Preface

This book has developed from the Authors' experience in teaching a course on the techniques of operational research at the University of Manchester.

The students included mathematicians, physicists, chemists, economists, econometricians and computer scientists, mostly with no background in operational research, so an approach starting at an elementary level was called for. The minimum prerequisites for the reader are an ability to handle sums (possibly infinite) and inequalities, elementary calculus and simple probability theory.

Chapters 2–13 cover a variety of techniques which might usefully be included in the tool kit of an operational researcher. No topic is dealt with in great depth (indeed whole books have been written on most of them) but even a nodding acquaintance with the basic ideas will prove useful to a potential user of operational research methods.

A full understanding of the material and of the common ideas underlying many of the techniques will only follow if the book is read as a whole. However, the text has been written so that individual chapters may, to a large degree, be read independently. In most cases references to other chapters can be ignored without losing the main thrust of the argument, but possibly at the risk of some impairment to the understanding of the finer points of a topic.

Chapters 1 and 14 set the techniques covered in the rest of the book in the wider context of operational research. Chapter 1 also summarises the contents of individual chapters.

The authors would like to thank Jill Weatherall for her superb typing and her ability to cope with manuscripts arriving often simultaneously from four different sources. They also wish to acknowledge the permission of the University of Manchester to reprint examination questions, or parts of examination questions, as exercises.

SF
RH
LT
DW   1986

Contents

1
Mathematics and Operational Research

Operational research is, in general terms, the application of scientific ideas and methods to improve the efficiency of an industrial process, an organisation or, in the most general of senses, the workings of any part of society. The range of problems that have been tackled by operational researchers is enormous. The following four examples indicate a small fraction of this range.

(1) The more check-outs a supermarket has, the more it must pay in cashiers' wages. The fewer it has, the more customers it loses, deterred by the length of the queues. What number of check-outs balances these conflicting costs most satisfactorily?
(2) Where should a hospital be sited so that it is conveniently situated for as many people as possible in the community that it serves?
(3) The more frequently a piece of equipment is serviced, the less likely it is to breakdown. What maintenance policy provides the best trade-off between servicing costs and the risk of break-down?
(4) What is the most economical way of distributing goods from a firm's factories to its warehouses?

Operational research is multidisciplinary: it draws heavily and simultaneously upon many different subject areas, such as mathematics, statistics, economics, psychology, the physical sciences and sociology. None of the examples of operational-research problems given above can be solved by methods that lie entirely within the province of a single discipline. Thus a successful operational-research worker must be a Jack of all trades and, to counter the proverb, the master of most as well.

Having said that, we shall concentrate almost myopically on the application of mathematics within operational research. We shall ignore all the behavioural, physical and methodological aspects of problem solving, and simply illustrate the role that mathematics has to play. This is not to claim that mathematics holds the central role within operational research. No subject holds that position. Rather we believe that a sound education in operational research requires a deep understanding of many subjects, and prominent among those is mathematical modelling; our purpose in this book is to introduce that mathematics. If we whet your appetite, then you can read more about both the mathematics of operational research and the roles played by other disciplines by referring to the books given in the bibliography at the end of the book.

Operational research is, as we have said, concerned with improving the workings of systems—ideally optimising them. Thus we would expect that we can apply the mathematics of optimisation to our operational research problems and that, indeed, is what we find. However, despite what we might expect from our school mathematics, calculus and differentiation have little part to play in the methods that we shall study; and it would be as well to pause and see why.

The simplest form of optimisation problem is

minimise $f(x)$ with respect to x.

In operational research this might be interpreted as follows. There is some system that we can control by varying the quantity x. Perhaps the system is an industrial process consuming an amount x of some raw material and $f(x)$ is the cost of running the process if we use the quantity x. Thus the minimisation problem might be translated as 'find the value of x that minimises the cost of the process.' If x can take any real value and if $f(x)$ is smooth enough, then this problem is simple enough to solve: simply differentiate $f(x)$ and solve

$$\frac{\mathrm{d}f}{\mathrm{d}x} = 0.$$

The solutions give the turning points of $f(x)$. Simple checks on higher derivatives find the local minima of the function and from these we can determine the global minimum. Unfortunately, few operational-research problems fall into this category, although one that does is investigated in Chapter 8.

The majority of operational-research optimisation problems are constrained; the variable x is not free to take any value. If x represents a quantity of raw material; then x is certainly limited to be a multiple of a given quantity, say a whole number of tons, and it may be limited to be less than a given amount. Such constraints can change an optimisation problem significantly.

Consider the following simple problem:

minimise $x^3 - 7x^2 + 14x + 8$

subject to $0 \leqslant x \leqslant 10$.

The function $x^3 - 7x^2 + 14x + 8$ is sketched in Fig. 1.1. The minimum in the range $0 \leqslant x \leqslant 10$ clearly occurs at $x = 0$, which equally clearly is not a turning point. Thus methods which search for a zero derivative will not succeed in optimising this function. We must use other methods.

Chapter 2 discusses *linear programming*, which is probably the most commonly used optimisation method in industry today. In linear programming it is assumed that the objective function and the constraints are given linearly. As a matter of terminology we might remark that 'programming' derives not from 'computer programming' but from 'mathematical programming', a general term for constrained optimisation.

Chapters 3 and 4 concern transportation and assignment problems respectively. These are special cases of linear programming problems with the additional

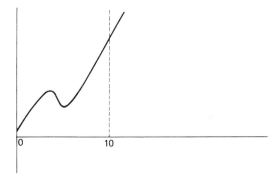

Fig. 1.1   Sketch of $x^3 - 7x^2 + 14x + 8$

constraints that the variables involved must be integers. Normally integer linear programming problems are very difficult to solve, but transportation and assignment problems have a special structure and their solution is relatively easy.

Chapters 5–7 concern a family of problems known as combinatorial optimisation. The defining property of these is that x is very severely constrained: it can only take one of a finite number of values. For instance, in the optimal-routing problems of Chapter 7, we seek the shortest route between two towns joined by a network of roads. There is only a finite number of possible routes (if we exclude driving round a loop hundreds of times) and so x may be thought of as taking a finite number of values, one labelling each possible route. Combinatorial optimisation problems sound very easy, and indeed the ones that we examine are. But in general their very 'finiteness' actually makes many of them among the hardest in mathematics—at least to solve practically.

Chapter 8 introduces inventory-control problems. These are the only problems that we treat in which standard differential calculus plays a significant role in their solution.

In Chapters 2–8 the problems treated are deterministic. All quantities are fixed and known in advance. Life, alas, is not always so certain. In much of operational research we face problems in which many of the quantities are uncertain. What will be the demand for umbrellas in three months time? How long will it be before a machine breaks down? And so on. The very quantities we need to define our problems are unknown. However, in such circumstances, we usually have a probability distribution describing our knowledge of their possible values. In Chapters 9–11 we consider the construction and optimisation of probabilistic models.

Several 'problems' that arise in operational research are not single optimisation problems, but a sequence of interrelated problems. Suppose that you own a car and that you need to fit it with new tyres. Suppose also that there is a variety of possible tyres available of different qualities and different prices. Lastly suppose that there is a possibility that you will sell your car next year. A little thought shows that you cannot choose a tyre until you have considered when you will sell the car. Dynamic programming is a method for solving such problems, and indeed, for solving a much wider class. We discuss it in Chapter 12.

Unfortunately, there are some optimisation problems that cannot be solved analytically. Despite all our battery of numerical techniques and theoretical results, they are beyond our current powers. But of course we cannot give up on such problems. They arose from some practical difficulty that needs to be overcome or, at least, eased. In such circumstances, simulation is often the answer. Using modern computers several possible policies can be tested to see which, if any, improves on the policy currently in use. We introduce the basic ideas of simulation in Chapter 13.

Finally, Chapter 14 broadens our perspective slightly. It attempts to set the mathematics that we have encountered into the context of the operational-research process, which involves, as we have said, many skills other than mathematical.

2
Linear Programming

2.1 What is linear programming?

In many problems in operational research, the aim is to maximise or minimise some objective, but there are certain constraints on what can be done in optimising this objective. The term **linear programming** (LP) is used to mean a way of modelling many of these problems so that they have a special structure, and it also denotes the way of solving problems with such a structure. It is a technique which can be applied in many different problem areas. For example, of the topics covered in this book, transportation (Chapter 3), assignment (Chapter 4), sequencing (Chapter 5), critical-path analysis (Chapter 6), routing problems (Chapter 7), and types of inventory problems (Chapter 8) and dynamic programming (Chapter 12) can all be modelled as linear programs.

Example 1—production problem

A paint manufacturer produces two types of paint, one type of standard quality (S) and the other of top quality (T). To make these paints, he needs two ingredients, the pigment and the resin. Standard quality paint requires 2 units of pigment and 3 units of resin for each unit made, and is sold at a profit of £1 per unit. Top quality paint requires 4 units of pigment and 2 units of resin for each unit made, and is sold at a profit of £1.50 per unit. He has stocks of 12 units of pigment, and 10 units of resin. How much of each type of paint should he make to maximise his profit?

2.2 Linear programming formulation

The first step in formulating a model of the problem is to decide which are the **decision variables**. These are the quantities which can be varied, and their variations affect the value of the objective. Here it is obvious that the quantities of each type of paint are the decision variables. Let x_1 be the number of units of standard quality paint to be made, and let x_2 be the number of units of top quality paint to be made.

The second step in the formulation is to express the objective in terms of the decision variables. Here we want to maximise the profit. For each unit of S paint there is a profit of £1, so if we make x_1 units, that will give a profit of £x_1. For each unit of T paint, there is a profit of £1.50, so if we make x_2 units, that will give a profit of £$1.5x_2$. So the **objective** is to

maximise $x_1 + 1.5x_2$.

Lastly in formulating the model, we must write down the constraints that restrict our choices of x_1 and x_2. In this case, there are two constraints due to limited resources and two that are just plain common sense. Those due to limited resources are that there are only 12 units of pigment and 10 units of resin that can be used. To make x_1 units of standard paint and x_2 units of top quality paint we need $2x_1 + 4x_2$ units of pigment and $3x_1 + 2x_2$ units of resin. The constraints are therefore

$$2x_1 + 4x_2 \leqslant 12$$
$$3x_1 + 2x_2 \leqslant 10.$$

The two commonsense constraints are that we cannot make negative amounts of paint, so $x_1 \geqslant 0$ and $x_2 \geqslant 0$. The problem has thus become

maximise $x_1 + 1.5x_2$

subject to $2x_1 + 4x_2 \leqslant 12$

             $3x_1 + 2x_2 \leqslant 10$

             $x_1 \geqslant 0, x_2 \geqslant 0$

2.3 Graphical solution

We can solve this problem by drawing a diagram of the region of values of x_1 and x_2 which satisfy all the constraints. This is called the **feasible** region.

For the constraint $2x_1 + 4x_2 \leqslant 12$, first draw the line $2x_1 + 4x_2 = 12$. One way is to notice that if $x_1 = 0$, then $x_2 = \frac{12}{4} = 3$ is on this line and when $x_2 = 0$, $x_1 = \frac{12}{2} = 6$. The line joining these points is the one we want.

Then we must identify on which side of this line are the points which satisfy $2x_1 + 4x_1 \leqslant 12$. A quick way to check this is to ask if the origin $x_1 = 0$, $x_2 = 0$ satisfies the constraint. In this case it does. So we want the shaded region of Fig. 2.1.

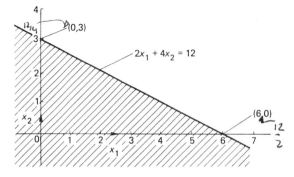

Fig. 2.1

If we repeat this procedure for the constraints $3x_1 + 2x_2 \leqslant 10$, $x_1 \geqslant 0$, $x_2 \geqslant 0$, we get the diagram in Fig. 2.2. The only points that satisfy all four constraints are those in the quadrilateral ABCD with corners $(0, 0)$ $(3\frac{1}{3}, 0)$ $(2, 2)$ and $(0, 3)$.

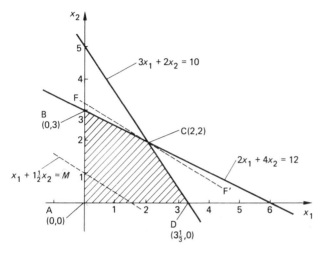

Fig. 2.2

To find which of these points maximises the profit, notice that all the points on the line $x_1 + 1.5x_2 = M$ have a profit £M. If we move this line parallel to itself in the north-eastern direction, we get another line $x_1 + 1.5x_2 = M'$, where $M' > M$. The points on this new line give more profit than the previous ones. Keep moving the line $x_1 + 1.5x_2 = M'$ as far to the north-east as we can, while there are still points in the feasible region on it. The furthest we can move it is to FF′, so that it just touches ABCD at the point C $(2, 2)$. This must be the line $x_1 + 1.5x_2 = 2 + 1.5(2) = 5$. Hence the maximum profit is £5 and is obtained when we make 2 units of standard quality paint and 2 units of top quality paint.

Example 2—diet problem

A dairy company wanted to promote its cheese products by saying you could slim by living on bread and cheese only, and yet still have a healthy diet. For such a healthy diet, you require 72 grammes of protein, 68 g of fats and 240 g of carbohydrates per day. The nutritional details for wholemeal bread and cheese are given in the table.

Food	Grammes per 10 oz of food			Number of calories per 10 oz of food
	Protein	Fat	Carbohydrates	
Wholemeal bread	2.0	0.5	10.0	40
Cheese	6.0	8.0	0.0	100

The question the company wanted to answer was 'What is the lowest daily calorie intake that produces a healthy diet?'

The decision variables are obviously the quantities of bread and cheese required. Let u_1 be the amount of bread required, in 10 oz units, and let u_2 be the amount of cheese required in 10 oz units again.

The objective is to minimise calorie intake, i.e.

$$\text{minimise } 40u_1 + 100u_2$$

The constraints are that the daily requirements for a healthy diet are satisfied i.e. $2u_1 + 6v_2 \geqslant 72$ (protein requirement)

$$0.5u_1 + 8u_2 \geqslant 68 \qquad \text{(fat requirement)}$$

$$10u_1 + 0u_2 \geqslant 240 \qquad \text{(carbohydrate requirement)}$$

$$u_1 \geqslant 0, \; u_2 \geqslant 0$$

The last two inequalities are the commonsense ones that prevent negative amounts of food being eaten.

In Fig. 2.3, we draw the region of u_1, u_2 values allowed by the constraints. The region of allowable or feasible solution is the unbounded one with corners at A $(24, 7)$ and B $(136, 0)$. Looking at lines of the form $40u_1 + 100u_2 = M$ and seeing how small we can make M and still cut this region is like moving the line CC' as far to the south-west as possible. In this case, M is smallest at the point A $(24, 7)$, which gives us the solution $u_1 = 24$, $u_2 = 7$ with calorie intake of $40.24 + 100.7 = 1660$. Notice that the protein requirement does not seem to matter, because the intakes of bread and cheese that satisfy the other two requirements automatically satisfy it. Such a constraint is called a **redundant** constraint.

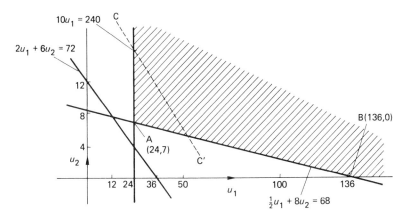

Fig. 2.3

2.4 Main results of linear programming

What do these two problems have in common that makes them linear programming problems? There are two requirements for an LP problem.

(1) The object is to maximise or minimise a linear combination of the decision variables, i.e. $x_1 + 1.5x_2$, $40u_1 + 100u_2$. Expressions of the form $ax_1 + bx_2$ are called linear in x_1 and x_2 because if we double the values of x_1 and x_2, then we double the value of the expression. If we were to plot the value of the expression as we varied x_1, we would get a line. A similar result holds for any other decision variable.

(2) The constraints are also linear, that is they are constraints on linear functions of the decision variables. They can be of the form $ax_1 + bx_2 \leqslant c$, $dx_1 + ex_2 \geqslant f$ or even $gx_1 + hx_2 = k$. The important point is that a region defined by linear constraints is convex; a set is said to be **convex** if a line joining any two points in it lies wholly in the set. In Fig. 2.4, the first two sets are convex but the second two are not convex.

Not only is the feasible region of any linear programming problem always convex, but also the region's boundary is a combination of straight edges, i.e. it is polyhedral. Looking at the convex polyhedral sets in Fig. 2.4, some special points which look like the corners of the region stand out. These are called **vertices**, and they have the property that they cannot lie on any line drawn wholly in the set, unless they are the end point of it.

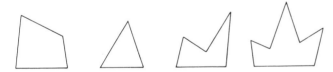

Fig. 2.4

In Example 1, the feasible region has four vertices. They are A with coordinates $(0, 0)$, B $(0, 3)$, C $(2, 2)$, and D $(3\frac{1}{3}, 0)$. In Example 2, there are only two vertices: A $(24, 7)$ and B $(136, 0)$. Vertices are so important because on the convex polyhedral feasible region arising from a linear program, which has non-negative decision variables, any linear function of the variable takes its maximum and minimum values (if they are finite) at a vertex.

If we calculate the value of the objective function only at the vertices, we can find the maximum and minimum value we want. Thus in Example 1, the profit was maximised at the vertex C $(2, 2)$. In example 2, the number of calories was minimised at the vertex A $(24, 7)$.

Example 3—manpower problem

An airline has 30 pilots, 24 co-pilots, 12 navigators and 132 cabin staff. It has two types of planes: nineteen 717 planes, which carry 180 passengers each, and fourteen 1110 planes, which carry 340 passengers each. A 717 plane needs a pilot, a co-pilot and four cabin staff, while a 1110 plane needs a pilot, a co-pilot, a navigator and seven cabin staff. Pilots can also act as co-pilots if required. What is the maximum number of passengers the airline can carry at one time?

Let x_1 be the number of 717 planes and x_2 be the number of 1110 planes to be used by the airline. The problem then is to

$$\begin{array}{ll}
\text{maximise} & 180x_1 + 340x_2 \\
\text{subject to} & x_1 \leqslant 19 \qquad\qquad \text{(717 planes constraint)} \\
& x_2 \leqslant 14 \qquad\qquad \text{(1110 planes constraint)} \\
& x_1 + x_2 \leqslant 30 \qquad\ \text{(pilots constraint)} \\
& 2x_1 + 2x_2 \leqslant 54 \qquad \text{(pilots and co-pilots constraint)} \\
& x_2 \leqslant 12 \qquad\qquad \text{(navigators constraint)} \\
& 4x_1 + 7x_2 \leqslant 132 \quad\ \text{(cabin staff constraints)} \\
& x_1, x_2 \geqslant 0.
\end{array}$$

We should also add the constraint that x_1 and x_2 are integers, but we will leave it out for now and see what happens.

The feasible region is given by Fig. 2.5. The vertices are A $(0,0)$, B $(0,12)$, C $(12,12)$, D $(19,8)$ and E $(19,0)$, and the objective function at each vertex is 0, 4080, 6240, 6140 and 3420 respectively. Thus the most passengers the airline can carry is 6240 with 12 717s and 12 1110s.

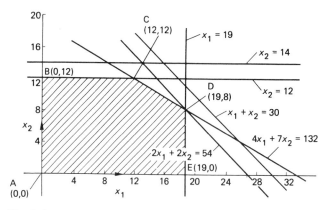

Fig. 2.5

2.5   Possible outcomes of linear programs

So far we have always been able to solve the problem and arrive at a unique solution. You might ask if this is always the case, and the answer is 'no'. Several possibilities might arise.

(1) *No feasible solution.* Look at the problem

maximise $x_1 + 2x_2$
subject to $x_1 + x_2 \leqslant 1$
                    $x_1 \geqslant 2$
                    $x_2 \geqslant 0.$

Figure 2.6 shows there is no point which satisfies all three constraints. Thus there is no solution to the problem.

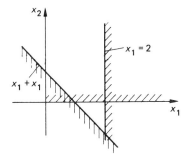

Fig. 2.6

(2) *Infinite number of solutions.* Consider the diet problem of Example 2 and instead of trying to minimise the calories in the diet, try to maximise them. Thus we have

maximise $40x_1 + 100x_2$
subject to $2x_1 + 6x_2 \geqslant 72$
                    $0.5x_1 + 8x_2 \geqslant 68$
                    $10x_1 \geqslant 240$
                    $x_1 \geqslant 0, x_2 \geqslant 0.$

Obviously the solution is infinite as we could eat as much as we can and still satisfy the constraints. The solution value is unbounded. Notice this can only happen if the feasible region is unbounded, i.e. if it goes on for ever in at least one direction.

(3) *Non-unique solutions.* Another possible outcome of an LP problem is that the optimal value occurs at more than one vertex. In that case, all the points on the line or face joining the optimal vertices also have the optimal value.

maximise $x_1 + x_2$
subject to $x_1 + x_2 \leqslant 1$
                    $x_1 \leqslant \tfrac{1}{2}$
                    $x_1, x_2 \geqslant 0.$

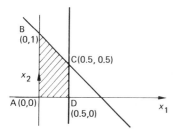

Fig. 2.7

In Fig. 2.7 both B $(0, 1)$ and C $(\frac{1}{2}, \frac{1}{2})$ give a value 1 which is the optimal value. So also do all the points $(\lambda, 1 - \lambda), 0 \leqslant \lambda \leqslant 0.5$, on the line BC, so they are all optimal solution points. So let us emphasise again that an optimal solution need not be a vertex, only that if the feasible region is bounded then one of the optimal solutions is a vertex.

(4)   *Degeneracy*. Normally the number of constraints which pass through a vertex equals the number of decision variables, but there are vertices where even more constraints meet. Such vertices are then said to be **degenerate**. This does not affect the existence or uniqueness of the optimal solution as for the other three cases discussed, but does cause modifications to be made in some of the solution algorithms. As an example, consider

$$\begin{aligned}
\text{maximise} \quad & 3x_1 + 2x_2 \\
\text{subject to} \quad & x_1 + x_2 \leqslant 1 \\
& x_1 \leqslant 1 \\
& x_1 \geqslant 0, x_2 \geqslant 0
\end{aligned}$$

which has a feasible region given by Fig. 2.8. The point C $(1, 0)$ is a degenerate vertex as three constraints $(x_2 \geqslant 0, x_1 \leqslant 1, x_1 + x_2 \leqslant 1)$ pass through it instead of the two through the other ones.

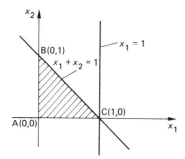

Fig. 2.8

2.6 Slack variables

The graphical method of constructing the region of feasible solutions no longer works if there are more than two decision variables, but the result about an optimal solution being at a *vertex* still holds. It is just that we cannot draw the feasible region. Is there a way of finding the optimal vertex which holds for all problems, no matter how many decision variables? In the next three sections we sketch a method called the **simplex algorithm**.

Consider again Example 1 (Fig. 2.9), which was modelled by

$$\text{maximise} \quad x_1 + 1.5x_2$$
$$\text{subject to} \quad 2x_1 + 4x_2 \leqslant 12$$
$$3x_1 + 2x_2 \leqslant 10$$
$$x_1 \geqslant 0, x_2 \geqslant 0.$$

Two of the boundary lines are $x_1 = 0$, $x_2 = 0$ while the other two are not so simply expressed. We introduce extra variables called **slack** and **surplus** variables to enable all constraints to be expressed as simply as possible. Thus $2x_1 + 4x_2 \leqslant 12$ is written as $2x_1 + 4x_2 + s_1 = 12$, $s_1 \geqslant 0$, and $3x_1 + 2x_2 \leqslant 10$ is rewritten $3x_1 + 2x_2 + s_2 = 10$, $s_2 \geqslant 0$. The constraint set is then

$$2x_1 + 4x_2 + s_1 = 12$$
$$3x_1 + 2x_2 + s_2 = 10$$
$$x_1 \geqslant 0, x_2 \geqslant 0, s_1 \geqslant 0, s_2 \geqslant 0.$$

If the constraint was $2x_1 + 6x_2 \geqslant 72$, we would take away the new variable and so write it as $2x_1 + 6x_2 - s = 72$, $s \geqslant 0$. If we add on the extra variable it is a **slack** variable; if we take it away it is a **surplus** variable. The point is that after introducing the new variable the constraint can be rewritten as $s \geqslant 0$.

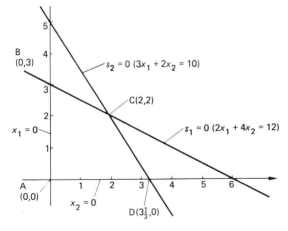

Fig. 2.9

Returning to Example 1, we see that every vertex now corresponds to setting two of the variables equal to zero and solving for the rest. If the others are non-negative then it is a vertex of the feasible set.

Thus   A is $x_1 = 0$, $x_2 = 0$ $(s_1 = 12,$ $s_2 = 10)$
        B is $x_1 = 0$ $s_1 = 0$ $(x_2 = 3,$ $s_2 = 4)$
        C is $s_1 = 0$ $s_2 = 0$ $(x_1 = 2,$ $x_2 = 2)$
and   D is $x_2 = 0$ $s_2 = 0$ $(x_1 = 3\frac{1}{3},$ $s_1 = 5\frac{1}{3})$

Notice $x_1 = 0, s_2 = 0$ gives $x_2 = 5, s_1 = -8$ and so is not a vertex of the feasible set.

In a general problem with n decision variables and m constraints, we have $n + m$ variables after introducing the slack and surplus variables. A vertex corresponds to the situation where n of the variables are 0 and the remaining m are non-negative. These set equal to 0 are called the **non-basic variables** for that vertex, and the other m are the **basic** variables for that vertex. In the degenerate case described in Section 2.5, some of the basic variables will also be zero at a vertex, but usually they are strictly positive.

This way of identifying the vertices leads to the **simplex algorithm**, which is a way of going from one vertex to an adjacent one, so that only one of the non-basic variables changes to become a basic variable. Each time we move to a new vertex, the value of the objective function improves (for a maximisation) or diminishes (for a minimisation) problem.

2.7   Simplex method (algebraic way)

We still concentrate on Example 1:

maximise $x_1 + 1.5x_2$
subject to $2x_1 + 4x_2 \leqslant 12$
         $3x_1 + 2x_2 \leqslant 10$
         $x_1 \geqslant 0, x_2 \geqslant 0.$

Step 1   Introduce slack or surplus variables to make the inequalities into equalities.

$2x_1 + 4x_2 + s_1 = 12$ (C1)
$3x_1 + 2x_2 + s_2 = 10$ (C2)
$x_1 \geqslant 0, x_2 \geqslant 0, s_1 \geqslant 0, s_2 \geqslant 0$ (C3)
where we maximise $M = 1x_1 + 1.5x_2 + 0s_1 + 0s_2$.   (OBJ)

Step 2   Look for an initial vertex, i.e. a solution of (C1), (C2), and (C3) with, in this case, two of the variables equal to zero. These are the non-basic variables. Often the origin works i.e. $x_1 = 0, x_2 = 0, s_1 = 12, s_2 = 10, M = 0$. This gives vertex A in Fig. 2.9.

Step 3 Write M and the basic variables in terms of the non-basic variables, so that only one basic variable appears in each equation and with coefficient 1. This is easy here:

$$M - x_1 - 1.5x_2 \quad = 0 \tag{OBJA}$$
$$2x_1 + 4x_2 + s_1 = 12 \tag{C1A}$$
$$3x_1 + 2x_2 + s_2 = 10. \tag{C2A}$$

Step 4 Check to see if we can improve M.

For each of the non-basic variables, which are at present zero, we ask what happens to M if we were to increase that variable by a small amount.

Choose the variable with the greatest increasing effect on M, which is just the one with the most negative coefficient in the equation (OBJA). Here increasing x_1 by 1 increases M by 1, increasing x_2 by 1 increases M by 1.5.

Step 5 Increase the chosen variable as much as possible. We want to increase our chosen variable x_2 as much as possible, keeping the other non-basic variable x_1 still equal to 0, and also satisfying (C1A) and (C2A).

(C1A) says $s_1 = 12 - 2x_1 - 4x_2$; if $x_1 = 0$, $s_1 \geqslant 0$, $x_2 \leqslant \frac{12}{4} = 3$

(C2A) says $s_2 = 10 - 3x_1 - 2x_2$; if $x_1 = 0$, $s_2 \geqslant 0$, $x_2 \leqslant \frac{10}{2} = 5$.

So the largest that x_2 can be is 3 since $\frac{12}{4} \leqslant \frac{10}{2}$. This corresponds to the vertex $x_2 = 3$, $x_1 = 0$, $s_1 = 0$, $s_2 = 4$, where $M = 4.5$, i.e. vertex B. The non-basic variables are x_1 and s_1 and the basic variables x_2 and s_2. Return to Step 3 and repeat the procedure.

Step 3 Divide (C1A) by 4 to get

$$\tfrac{1}{2}x_1 + x_2 + \tfrac{1}{4}s_1 = 3. \tag{C1B}$$

Take (C2A) minus twice (C1B) to get only s_2 in the other equation:

$$3x_1 + 2x_2 + s_2 - 2(\tfrac{1}{2}x_1 + x_2 + \tfrac{1}{4}s_1) = 10 - 2(3)$$
$$2x_1 - \tfrac{1}{2}s_1 + s_2 \qquad\qquad = 4. \tag{C2B}$$

Take (OBJ) $+1.5$ times (C1B) to get

$$M - x_1 - 1.5x_2 + 1.5(\tfrac{1}{2}x_1 + x_2 + \tfrac{1}{4}s_1) = 4.5$$
$$M - \tfrac{1}{4}x_1 + \tfrac{3}{8}s_1 = 4.5. \tag{OBJB}$$

From (OBJB), if we increase x_1 by 1 the objective value increases by $\tfrac{1}{4}$, but if we increase s_1 by 1 it decreases by $\tfrac{3}{8}$. So we want to increase x_1. Again we have chosen the most negative coefficient in (OBJB).

How much can we increase x_1 and still satisfy the constraints while keeping the other non-basic variable s_1 equal to zero?

(C1B) has $\tfrac{1}{2}x_1 + x_2 + \tfrac{1}{4}s_1 = 3$; if $s_1 = 0$, $x_2 \geqslant 0$, $x_1 \leqslant \frac{3}{0.5} = 6$.

(C2B) has $2x_1 - \tfrac{1}{2}s_1 + s_2 = 4$; if $s_1 = 0$, $s_2 \geqslant 0$, $x_1 \leqslant \frac{4}{2} = 2$.

So we can only increase x_1 to 2, and arrive at the vertex $x_1 = 2$, $s_1 = 0$, $x_2 = 2$, $M = 5$, i.e. vertex C.

Repeating steps 3, 4 and 5 for this vertex we first write M, x_1, x_2 in terms of the non-basic variables s_1 and s_2. Halving (C2B) gives

$$x_1 - \tfrac{1}{4}s_1 + \tfrac{1}{2}s_2 = 2 \tag{C2C}$$

$$(\text{C1B}) - \tfrac{1}{2}(\text{C2C}) \text{ gives } x_2 + \tfrac{3}{8}s_1 - \tfrac{1}{4}s_2 = 2 \tag{C1C}$$

while $(\text{OBJB}) + \tfrac{1}{4}$ (C2C) gives

$$M - \tfrac{1}{4}x_1 + \tfrac{3}{8}s_1 + \tfrac{1}{4}(x_1 - \tfrac{1}{4}s_1 + \tfrac{1}{2}s_2) = 4\tfrac{1}{2} + \tfrac{1}{4}(2);$$

that is, $M + \tfrac{5}{16}s_1 + \tfrac{1}{8}s_2 = 5.$ (OBJC)

When we try to increase s_1 or s_2 from 0, (OBJC) tells us the objective value M will decrease. So we cannot improve on M and $x_1 = 2, x_2 = 2, s_1 = 0, s_2 = 0, M = 5$ is the optimal solution.

To summarise the method again, we have the following steps.

Step 1   Introduce slack variables.

Step 2   Find a feasible vertex (a solution of the constraint equations, where the number of variables taking a value zero is at least the number of original decision variables—often the origin will do).

Step 3   Write M, the objective function and the basic variables in terms of the non-basic variables.

Step 4   Find which non-basic variable has the most negative coefficient in expression for M.

Step 5   Increase the value of this variable as much as possible, while ensuring all other non-basic variables remain zero and the constraints are satisfied. Return to Step 3 and repeat the process until M is written in terms of non-basic variables, all of which have non-negative coefficients.

2.8   Simplex method (tableau way)

One can perform exactly these calculations much more quickly by dropping the variable names, x_1 and x_2 etc., and writing only their coefficients in a tableau. This then is the standard simplex method, or at least one variation of it. We will repeat the calculations to solve Example 1 again:

$$\begin{aligned} \text{maximise} \quad & x_1 + 1.5x_2 \\ \text{subject to} \quad & 2x_1 + 4x_2 \leqslant 12 \\ & 3x_1 + 2x_2 \leqslant 10 \\ & x_1 \geqslant 0, x_2 \geqslant 0. \end{aligned}$$

Step 1   Introduce slack variables (see Table 2.1).

Step 2   Find an initial vertex. This corresponds, in a problem with m constraints or rows, to there being m variables or columns, each of which has only one entry of 1, the rest of the entries being zero. The 1s appear in different rows from each other,

Table 2.1

	x_1	x_2	s_1	s_2	
(C1)	2	4	1	0	12
(C2)	3	2	0	1	10
M	−1	−1.5	0	0	0

and the last column of the tableau, which corresponds to the right-hand sides of the equation, must have non-negative entries. In this example, the columns s_1 and s_2 satisfy these requirements.

Step 3   Look for the most negative number in the (OBJ) line. This gives the *pivot column*, and the variable corresponding to that column becomes a new basic variable. Here it is − 1.5, so x_2 is the pivot column.

Step 4   In each constraint row divide the value of the pivot column into the value of the last column, provided the pivot column value is positive (ignore the rows with negative values). Choose as the pivot row the row with the smallest result. Here (C1) gives $\frac{12}{4} = 3$ and (C2) is $\frac{10}{2} = 5$. So (C1) is the pivot row and the (C1, x_2) entry 4 is the pivot element.

Step 5   Divide pivot row by value of pivot element

$$
\text{(C1B)} \quad
\begin{array}{cccc}
x_1 & x_2 & s_1 & s_2 \\
\frac{1}{2} & 1 & \frac{1}{4} & 0
\end{array}
\qquad 3.
$$

and subtract multiples of this row from the other rows so they have 0s in pivot column.

Table 2.2

	x_1	x_2	s_1	s_2		
(C1B)	$\frac{1}{2}$	1	$\frac{1}{4}$	0	3	$3/\frac{1}{2}$ = 6
(C2B) = (C2A) − 2(C1B)	2	0	$-\frac{1}{2}$	1	4	4/2 = 2 ←
(OBJB) = (OBJA) + 1.5(C1B)	$-\frac{1}{4}$	0	$\frac{3}{8}$	0	4.5	
	↑					

As you may check, this is exactly what we were doing in the last section when we derived (C1B), (C2B), (OBJB). Now repeat Steps 3–5 for Table 2.2 to get the new tableau of Table 2.3. If all coefficients in the (OBJ) line are non-negative, then this is an optimal solution. We can read off values of the solution from the last column of the tableau, identifying the variable with that value as the one which has a 1 in that row. These are the basic variables. So $x_1 = 2$, $x_2 = 2$, (OBJ) = 5 is the solution.

Table 2.3

	x_1	x_2	s_1	s_2	
(C2C)	1	0	$-\frac{1}{4}$	$\frac{1}{2}$	2
(C1C) = (C1B) $-\frac{1}{2}$(C2C)	0	1	$\frac{3}{8}$	$-\frac{1}{4}$	2
(OBJC) = (OBJB) $+\frac{1}{4}$(C2C)	0	0	$\frac{5}{16}$	$\frac{1}{8}$	5

If, instead of maximising $M = x_1 + 1.5x_2$, we wanted to minimise $N = 2x_1 + x_2$, say, we first change this into a maximisation problem. Notice that since

$$\min \{1, 3, 5, 7\} = 1 = -\max \{-1, -3, -5, -7\},$$

minimising N is the same as maximising $(-N)$. So we maximise $-2x_1 - x_2$ and when the final solution is obtained just change the sign of the objective function.

Sometimes there is no obvious vertex of the feasible region to start with. There is a way, called the two-phase simplex method, of modifying the algorithm, so that finding a first vertex involves using the simplex method on a modified problem. If there is no feasible solution, then this method will display that fact.

The other non-standard solutions of LP discussed in Section 2.8 can also be recognised in the simplex algorithm. If the solution is unbounded, then a pivot column will occur with all the entries zero or negative. If there are alternative solutions, then the final tableau will have more zeros in the objective function row than there are basic variables. Pivoting on one of these columns corresponds to a non-basic variable which has a zero in the objective function row. Degeneracy occurs when a zero appears in the last column of the tableau, which corresponds to a basic variable taking a value of zero.

2.9 Duality

Another important fact about linear program problems is that every problem has a companion or **dual** problem. We will show how to find this dual problem with reference to good old Example 1:

> maximise $x_1 + 1.5x_2$
> subject to $2x_1 + 4x_2 \leq 12$
> $3x_1 + 2x_2 \leq 10$
> $x_1 \geq 0, x_2 \geq 0.$

(1) First you have to check that the original, or **primal**, problem is of the correct form. If it is a maximisation problem then all the non-trivial constraints must be of the form

> variable expression $\leq$ numbers.

$12u_1 + 10u_2$

$2u_1 + 3u_2 \geq 1$

$4u_1 + 2u_2 \geq 1.5$

This is already satisfied in this case. If it is a minimisation problem, the constraints must be put in the form

variable expression $\geqslant$ number.

(2) The number of variables in the dual problem is the number of non-trivial constraints in the original problem. So there are two in this case. Call them u_1 and u_2. Each variable is associated with a constraint in the original problem. Here we say $2x_1 + 4x_2 \leqslant 12$ is associated with u_1.
and $3x_1 + 2x_2 \leqslant 10$ is associated with u_2.

(3) If the original problem is a maximisation one, the dual is a minimisation one and vice versa. So the dual here must minimise the objective function. The coefficients of u_1 and u_2 in the objective function are the right-hand side values of the constraints in the original problem, which are associated with these variables. So u_1 has coefficient 12, u_2 has coefficient 10 and the objective function is

$$12u_1 + 10u_2.$$

(4) The number of non-trivial constraints in the dual is the number of variables in the original problem, i.e. two in this problem. Each constraint in the dual problem is associated with a variable in the original problem. So here one constraint is associated with x_1 and the other is associated with x_2. The coefficient of u_1 in the constraint associated with x_1 is the coefficient of x_1 in the constraint in the original problem, which is associated with u_1 i.e. 2. Similarly the coefficient of u_2 in the constraint associated with x_1 is 3, as this is the coefficient of x_1 in the constraint associated with u_2. The right-hand side of the constraint related to x_1 is the coefficient of x_1 in the objective function of the original problem, i.e. 1. So the constraint related to x_1 becomes

$$2u_1 + 3u_2 \geqslant 1.$$

Notice that because the dual problem is a minimisation, we write the constraint as

variable expression $\geqslant$ number.

The same rules give the constraint related to x_2 as

$$4u_1 + 2u_2 \geqslant 1.5.$$

So the dual problem is

$$\begin{array}{ll} \text{minimise} & 12u_1 + 10u_2 \\ \text{subject to} & 2u_1 + 3u_2 \geqslant 1 \\ & 4u_1 + 2u_2 \geqslant 1.5 \\ & u_1 \geqslant 0,\ u_2 \geqslant 0. \end{array}$$

The dual problem of the dual problem is the original problem, which you can check by applying the rules to the dual problem.

If there are equality constraints, i.e. $2x_1 + 4x_2 = 12$, then we can consider each as two inequality constraints, i.e. $2x_1 + 4x_2 \leqslant 12$, and $2x_1 + 4x_2 \geqslant 12$ (i.e. $-2x_1 - 4x_2 \leqslant -12$). There will then be two dual variables associated with the original constraint. They will always appear in the dual with the coefficient of one equal to minus the coefficient of the other, i.e. $2u_1 - 2u_2$, in constraint associated with x_1; $4u_1 - 4u_2$ in constraint associated with x_2, and $12u_1 - 12u_2$ in the objective function. If we take $u_1 - u_2$ as a new variable, u_3, say, it can be unrestricted in sign, i.e. it does not have to be greater than zero, but its coefficients in the dual correspond to the usual rule described above, if we assumed the original constraint was an inequality one. Conversely, if a variable is allowed to take negative as well as positive values in an LP problem, the corresponding constraint in the dual problem is an equality. Thus if the primal problem is

$$\begin{aligned}
\text{maximise} \quad & x_1 + 2x_2 + 3x_3 \\
\text{subject to} \quad & 4x_1 - x_2 + 2x_3 = 4 \\
& 5x_1 + 2x_2 + 6x_3 \leqslant 2 \\
& x_1 \geqslant 0, \ x_2 \geqslant 0, \ x_3 \text{ any value}
\end{aligned}$$

the dual problem is

$$\begin{aligned}
\text{minimise} \quad & 4u_1 + 2u_2 \\
\text{subject to} \quad & 4u_1 + 5u_2 \geqslant 1 \\
& -u_1 + 2u_2 \geqslant 2 \\
& 2u_1 + 6u_2 = 3 \\
& u_1 \text{ any value}, \ u_2 \geqslant 0.
\end{aligned}$$

2.10 Duality theorem

Let us solve the dual of Example 1, which we generated in the last section. From Sections 2.2 and 2.3, we know that the original problem is

$$\begin{aligned}
\text{maximise} \quad & x_1 + 1.5x_2 \\
\text{subject to} \quad & 2x_1 + 4x_2 \leqslant 12 \\
& 3x_1 + 2x_2 \leqslant 10 \\
& x_1, x_2 \geqslant 0
\end{aligned}$$

with solution of a maximum value of 5 when $x_1 = 2$ and $x_2 = 2$. From Section 2.9, we know that its dual is

$$\begin{aligned}
\text{minimise} \quad & 12u_1 + 10u_2 \\
\text{subject to} \quad & 2u_1 + 3u_2 \geqslant 1 \\
& 4u_1 + 2u_2 \geqslant 1.5 \\
& u_1, u_2 \geqslant 0.
\end{aligned}$$

The dual is solved graphically using Fig. 2.10. The vertices of the feasible region are A $(0.5, 0)$, with objective value 6, B $(\frac{5}{16}, \frac{1}{8})$ with value 5 and C $(0, \frac{3}{4})$ with value 7.5. Thus the solution is $u_1 = \frac{5}{8}$, $u_2 = \frac{1}{8}$ with value 5.

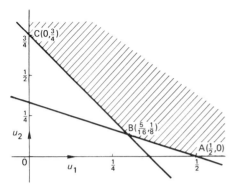

Fig. 2.10

The optimal value of the dual problem in this case is the same as the optimal value of the primal problem. This is no fluke, as it is always true that the value of the optimal solution of a primal problem is the same as the value of the optimal solution of its dual problem, provided at least one has a finite solution. Thus if $c_1 x_1 + c_2 x_2 + \cdots + c_n x_n$ is the objective function for a problem and $b_1 u_1 + b_2 u_2 + \cdots + b_m u_m$ the objective function of its dual, we have

$$c_1 x_1^* + c_2 x_2^* + \cdots + c_n x_n^* = b_1 u_1^* + b_2 u_2^* + \cdots + b_m u_m^*$$

where x_i^*, $i = 1, \cdots, n$, are the solution values to the primal and u_i^*, $i = 1, \ldots, n$, are the solution values to the dual.

2.11 Complementary slackness

We do not have to solve the dual problem to find its optimal value since this is the same as the optimal value of the primal problem. Moreover we do not need to solve it to find the values of the variables at its optimal solution, if we already know the values of the variables in the primal problem at its optimal solution point. This is because of the *principle of complementary slackness*, which says 'At the solution points to the primal and dual problems, either a variable has zero value, or the constraint associated with that variable in the dual problem is an equality when the optimal solution values are substituted in.' This result is really only a restatement of the duality theorem, which says the two problems have the same optimal value.

Recall Example 1 and its dual.

Primal	*Dual*
maximise $x_1 + 1.5x_2$	minimise $12u_1 + 10u_2$
subject to $2x_1 + 4x_2 \leqslant 12\ (u_1)$	subject to $2u_1 + 3u_2 \geqslant 1\ (x_1)$
$3x_1 + 2x_2 \leqslant 10\ (u_2)$	$4u_1 + 2y_2 \geqslant 1.5\ (x_2)$
$x_1 \geqslant 0,\ x_2 \geqslant 0$	$u_1 \geqslant 0,\ u_2 \geqslant 0$

where the brackets indicate the dual variable associated with that constraint. If $x_1^*, x_2^*, u_1^*, u_2^*$ are the values of the variables at the solutions of the two problems, applying complementary slackness gives:

either $x_1^* = 0$ or $2u_1^* + 3u_2^* = 1$;

either $x_2^* = 0$ or $4u_1^* + 2u_2^* = 1.5$;

either $u_2^* = 0$ or $2x_1^* + 4x_2^* = 12$;

either $u_2^* = 0$ or $3x_1^* + 2x_2^* = 10$;

Since $x_1^* = 2$, $x_2^* = 2$ is the solution to Example 1, this implies

$$2u_1^* + 3u_2^* = 1$$
$$4u_1^* + 2u_2^* = 1.5.$$

We can solve this to get $u_1^* = \frac{5}{16}$, $u_2^* = \frac{1}{8}$, which is the original solution to the dual problem. Those interested in the simplex algorithm should note that the solution of the dual problem can be obtained from the (OBJ) row of the last tableau. The numbers in this row of the columns corresponding to slack variables are the values of the dual variables corresponding to the constraints with those slack variables.

2.12   Interpretation of duality

The dual problem can be obtained from the original problem; its solution can be obtained from that of the primal, and moreover its solution gives us an insight into the implications of the solution of the original problem. In the case of the paint problem of Example 1, paint is sold at a certain price, but the paint itself is made up from pigment and resin. Thus these resources of pigment and resin also have a value given indirectly by the profit obtained by selling the paint. What are these values? One way of identifying this value is to ask how much extra profit we can make if we increase the amount of resin by a small amount. The extra profit for a unit increase in the amount of pigment is the *shadow value* of pigment, and similarly the increase in profit for a unit amount of resin extra is the shadow value of resin. If we let u_1 be the value of a unit of pigment and u_2 the value of a unit of resin, since 2 units of pigment and 3 units of resin produce one unit of standard quality paint, which is worth £1, we could argue that they are worth at least £1.

Thus

$$2u_1 + 3u_2 \geqslant 1.$$

A similar argument about top quality paint implies

$$4u_1 + 2u_2 \geqslant 1.5.$$

It is obviously reasonable to assume that these shadow values, u_1 and u_2, must be non-negative. The total value we have in resin and pigment, with 12 units of pigment and 10 units of resin, is $12u_1 + 10u_2$. The value of these commodities is the lowest value of $12u_1 + 10u_2$ which satisfies all the constraints described above, i.e.

minimise $\quad 12u_1 + 10u_2$

subject to $\quad 2u_1 + 3u_2 \geqslant 1$

$\qquad\qquad 4u_1 + 2u_2 \geqslant 1.5$

$\qquad\qquad u_1, u_2 \geqslant 0.$

This is the dual we generated from the rules described in Section 2.9 and solved with $u_1 = \frac{5}{16}$, $u_2 = \frac{1}{8}$ in Section 2.10. This solution of the dual means that if we increase the amount of pigment slightly, then the profit on the paint sold will increase at a rate of $\pounds\frac{5}{16}$ per unit of pigment. Similarly changes in the amount of resin affect the profit at the rate of only $\pounds\frac{1}{8}$ per unit, provided the changes in amount are small.

Example 4—cutting mill problem

Sometimes it is easier to solve the dual problem rather than the primal one, because the change in the number of constraints and variables makes it more amenable. We give one such example, which we can solve graphically.

A cutting mill receives reels of paper with a standard width of 540 cm. Customers require 900 m of width 150 cm and 900 m of width 80 cm, which have to be cut from these reels. The problem is to decide how to cut the reels and in what lengths, so as to minimise the length of the original reel used, since the waste pieces (or trim losses) are thrown away.

There are four possible ways of cutting 540 cm width into widths of 150 cm and 80 cm. These are shown in Table 2.4.

Table 2.4

Method	1	2	3	4
Number of 150 cm pieces	3	2	1	0
Number of 80 cm pieces	1	3	4	6
Trim loss	10	0	70	60

Let x_i, $i = 1, 2, 3, 4$, be the length of reel cut, using method i. So to minimise total length cut and to satisfy the customers' requirements, we want to

minimise $\quad x_1 + x_2 + x_3 + x_4$

subject to $\quad 3x_1 + 2x_2 + x_3 \geqslant 900$

$\qquad\qquad x_1 + 3x_2 + 4x_3 + 6x_4 \geqslant 900$

$\qquad\qquad x_1 \geqslant 0,\ x_2 \geqslant 0,\ x_3 \geqslant 0,\ x_4 \geqslant 0.$

This problem has four variables and two constraints, so the dual problem will have two variables and four constraints, and we can solve it graphically. Using the rules of Section 2.19, the dual problem is

maximise $\quad 900u_1 + 900u_2$

subject to $\quad 3u_1 + u_2 \leqslant 1$

$\qquad\qquad 2u_1 + 3u_2 \leqslant 1$

$\qquad\qquad\ u_1 + 4u_2 \leqslant 1$

$\qquad\qquad\quad\ 6u_2 \leqslant 1$

$\qquad\qquad u_1 \geqslant 0,\ u_2 \geqslant 0.$

From Fig. 2.11 we can read off the vertices and the objective function value at each. At A $(0, 0)$ the value is 0, at B $(0, \frac{1}{6})$ the value is 150; at C $(\frac{1}{4}, \frac{1}{6})$ it is 375, at D $(\frac{2}{7}, \frac{1}{7})$ it is $385\frac{5}{7}$; and at E$(\frac{1}{3}, 0)$ it is 300. Thus the solution is $385\frac{5}{7}$ with $u_1^* = \frac{2}{7}$,

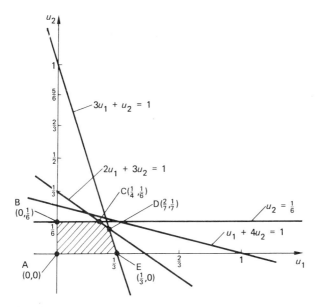

Fig. 2.11

$u_2^* = \frac{1}{7}$. Using the complementary slackness conditions we get

$$
\begin{array}{lll}
x_1^* = 0 & \text{or} & 3u_1^* + u_2^* = 1 \\
x_2^* = 0 & \text{or} & 2u_1^* + 3u_2^* = 1 \\
x_3^* = 0 & \text{or} & u_1 + 4u_2^* = 1 \\
x_4^* = 0 & \text{or} & 6u_2^* = 1 \\
u_1^* = 0 & \text{or} & 3x_1^* + 2x_2^* + x_3^* = 900 \\
u_2^* = 0 & \text{or} & x_1^* + 3x_2^* + 4x_3^* + 6x_4^* = 900.
\end{array}
$$

With $u_1^* = \frac{2}{7}$, $u_2^* = \frac{1}{7}$, $u_1^* + 4u_2^* \neq 1$, so $x_3^* = 0$, and $6u_2^* \neq 1$, so $x_4^* = 0$. Since $u_1^* \neq 0$, $u_2^* \neq 0$ and $x_3^* = x_4^* = 0$, the last two conditions become

$$
\begin{array}{l}
3x_1^* + 2x_2^* = 900 \\
x_1^* + 3x_2^* = 900
\end{array}
$$

i.e. $x_1^* = 128\frac{4}{7}$, $x_2^* = 257\frac{1}{7}$ and the total length is $385\frac{5}{7}$ m.

The fact that the dual values were $u_1^* = \frac{2}{7}$ and $u_2^* = \frac{1}{7}$ means that if we required 1 m more of 150 cm width we would need $\frac{2}{7}$ of a metre more of the 540 cm reel to make it, while if we needed 1 m more of 80 cm width we would need $\frac{1}{7}$ of a metre more of the 540 cm reel to make it.

2.13 Sensitivity analysis

Solving the linear program is not the end of the analysis. Often we want to know how the solution will vary if the data in the program change. This is because such data are often subject to variation—in Example 1, for example, the price of paint might change, or some of the pigment might be lost. If the optimal solution does not change much under small variations in the problem data, then it seems sensible to implement that solution. However, if small variations in the data cause considerable changes in the form or value of the optimal solution, then we must be much more careful and check the data available very thoroughly. This idea of checking how changes in the data affect the solution is called **sensitivity analysis**.

Consider, yet again, the paint problem of Example 1, which led to the linear program

$$
\begin{array}{ll}
\text{maximise} & x_1 + 1.5x_2 \\
\text{subject to} & 2x_1 + 4x_2 \leqslant 12 \\
& 3x_1 + 2x_2 \leqslant 10 \\
& x_1, x_2 \geqslant 0.
\end{array}
$$

The solution is $x_1^* = 2$, $x_2^* = 2$ and the dual solution is $u_1^* = \frac{5}{16}$ and $u_2^* = \frac{1}{8}$, with optimal profit of 5.

Suppose in fact instead of 12 units of pigment being available, there were $12 + h$ units available, where h is small. We know from the duality results that since the corresponding dual variable u_1 to the constraint has value $\frac{5}{16}$ initially the total profit will change by $\frac{5}{16}h$; but for what range of h is this true? If we look at the equations in the final tableau of the simplex method ((C1C), (C2C), (OBJC) of Section 2.7 or Table 2.3 of Section 2.8) we notice that at this vertex we have $s_1 = s_2 = 0$, as these are the non-basic variables. Our constraints are now

$$2x_1 + 4x_2 + s_1 = 12 + h,$$
$$3x_1 + 2x_2 + s_2 = 10$$

and solving this with $s_1 = s_2 = 0$ gives $x_1 = 2 - \frac{1}{4}h$, $x_2 = 2 + \frac{3}{8}h$. The objective function equation (OBJC) is now $M + \frac{5}{16}s_1 + \frac{1}{8}s_2 = 5 + \frac{5}{16}h$. (Notice a quick way of getting this result is to replace s_1 by $s_1 - h$ in the last set of equations.) These solutions will then remain optimal while they are still feasible, i.e. provided $x_1 = 2 - \frac{1}{4}h \geqslant 0$ and $x_2 = 2 + \frac{3}{8}h \geqslant -0$ or $-\frac{16}{3} \leqslant h \leqslant 8$.

Instead of a change in the level of a constraint, we might want to investigate a change in a coefficient in the objective function. Suppose the profit of standard paint changes from £1 per unit to (£$1 + h$) per unit: the objective function is then $(1 + h)x_1 + 1.5x_2$. This time, since there is no change in the constraints, the solution $x_1 = 2$, $x_2 = 2$ remains optimal for small values of h. The new objective function equation is $M - (1 + h)x_1 - 1.5x_2 = 0$, or

$$M - (1 + h)(2 + \tfrac{1}{4}s_1 - \tfrac{1}{2}s_2) - 1.5(2 - \tfrac{3}{8}s_1 + \tfrac{1}{4}s_2) = 0,$$

or

$$M + (\tfrac{5}{16} - \tfrac{1}{4}h)s_1 + (\tfrac{1}{8} + \tfrac{1}{2}h)s_2 = 5 + 2h, \tag{OBJ'}$$

where we have used the equations (C1C) and (C2C) of Section 2.9 which give x_1 and x_2 in terms of s_1 and s_2. So $x_1 = 2$, $x_2 = 2$ with solution value $5 + h$ will remain optimal provided the coefficients of s_1 and s_2 in (OBJ') are non-negative, i.e. if $\frac{5}{16} - \frac{1}{4}h \geqslant 0$ and $\frac{1}{8} + \frac{1}{2}h > 0$. This will hold if $-\frac{1}{4} \leqslant h \leqslant \frac{5}{4}$.

If we want to know what happens if we vary the coefficients outside these ranges we have to change to another vertex and this will involve another iteration in the simplex method.

2.14 Multi-objective linear programming and goal programming

In recent years, there have been many advances in linear programming. On the programming side, the simplex algorithm has been modified to take advantage of modern computers and to avoid too many round-off errors, and other algorithms have been developed which use information from the dual as well as the primal problem at each iteration. On the actual formulation of the models it was realised that, in many cases, there is more than one objective function to be optimised.

In the paint example, as well as maximising the profit, you might also want to maximise the amount of top quality paint made. So you have two objectives— maximise $x_1 + 1.5x_2$ and maximise x_2. It is not possible to maximise both these at the same time. In Example 1 the profit is maximised by $x_1 = 2$, $x_2 = 2$ with value 5 and 2 units of top quality paint, whereas the amount of top quality paint is maximised at $x_1 = 0$, $x_2 = 3$, with profit 4.5 and 3 units of top quality paint. We would write this as

maximise $\quad x_1 + 1.5x_2$

$\qquad\qquad x_2$

subject to $\quad 2x_1 + 4x_2 \leqslant 12$

$\qquad\qquad 3x_1 + 2x_2 \leqslant 10$

$\qquad\qquad x_1, x_2 \geqslant 0.$

Multi-objective linear programming and goal programming are two ways of dealing with such problems. In multi-objective linear programming problems you try to find all the efficient solutions, which are those with the property that there is not another solution which is better or as good as it in all the objectives. In goal programming, you set levels which you would like your objectives to reach, and see if there is a solution which attains all these goals, or if not, find one which is close to doing so.

For the example above, the multi-objective linear programming problem would give as a solution the set of efficient solutions $\{(6 - 2x, x): 2 \leqslant x \leqslant 3\}$ i.e. $x_1 = 6 - 2x$, $x_2 = x$, which gives objective values, $(6 - \frac{1}{2}x)$ for profit and x for amount of top quality paint. In goal programming we might say we want to have 2.5 units of top quality paint and a profit of £4. The undominated solutions which satisfy these levels are $x_1 = 6 - 2x$, $x_2 = x$, $2.5 \leqslant x \leqslant 3$.

Exercises

1 An oil firm operates two processes, I and II. The maximum capacity per day of processes I and II is respectively 1.5 and 3 tons. The input to the processes is a single grade crude oil. Each ton of crude oil input to process I requires 20 men, and produces an output of $\frac{3}{4}$ ton of a product A, and $\frac{1}{4}$ ton of a product B. Each ton of crude oil input to process II requires 10 men, and produces an output of $\frac{1}{4}$ ton of product A and $\frac{3}{4}$ ton of product B. In addition, there are costs of £60 and £30 respectively for each ton treated by processes I and II. The firm has 40 men available, and can obtain 4 tons of crude oil each day. The selling prices of products A and B are respectively £285 and £105 per ton.

Treat all variables as continuous variables. Formulate and solve the problem of maximising net revenue as a linear program.

2 A diesel train needs 1 driver, 1 guard, 2 cleaners and 4 fitters to run it, while an electric train needs 1 driver, 2 guards, 1 cleaner and 3 fitters to keep it running. The local depot has 60 diesel trains, 35 electric trains, 84 drivers, 114 guards, 250 cleaners and 309 fitters. Using linear programming techniques, find the maximal number of trains that can be run.

How many (a) drivers, (b) guards, (c) cleaners and (d) fitters can be sacked and yet still run the same number of trains? If 4 guards and 4 fitters leave, how many trains can now be run?

If running a diesel train costs £50 per day and running an electric train costs £80 per day, and the depot has the same number of personnel as in the first part of the question, what is the cheapest number of trains of each type to run? (Don't work too hard.)

3 It is required to supply, over 3 weeks, a total flying effort of 720 man-weeks, with at least 100 flying each week. The conditions are as follows.

(a) In any given week, qualified airmen may be flying, resting or instructing, and may be involved, for that week, in only one of these activities, for the whole week.

(b) At the beginning of the first week there are 120 qualified airmen available.

(c) When a qualified airman is instructing he trains 20 newly qualified airmen who will be available for any 1 of the activities at the beginning of the next week.

(d) There is no limit on the availability of unqualified airmen for training.

(e) At the beginning of each week, any airman who is qualified may rest for the next week, and if he has been flying in the previous week, he must not fly this week. In the first week any qualified airman may rest.

(f) The number of airmen flying in any given week must be at least as great as those flying in the immediately preceding week.

(g) The weekly costs per airman for flying, resting and instructing are respectively 80, 5 and 200.

Formulate, as a linear program, with equalities and inequalities, the problem of finding a schedule of activities, to minimise the total costs over the 3 weeks. Do not solve the problem. For interest, the answer is to have 100 airmen flying, 4 instructing in the first week, 100 flying, 21 instructing in the second, and 520 flying, 0 instructing in the third.

4 Consider the following linear program (shades of Exercise 1):

$$\text{maximise} \quad M = 180x_1 + 120x_2$$
$$\text{subject to} \quad x_1 + x_2 \leqslant 4$$
$$x_1 \leqslant 1.5$$
$$x_2 \leqslant 3$$
$$20x_1 + 10x_2 \leqslant 40$$
$$x_1 \geqslant 0, x_2 \geqslant 0.$$

Solve this problem using the algebraic method, start with $x_1 = 0$, $x_2 = 0$.

5 Consider the following linear program:

$$\text{maximise} \quad 3x + 2y$$

subject to

$$z \quad +0.5u - \frac{v}{20} = 1$$

$$y \quad + \quad u \quad = 3$$

$$x \quad -0.5u + \frac{v}{20} = 0.5$$

$$w - 0.5u - \frac{v}{20} = 0.5$$

$x \geq 0, \ y \geq 0, \ w \geq 0, \ u \geq 0, \ v \geq 0.$

(a) Show that the solution $u = 0, \ v = 0, \ x = 0.5, \ y = 3, \ z = 1, \ w = 0.5$ is optimal by checking in the algebraic method.

(b) Given that the objective function is $\alpha x + \beta y$, find inequalities between α and β which are necessary and sufficient for the solution in (a) to be optimal.

6 A wholesale company has a warehouse of 2000 ft³. It stocks three types of food mixer: Pixie Mixie, Super Mixer and Mixmaster. A Pixie Mixie costs £10 for the company to buy, occupies 1 ft³ and can be sold at a profit of £2. A Super Mixer costs £12, occupies 2.5 ft³ and makes a profit of £3, while a Mixmaster occupies 3 ft³, costs £18 to buy and yields a profit of £4. The company has a maximum of £12 200 for the purchase of stock. Set up the problem of maximising the company's profit in LP formulation and state the dual. Solve the dual problem graphically and, by complementary slackness, or otherwise, find the solution to the original problem. If another company wants to rent some storage space from this company, how much rent per cubic foot should they charge? Explain your answer.

7 A firm manufactures colour televisions, black and white televisions, radios, record players and speakers for record players. The costs of manufacture and the number of hours of labour involved are given in Table 2.5. Labour costs are £1 per hour.

Table 2.5

Item	Cost of parts	No. of hours of labour	Sale price (£)
Colour TV	160	20	230
B/W TV	20	10	70
Radio	7	5	22
Record player	35	8	73
Speakers	10	2	20

At least 10 more record players than speakers are required each week. The total number of hours of labour available each week is 1000.

Express the problem of maximising the profit (sales revenue – costs) per week in linear programming form.

State the dual problem, and solve this dual problem graphically. Treat all variables as continuous variables.

8   Two warehouses A, B, supply three stores, C, D, E. The supplies available from A and B are 10 and 6 units respectively. The requirements for C, D, E are 3, 7, 6 units respectively. It costs a certain amount to supply each store with 1 unit from each of the warehouses, as given in Table 2.6.

Table 2.6

	C	D	E	
A	5	4	2	Unit supply costs
B	4	6	3	

(a)   Formulate and solve graphically as a standard linear program with *all inequality* constraints, the problem of supplying all the requirements at a minimal total cost, using only *two* decision variables.

(b)   Formulate the same problem as a problem with six decision variables and equality constraints.

(c)   Write down the dual problem to (b) and check by complementary slackness that the solution in (a) is optimal.

9   In Exercises 1 (and 4) above, carry out a post-optimality sensitivity analysis on the right-hand constraints.

(a)   Find the possible sets of right-hand constraint levels (i.e. $x_1 + x_2 \leqslant a$, $x_1 \leqslant b$, $x_2 \leqslant c$, $20x_1 + 10x_2 \leqslant d$) for which the solution in Exercises 1 (and 4) ($x_1 = 0.5$, $x_2 = 3$) is still optimal.

(b)   Find how the value of the objective function $180x_1 + 120x_2$ varies as the right-hand side constraint level changes in this region.

10   At Christmas, I buy either expensive presents at £20 each or cheap ones at £5 for the children in my family. I have 12 children to buy presents for (though I may buy more than one present for a child). I must buy expensive presents for my three favourite children. However, cheap presents tend to weigh 5 kg, while expensive ones weigh only 1 kg. In order to make Santa's sack look right, I want the presents to weigh at least 20 kg.

(a)   Set up in LP form and solve the problem of buying the presents so as to minimise the costs.

(b)   It takes 1 hour to choose each expensive present but 2 hours to choose each cheap present. Set up in LP form and solve the problem of buying the presents in the shortest possible time.

(c) Think of the problem with the two criteria of minimising cost and minimising time to buy. Find all the solutions which are not dominated in the sense that there is another solution which is as cheap and as quick (and is strictly better in one of the criteria). These are called the efficient points.

(d) In a goal programming approach to the problem, find all the undominated solutions in which I spend less than £120 and shop for less than 22 hours.

3
Transportation Problems

3.1 Introduction

In Chapter 2 we have discussed linear programming in general. There are some problems which give rise to special forms of linear programming. In this chapter, and the next, we will consider two such classes—transportation and assignment problems.

In order to illustrate the class of transportation problems, we will consider a simple example related very much to the pioneering developments in this area.

An electricity utility has four power stations, which we label $j = 1, 2, 3, 4$. They are supplied by three collieries, which we label $i = 1, 2, 3$. The total supply of coal at the collieries is equal to the total requirement by the power stations in appropriate units. There is a cost of transporting one unit of coal from each colliery to each power station. Table 3.1 gives the available supplies, the requirements, and the unit transportation costs.

Table 3.1

		Power station j				
		1	2	3	4	Available supplies
	1	2	3	4	5	10
Colliery i	2	5	4	3	1	15
	3	1	3	3	2	21
Requirements		6	11	17	12	

The transportation problem is to determine how many units to transport from each colliery to each power station in order to minimise the total cost in meeting all requirements.

Readers may wish to see if they can solve this problem themselves before looking at the standard way of solving the problem. The minimal total cost is 102 and the unique, optimal, solution is to transport 10, 3, 12, 6, 1, 14 units from collieries 1, 2, 2, 3, 3, 3 to power stations 2, 3, 4, 1, 2, 3 respectively.

As has been indicated, the transportation problem may be considered to be a special class of linear program, and we will now look at this.

3.2 A linear programming formulation

We will proceed to identify the decision variables, constraints, and objective functions as we do in general linear programming.

We will initially formulate the problem as one in which *no more than* the available supplies may be used, and *at least* the specified requirements must be met, so that the problem is in *inequality* form.

Let x_{ij} be the amount to be transported from colliery i to power station j.
The constraints are as follows.

$$x_{11} + x_{12} + x_{13} + x_{14} \leqslant 10 \qquad \text{(colliery 1)}$$
$$x_{21} + x_{22} + x_{23} + x_{24} \leqslant 15 \qquad \text{(colliery 2)}$$
$$x_{31} + x_{32} + x_{33} + x_{34} \leqslant 21 \qquad \text{(colliery 3)}$$

$$x_{11} + x_{21} + x_{31} \qquad \geqslant 6 \qquad \text{(power station 1)}$$
$$x_{12} + x_{22} + x_{32} \qquad \geqslant 1 \qquad \text{(power station 2)}$$
$$x_{13} + x_{23} + x_{33} \qquad \geqslant 7 \qquad \text{(power station 3)}$$
$$x_{14} + x_{24} + x_{34} \qquad \geqslant 2 \qquad \text{(power station 4)}$$

The problem has been formulated as one of at least meeting the requirements, and hence we use $\geqslant$ rather than $=$ for the moment. For general linear programming problems it is not necessarily true that optimal solutions require that all constraints be satisfied as *equalities*.

$$x_{ij} \geqslant 0 \text{ for all } i \text{ and } j.$$

The objective function is as follows.

$$\text{Total cost} = M = 2x_{11} + 3x_{12} + 4x_{13} + 5x_{14} + 5x_{21} + 4x_{22} + 3x_{23} + 1x_{24} + 1x_{31} + 3x_{32} + 3x_{33} + 2x_{34}.$$

The problem is to minimise M subject to the specified constraints.
In terms of the above notation, the optimal solution is given by

$$M = 102, x_{12} = 10, x_{23} = 3, x_{24} = 12, x_{31} = 6, x_{32} = 1, x_{33} = 14,$$
$$x_{11} = x_{13} = x_{14} = x_{21} = x_{22} = x_{34} = 0.$$

This linear programming problem may be solved using the simplex method of Chapter 2. If the availability levels are whole numbers, then the simplex method always gives whole number solutions for every iteration (i.e. for all basic feasible solutions). However, there is a simpler method of solving this problem, related to the *simplex* algorithm and to *duality* as discussed in Chapter 2. This method is known as the *transportation algorithm*, and we will restrict ourselves to this in this text. It is the simplex method done more efficiently than for general linear programming problems. Before doing so, we must convert our *inequality* problem to an *equality* problem in which the inequalities for the availability and requirement constraints are replaced by equalities. The reader should check that this is valid for our problem in which total availability equals total requirements.

3.3   The transportation algorithm

There are two essential steps in the transportation algorithm: (a) *finding starting solutions*; and (b) *improving on solutions*, if possible, until no further improvement is possible.

Before proceeding with the method, it is to be noted that all approaches involve essentially the same operations in that they

(1)   select a cell (i, j)
(2)   make x_{ij} as large as possible
(3)   delete a row or column
(4)   return to (1).

The differences in the three approaches which we will use lie solely in the mechanism for selecting (i, j) in (1) for the starting solution only. Thereafter, the operations are identical.

This feature of finding a starting solution, improving on it in some way, and repeating the procedure, is a common one in other chapters in this text. At each stage, there will be checks to determine whether or not an improvement is possible (e.g. see the next chapter on the assignment problem).

Finding a starting solution

By a *starting solution* we mean a set of transportation quantities which will satisfy all the constraints. There are several ways of finding starting solutions. We will deal with three: the north-west corner rule method, minimal unit cost method, and Vogel's method. The first method is the more easily applied method, but the latter methods, although involving extra work, seek to begin with *good* starting solutions in an attempt to speed up the algorithm. They work loosely on a principle of the kind *smallest in a row, or column, is best*.

Throughout the application of the method, each solution will have $m + n - 1$ positive values of x_{ij}, if the problem has m supply sources and n requirements points (i.e. m rows and n columns in the formulation), with the exception of degenerate situations, which we will briefly discuss later on. For our example, this means that solutions will have $6 (= 3 + 4 - 1)$ positive transportation quantities.

North-west corner rule

We begin in the top left-hand corner (i.e. north-west position) and make x_{11} as large as possible compatible with the constraints. This gives $x_{11} = 6$

(= minimum of available supply of 10 and requirement of 6). This exhausts the requirement in column 1, which we delete, with a residual supply left, for row 1, of 4 units. The new sub-problem is then given in Table 3.2.

Table 3.2

		\multicolumn{4}{c}{Power station j}	Available supplies
		1	2	3	4	
	1	6				4
Colliery i	2		sub-problem			15
	3					21
Requirements			11	17	12	

We now repeat the procedure with the sub-problem of Table 3.2, and make x_{12} as large as possible compatible with the new constraints. This gives $x_{12} = 4$ (= minimum of available supply of 4 and requirement of 11). This exhausts the supply in row 1, which we delete, with a residual requirement of 7 for column 2.

The procedure is repeated until we arrive at the north-west corner rule solution of Table 3.3. Each time a row or column is exhausted it is deleted, and the procedure applied to the new sub-problem arising from this.

Table 3.3

		\multicolumn{4}{c}{Power station j}	Available supplies
		1	2	3	4	
	1	6	4			10
Colliery i	2		7	8		15 Total cost = 127
	3			9	12	21
Requirements		6	11	17	12	

Although we have explained the step-by-step procedure in terms of sub-problems, it is quite easy to do the calculations in one go on a single table.

For some problems we may simultaneously exhaust a row *and* a column when the availability and requirements are equal for that row and column. This will result in a *degenerate* situation to which we will return later on.

The minimal unit cost method

This method proceeds by allocating as much as possible to the cell (i, j) which has the smallest unit cost, deleting the row or column whose availability or requirement is exhausted, and repeating the procedure until all rows and columns have been deleted. The calculations proceed as in Tables 3.4–3.8.

Table 3.4

		Power station j				Available supplies
		1	2	3	4	
	1	2	3	4	5	10
Colliery i	2	5	4	3	(1)	15
	3	1	3	3	2	21
Requirements		6	11	17	12	

We may make x_{24} or x_{31} as large as possible. We choose $x_{24} = 12$, and column 4 is deleted (Table 3.5)

Table 3.5

		Power station j				Available supplies
		1	2	3	4	
	1	2	3	4		10
Colliery i	2	5	4	3	12	3
	3	(1)	3	3		21
Requirements		6	11	17		

We make x_{31} as large as possible, i.e. $x_{31} = 6$, and column 1 is deleted (Table 3.6).

We may make x_{12}, x_{23}, x_{32} or x_{33} as large as possible. We choose $x_{12} = 10$, and row 1 is deleted to give Table 3.7.

We may make x_{23}, x_{32}, or x_{33} as large as possible. We choose $x_{23} = 3$. Then $x_{32} = 1, x_{33} = 14$, and we obtain the starting solution in Table 3.8.

This happens to be the optimal solution, but the method need not give optimal solutions, even for the case $m = n = 2$.

Table 3.6

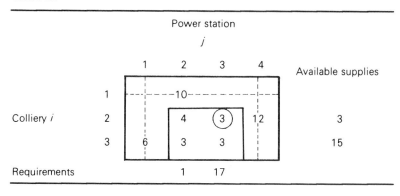

		Power station j				Available supplies
		1	2	3	4	
Colliery i	1		③	4		10
	2		4	3	12	3
	3	6	3	3		15
Requirements			11	17		

Table 3.7

		Power station j				Available supplies
		1	2	3	4	
Colliery i	1	----10----				3
	2		4	③	12	3
	3	6	3	3		15
Requirements			1	17		

Table 3.8

		Power station j				Available supplies
		1	2	3	4	
Colliery i	1		10			10
	2			3	12	15 Total cost = 102
	3	6	1	14		21
Requirements		6	11	17	12	

For the example of Table 3.9, it may be shown that for $m = n = 2$, the minimal unit cost rule will not give an optimal starting solution.

Table 3.9

		Destination j		Available supplies
		1	2	
Source i	1	1	2	2
	2	2	4	1
Requirements		1	2	

The appeal of the method derives from the intuitively desirable feature of using up as much of the available supplies or requirements at as small a cost as possible.

Vogel's method

As has been indicated, it seems prudent to seek *good* starting solutions. Vogel's method does this by looking, in effect, at *relative* unit costs. More specifically, at each step the procedure determines, for the sub-problem being considered, the two smallest unit costs in each row and the two smallest unit costs in each column. If several unit costs are equally the smallest, then any two of these may be used. The procedure then takes the difference between the pair so determined for each row and column. Again, note that the smallest and second smallest may be equal, so this difference may be zero. For the row, or column, where this difference is largest, the minimal unit cost is determined and, as for the north-west corner rule, the maximal transportation amount, x_{ij}, compatible with the availabilities and requirements is determined for the cell (i, j) where this minimum is located. The row or column which is thereby exhausted is then deleted, and the procedure is repeated until all rows and columns have been deleted and a starting solution is obtained.

For our specimen problem, we obtain Tables 3.10–3.14.

Table 3.10

		Power station j				Unit cost difference
		1	2	3	4	
Colliery i	1	2	3	4	5	1
	2	5	4	3	①	2 ← Largest
	3	1	3	3	2	1
Unit cost difference		1	0	0	1	

The maximal difference in Table 3.10 is in row 2, and the smallest unit cost in this row is 1 in cell (2, 4) (i.e. row 2, column 4). We make x_{24} as large as possible compatible with availability and requirement levels, to give $x_{24} = 12$, and column 4 is deleted to give Table 3.11.

Table 3.11

		Power station j					
		1	2	3	4	Available supplies	Unit cost difference
	1	2	3	4		10	1
Colliery i	2	5	4	3	12	3	1
	3	(1)	3	3		21	2 ← largest
Requirements		6	11	17			
Unit cost difference		1	0	0			

We make x_{31} as large as possible, i.e. $x_{31} = 6$, and column 1 is deleted to give Table 3.12.

Table 3.12

		Power station j					
		1	2	3	4	Available supplies	Unit cost difference
	1		(3)	4		10	1 ← largest
Colliery i	2		4	3	12	3	1
	3	6	3	3		15	0
Requirements			11	17			
Unit cost difference			0	0			

We make x_{12} as large as possible, i.e. $x_{12} = 10$, and row 1 is deleted to give Table 3.13.

We make x_{23} as large as possible, i.e. $x_{23} = 3$. We must then have $x_{32} = 1$ and $x_{33} = 14$, to give the Vogel starting solution in Table 3.14.

Table 3.13

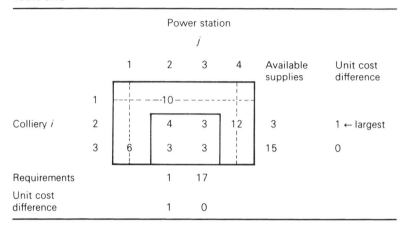

Table 3.14

		1	2	3	4	Available supplies
	1		10			10
Colliery i	2			3	12	15 Total cost = 102
	3	6	1	14		21
Requirements		6	11	17	12	

For this problem it so happens that the optimal solution is obtained, but this is not generally so unless $m = n = 2$.

For the problem of Table 3.15, neither the minimal unit cost method nor Vogel's method will give optimal solutions, as the reader should check once he has learnt how to get optimal solutions.

The question arises of why Vogel's method works so well. Let us look at Table 3.10. The method requires that we allocate as much as possible to the cell (2, 4). If we did not do so, then there would be subsequent allocations to row 2 with a minimal increase in unit cost of 2 units per unit allocation, and this is the largest increase possible if we had chosen to allocate the maximal amount to any cell other than (2, 4). By choosing (2, 4) we try to avoid this maximal penalty of 2 units which might be incurred by later allocations.

Table 3.15

		Destination			
		j			
		1	2	3	Available supplies
Source *i*	1	4	4	6	10
	2	10	8	8	15
	3	9	12	10	21.
Requirements		6	16	24	

Improving the solution

We will use the north-west corner rule to find our starting solution (see Table 3.3), although the method now to be described for improving the solution also applies to any other starting solution method.

The method we will describe is called the *stepping-stone method* since it involves an operation which looks like stepping from one stone to another. Let us first of all illustrate this stepping-stone operation beginning with Table 3.3, which we now restate as Table 3.16 for convenience.

Table 3.16

		Power station				
		j				
		1	2	3	4	Available supplies
Colliery *i*	1	6	4			10
	2		7	8		15
	3			9	12	21
Requirements		6	11	17	12	

Let us suppose that we wish to consider what change in the cost arises if we allocate a quantity θ to the cell $(1, 3)$, i.e. make $x_{13} = \theta$. We must now adjust the other allocations to maintain row and column availability and requirement levels. In doing so we will allow changes in only the positive entries in Table 3.16. This corresponds to the simplex procedure in linear programming, where a vertex (basic feasible solution) has at most $m + n - 1$ positive entries if our transportation problem has m rows and n columns, a point to which we will return later on.

The positive entry cells are the *stones* in the stepping stone operation. We will seek a circuit of such stones, including the new stone in cell (1, 3), with exactly two stones in each row and column. The circuit, which is unique in any problem, is given in Table 3.17.

Table 3.17

		1	2	3	4	Available supplies
			Power station	*j*		
Colliery *i*	1	6	$4-\theta\leftarrow$ $\downarrow$	θ $\uparrow$		10
	2		$7+\theta\rightarrow$	$8-\theta$		15
	3			9	12	21
Requirements		6	11	17	12	

From the unit cost Table 3.1, the additional cost arising from Table 3.17 is

$$\theta(4-3+4-3) = 2\theta > 0$$

if $\theta > 0$. Hence we would not allocate θ to cell (1, 3). If we, for example, allocate θ to cell (2, 4) we have Table 3.18.

Table 3.18

		1	2	3	4	Available supplies
			Power station	*j*		
Colliery *i*	1	6	4			10
	2		7	$8-\theta\leftarrow$ $\downarrow$	θ $\uparrow$	15
	3			$9+\theta\rightarrow12-\theta$		21
Requirements		6	11	17	12	

The additional cost is

$$\theta(1-3+3-2) = -\theta$$

and if $\theta > 0$ we reduce the cost. We must keep all allocations non-negative, and, in Table 3.17, the maximal value of θ consistent with this is $\theta = 4$, whereas in

Table 3.18 the maximal value of θ is 8. This is, in effect, the standard *pivot row* selection rule used in the simplex method. Putting $\theta = 8$ in Table 3.18 we obtain an improved solution given in Table 3.19.

Table 3.19

		\multicolumn{4}{c}{Power station}		
		\multicolumn{4}{c}{j}		
		1	2	3	4	Available supplies
	1	6	4			10
Colliery i	2		7		8	15 Total cost $= 119$
	3			17	4	21
Requirements		6	11	17	21	

It would be possible to treat each location, with a non-positive allocation, in a similar manner and terminate the calculations if all the associated changes in cost were positive. For a problem with m rows and n columns this would involve $mn - m - n + 1$ cells to be checked, with the corresponding stepping-stone operation, and could be quite time consuming if m or n were large. Fortunately, we can avoid having to do this by making use of a little of our linear programming knowledge. Let us now look at the full transportation method. Before doing so, however, let us examine the general balanced transportation problem in a linear programming context so that we will be able to see why the method works.

If we have m supply sources, n requirement points, and the total supply equals the total requirement, we have a *balanced problem*. If $\{a_i\}$ are the supply levels, and $\{b_j\}$ are the requirement levels, the linear programming formulation is as follows (check against the linear programming formulation of the colliery–power station example, noting that the inequalities for that problem may be reduced to equalities since it is a balanced problem):

minimise $\quad M = \sum_i \sum_j c_{ij} x_{ij}$

subject to

$\sum_j x_{ij} = a_i, \; i = 1, 2, \ldots, m \qquad$ (availabilities)

$\sum_i x_{ij} = b_j, \; j = 1, 2, \ldots, n \qquad$ (requirements)

$x_{ij} \geqslant 0$ for all i and j,

where x_{ij} is the amount transported from supply point i to requirement point j.

We have $m + n$ equations in mn variables. The equations are dependent in that any one may be deduced from the remaining $m + n - 1$. From our linear programming results we seek $m + n - 1$ basic variables, and this is why we keep $m + n - 1$ allocations in each solution at each stage. The dual problem is easily stated:

$$\text{maximise } M = \sum_i a_i u_i + \sum_j b_j v_j$$

subject to

$$u_i + v_j \leqslant c_{ij} \qquad \text{for all } i, j$$

with $\{u_i\}$, $\{v_j\}$ unsigned because the primal problem is in equality form. The complementary slackness conditions require that, if $x_{ij} \neq 0$, then the corresponding dual constraint should be an equality (i.e. the slack variable of the dual constraint is 0) and, as will be seen in step (2) of the stepping-stone method, we require $u_i + v_j = c_{ij}$ whenever $x_{ij} > 0$. In the simplex method, the numbers $\{c_{ij} - u_i - v_j\}$ are the coefficients, in the objective function, of the variable $\{x_{ij}\}$ and, as with the linear programming method, we can increase x_{ij}, where $c_{ij} - u_i - v_j < 0$.

It should be noted that, whereas in the linear programming chapter, the complementary slackness conditions were used only at an *optimal* solution, for the transportation problem they are used at each step of the algorithm, and this is a special feature of the transportation problem and not of *all* linear programming problems.

Before proceeding with the algorithm, let us recall, from the linear programming chapter, that the dual problem can be given physical interpretations in terms of market prices for constraint levels. Thus, in this problem, suppose that the manager responsible for the transportation problem was given a price u_i for each unit loaded at supply point i, and price v_j for unloading a unit at destination j. Then the total price paid to the market is exactly the objective function given for all the operations required to move the goods from the supply points to the destination points. The constraints placed by the manager would be that his unit costs should be no higher than they were before, and the market would seek to maximise its income.

Let us now look at the steps we follow in the transportation algorithm once we have a starting solution.

(1)   Identify the unit costs associated with the positive allocations of the starting solution. These are given in Table 3.20.

(2)   With each row i associate a dual variable u_i, which we will call a row *shadow cost*, and with each column j associate a dual variable v_j, which we will call a column *shadow cost*, in such a way that the sum of u_i and v_j equals the unit cost in cell (i, j) for all positive cells. Thus we require

$$u_1 + v_1 = 2$$
$$u_1 + v_2 = 3$$

Table 3.20

		Power station				
				j		
		1	2	3	4	Available supplies
Colliery i	1	2	3			10
	2		4	3		15
	3			3	2	21
Requirements		6	11	17	12	

$$u_2 + v_2 = 4$$
$$u_2 + v_3 = 3$$
$$u_3 + v_3 = 3$$
$$u_3 + v_4 = 2$$

We have 6 ($= m + n - 1$) equations in 7 ($= m + n$) variables, and can set any one of the 7 variables equal to any number (we choose the number 0) and solve for the rest.

It is easily seen, for example, that in the above equations we can add any constant k to the values of $\{u_i\}$, and subtract the same constant k from the values of $\{v_j\}$, and still get a solution to the equations.

An alternative way of seeing that we have a degree of freedom in our solution for the $\{u_i\}$ and $\{v_j\}$ is to note, as has already been indicated, that there is no loss in removing any single constraint, and that hence we merely drop the corresponding dual variable by setting it equal to 0 (or, indeed, to any value). The calculations can be done quite easily on Table 3.20 directly to give Table 3.21.

Table 3.21

			Power station				
					j		
			$v_1 = 0$	$v_2 = 1$	$v_3 = 0$	$v_4 = -1$	
			1	2	3	4	Available supplies
Colliery i	$u_1 = 2$	1	2	3			10
	$u_2 = 3$	2		4	3		15
	$u_3 = 3$	3			3	2	21
Requirements			6	11	17	12	

(3)   For each cell (i, j) subtract the sum of the row and column shadow costs from the unit cost for that cell. Cells corresponding to the positive allocations will, because of step (2), always have a zero value for this. Table 3.22 gives the results of this step.

Table 3.22

		\multicolumn{4}{c}{Power station j}	
		1	2	3	4	Available supplies
Colliery i	1	0	0	2	4	10
	2	2	0	0	−1	15
	3	−2	−1	0	0	21
Requirements		6	11	17	12	

From our knowledge of linear programming, it may be shown that the entries in Table 3.22 are the coefficients of the objective function we would obtain if our basic variables had been chosen to correspond to the positive allocation cells, the entries being zero for the latter. Any extra allocation θ to any cell, followed by an adjustment using the stepping stone operation, will change the total cost by an amount $\theta \times$ the corresponding entry in Table 3.22, just as in linear programming. This may also be checked a different way using the derivation of $\{u_i\}, \{v_j\}$ in step (3). Thus suppose we allocate θ to cell $(3, 1)$, and use the stepping stone operation. We obtain Table 3.23.

Table 3.23

		\multicolumn{4}{c}{Power station j}	
		1	2	3	4	Available supplies
Colliery i	1	$6 - \theta$	$4 + \theta$			10
	2		$7 - \theta$	$8 + \theta$		15
	3	θ		$9 - \theta$	12	21
Requirements		6	11	17	12	

The addition to the total cost is

$$\theta(1 - 2 + 3 - 4 + 3 - 3)$$
$$= \theta((1 - u_3 - v_1) - (2 - u_1 - v_1) + (3 - u_1 - v_2)$$
$$\quad - (4 - u_2 - v_2) + (3 - u_2 - v_3) - (3 - u_3 - v_3)) \quad \text{(as is easily checked)}$$
$$= \theta(1 - u_3 - v_1) \quad \text{(since the remaining brackets are all zero by virtue of step (3))}$$
$$= -2\theta.$$

(4)   We make θ as large as possible (i.e. $\theta = 6$) to derive Table 3.24, which becomes the starting solution for a repetition of all the steps (1)–(4).

Table 3.24

		Power station				
		j				
		1	2	3	4	Available supplies
	1		10			10
Colliery i	2		1	14		15 Total cost = 115
	3	6		3	12	21
Requirements		6	11	17	12	

The steps are repeated until the table corresponding to Table 3.22 has all entries non-negative, and the corresponding allocation solution will be optimal. Again note that this is the simplex method at work. In carrying out the calculation it is much simpler to put some calculations on the same table. We will use the convention shown in Table 3.25 in constructing Table 3.26 for a given cell (i, j).

Table 3.25

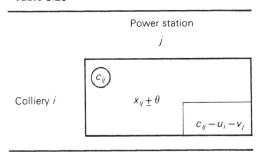

Here c_{ij} is the unit cost and we put the most negative value of $c_{ij} - u_i - v_j$ inside a square, and encircle the $\{c_{ij}\}$ corresponding to the positive allocations x_{ij} at each stage. Tables 3.27 and 3.28 complete the calculations.

Table 3.26

Power station j

		$v_1=0$ 1	$v_2=3$ 2	$v_3=2$ 3	$v_4=1$ 4	Available supplies
	$u_1=0$ 1	2 2	③ 10 0	4 0	5 4	10
Colliery i $u_2=1$ 2		5 4	④ $1-\theta$ 0	③ $14+\theta$ 0	1 -1	15
	$u_3=1$ 3	① 6 0	3 θ -1	③ $3-\theta$ 0	② 12 0	21 Total cost $=115$
Requirements		6	11	17	12	$\theta_{max}=1$

Table 3.27

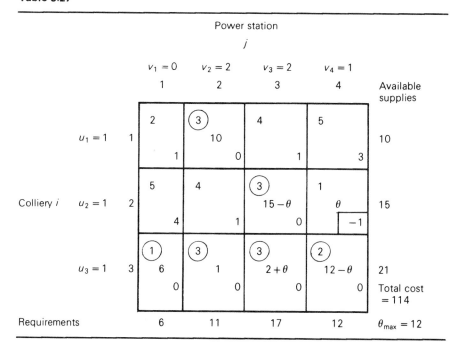

Power station j

		$v_1=0$ 1	$v_2=2$ 2	$v_3=2$ 3	$v_4=1$ 4	Available supplies
	$u_1=1$ 1	2 1	③ 10 0	4 1	5 3	10
Colliery i $u_2=1$ 2		5 4	4 1	③ $15-\theta$ 0	1 θ -1	15
	$u_3=1$ 3	① 6 0	③ 1 0	③ $2+\theta$ 0	② $12-\theta$ 0	21 Total cost $=114$
Requirements		6	11	17	12	$\theta_{max}=12$

Table 3.28

Note that we have two equally negative values of $c_{ij} - u_i - v_j$ equal to -1 and we choose cell $(3, 3)$. We may equally well choose cell $(2, 4)$ for the next step. Either choice will work.

In Table 3.28 all the entries $c_{ij} - u_i - v_j$ in the bottom right-hand quarters of each square are non-negative, and hence the solution is optimal:

$$x_{12} = 10, \; x_{23} = 3, \; x_{24} = 12, \; x_{31} = 6, \; x_{32} = 1, \; x_{33} = 14,$$
$$x_{11} = x_{13} = x_{14} = x_{21} = x_{22} = x_{34} = 0, \; M = 102.$$

Let us now consider some special points relating to the transportation problem.

3.4 Special aspects

(i) Unbalanced transportation problems

For some problems we may have total supply not equal to total requirement. Consider the example in Table 3.29.

Table 3.29

		Power station				
		j				
		1	2	3	4	Available supplies
Colliery *i*	1	2	3	4	5	11
	2	5	4	3	1	16
	3	1	3	3	2	22
Requirements		6	11	17	12	

The total available supplies (49) are greater than the total requirement (46). Hence, some supplies will not be used. We add a dummy column to obtain a balanced transportation problem in Table 3.30, where $\{p_i\}$ are the penalties for each unit of supply i not being used.

Table 3.30

		Power station					
		j				Dummy	
		1	2	3	4	5	Available supplies
Colliery *i*	1	2	3	4	5	p_1	11
	2	5	4	3	1	p_2	16
	3	1	3	3	2	p_3	22
Requirements		6	11	17	12	3	

Unless stated otherwise the $\{p_i\}$ are usually equal to 0.

Likewise if total supplies are less than total requirements, we construct a standard balanced transportation problem with a dummy row.

In general, whether the problem is balanced or not, we may not need to use all the supplies or to meet all the requirements. We then add a dummy row and a dummy column to obtain Table 3.31, where $\{p_i\}$, $\{q_j\}$ are specified penalties for units of supply not used or requirements not met respectively. Here a_4 is the dummy supply level and b_5 the dummy requirement level. We require $a_1 + a_2 + a_3 + a_4 = b_1 + b_2 + b_3 + b_4 + b_5$. The values of a_4, b_5 merely have to be big enough to allow no requirements to be met or no supplies to be used in the original problem; e.g.

$$a_4 = b_1 + b_2 + b_3 + b_4, \quad b_5 = a_1 + a_2 + a_3$$

will do.

Table 3.31

		Power station					
				j		Dummy	
		1	2	3	4	5	Available supplies
Colliery *i*	1	2	3	4	5	p_1	a_1
	2	5	4	3	1	p_2	a_2
	3	1	3	3	2	p_3	a_3
Dummy	4	q_1	q_2	q_3	q_4	0	a_4
Requirements		b_1	b_2	b_3	b_4	b_5	

(ii)   Non-unique optimal solutions

Suppose that in Table 3.1 we had $c_{13} = 3$ instead of $c_{13} = 4$. Then, following the stepping-stone procedure we would end up with Table 3.32 instead of Table 3.28.

Table 3.32

We can see that $c_{13} - u_1 - v_3 = 0$. If we allocate a quantity θ to the cell $(1, 3)$, and use the stepping-stone operation, the change in cost is $\theta.0 = 0$ for all θ such that $0 \leqslant \theta \leqslant 10$. Thus for all such θ we will obtain solutions each with a cost of 102, and the solution arrived at with $\theta = 0$ is not uniquely optimal. Again this is the simplex method at work (see Chapter 1 for non-uniqueness in general linear programming).

(iii)   Degeneracy

As we have seen in linear programming, degeneracy can arise when one, at least, of the basic variables is zero. In the transportation problem this corresponds to one of the $m + n - 1$ allocations of our solutions being zero. Let us see how this may arise. Suppose that instead of Table 3.1 we have Table 3.33.

Table 3.33

		Power station j				Available supplies
		1	2	3	4	
Colliery i	1	2	3	4	5	10
	2	5	4	3	1	15
	3	1	3	3	2	21
Requirements		10	11	11	14	

If we use the north-west corner rule we obtain $x_{11} = 10$ and row 1 *and* column 1 would be exhausted. If we deleted both and continued with the north-west corner rule we would obtain Table 3.34. This has only 5, instead of 6, positive allocations and gives a degenerate solution.

Table 3.34

		Power station j				Available supplies
		1	2	3	4	
Colliery i	1	10				10
	2		11	4		15
	3			7	14	21
Requirements		10	11	11	14	

A look at the stepping-stone method will show that each allocation x_{ij} will be equal to $\pm$ (the sum (may be zero) of some of the available source levels $\{a_i\}$ minus the sum (may be zero) of some of the requirement levels $\{b_j\}$). Thus in Table 3.16

$$x_{11} = b_1 - 0 = 6, \quad x_{12} = a_1 - b_1 = 10 - 6 = 4, \quad x_{13} = 0 - 0 = 0,$$
$$x_{14} = 0 - 0 = 0, \quad x_{21} = 0 - 0 = 0,$$
$$x_{22} = b_2 - (a_1 - b_1) = b_1 + b_2 - a_1 = 7;$$

and so on. Thus we can avoid any of the stepping-stone entries being zero if we can avoid any non-null differences of the sums of available supply levels and requirements levels being zero. We do this by changing Table 3.33 to Table 3.35.

Table 3.35

		\multicolumn{4}{c}{Power station}			

		\multicolumn{4}{c}{j}	
		1	2	3	4	Available supplies
	1	2	3	4	5	$10 + \varepsilon$
Colliery i	2	5	4	3	1	$15 + \varepsilon$
	3	1	3	3	2	$21 + \varepsilon$
Requirements		$10 + 3\varepsilon$	11	11	14	

It is easily checked that the above property regarding the differences of the sums of sub-sets of the available supply levels and requirement levels is satisfied if ε is small enough, e.g. $\varepsilon = \frac{1}{4}$. For a general $m \times n$ problem, with $n \geq m$, with whole number supply and requirement levels, we change a_i to $a_i + \varepsilon$, b_1 to $b_1 + m\varepsilon$, and leave the remaining levels unaltered. The calculations then proceed as before and ε is set equal to 0 when they terminate. For computer applications it is sufficient to put $\varepsilon = 1/2n$. The modification is usually done at the beginning, even though degeneracy may not have arisen without it. Alternatively, one can wait until degeneracy arises and modify the solution at that stage, although this may require some searching of the empty allocation cells before a solution is found. Thus if we arrive at Table 3.34, then Table 3.36 will suffice.

(iv) Post-optimality sensitivity analysis

We have dealt with sensitivity analysis in linear programming. We do so with respect to variations in the unit costs only. Suppose that Table 3.1 is replaced by Table 3.37.

Table 3.36

		1	2	3	4	Available supplies
			Power station			
			j			
Colliery i	1	$10 + \varepsilon$				$10 + \varepsilon$
	2	2ε	11	$4 - \varepsilon$		$15 + \varepsilon$
	3			$7 + \varepsilon$	14	$21 + \varepsilon$
Requirements		$10 + 3\varepsilon$	11	11	14	

Table 3.37

		1	2	3	4	Available supplies
			Power station			
			j			
Colliery i	1	$2 + \delta_{11}$	3	$4 + \delta_{13}$	$5 + \delta_{14}$	10
	2	$5 + \delta_{21}$	$4 + \delta_{22}$	3	1	15
	3	1	3	3	$2 + \delta_{34}$	21
Requirements		6	11	17	12	

In order to keep matters simple, we have kept the unit costs associated with the positive solution allocations unaltered, and made small perturbations $\{\delta_{ij}\}$ in the remaining unit cost entries. We stress that this is merely to keep computations simple and that, in practice, variations in *all* the unit costs would be considered.

If we take the solution given in Table 3.28 for the original problem, the $\{c_{ij} - u_i - v_j\}$ entries for the new cost table are given in Table 3.38, noting that the $\{u_i\}, \{v_j\}$ values remain the same since we have calculated these for the same final solution of Table 3.28.

Then the original solution given in Table 3.28 is still optimal for the new unit cost matrix if all the entries in Table 3.38 are non-negative, i.e.

$$\delta_{11} \geqslant -1, \quad \delta_{13} \geqslant -1, \quad \delta_{14} \geqslant -4, \quad \delta_{21} \geqslant -4,$$
$$\delta_{22} \geqslant -1, \quad \delta_{34} \geqslant -1.$$

This is equivalent to

$$c_{11} \geqslant 1, \quad c_{13} \geqslant 3, \quad c_{14} \geqslant 4, \quad c_{21} \geqslant 1, \quad c_{22} \geqslant 3, \quad c_{34} \geqslant 1.$$

Table 3.38

			$v_1 = 0$	$v_2 = 2$	$v_3 = 2$	$v_4 = 0$	
			Power station j				
			1	2	3	4	Available supplies
	$u_1 = 1$	1	$1 + \delta_{11}$	0	$1 + \delta_{13}$	$4 + \delta_{14}$	10
Colliery i	$u_2 = 1$	2	$4 + \delta_{21}$	$1 + \delta_{22}$	0	0	15
	$u_3 = 1$	3	0	0	0	$1 + \delta_{34}$	21
Requirements			6	11	17	12	

If we allow the unit costs associated with the positive allocation solutions in Table 3.28 to change also, then a similar analysis is possible, but the $\{u_i\}, \{v_j\}$ must be recalculated, i.e.

$$v_1 = 0, \quad u_3 = 1 + \delta_{31}, \quad v_2 = 2 + \delta_{32} - \delta_{31}, \quad v_3 = 2 + \delta_{33} - \delta_{31},$$
$$u_2 = 1 + \delta_{23} - \delta_{33} + \delta_{31}, \quad v_4 = \delta_{24} - \delta_{23} + \delta_{33} + \delta_{31},$$
$$u_1 = 1 + \delta_{12} - \delta_{32} + \delta_{31}.$$

(v) Non-transportation problems formulated as transportation problems

There are problems which are not physically transportation problems but which, by appropriate identification of sources and destinations, may be profitably formulated as such. Consider the following problems.

A caterer problem

A caterer undertakes to organise garden parties for a week and decides that he will need a supply of new napkins, each of which costs a pence. He will buy as few as possible, and make use of a laundry service by sending used napkins for laundering. There is a standard laundry service, costing b pence per napkin, which returns napkins within 4 days. There is an express service, costing c pence per napkin, which returns napkins within 2 days. The caterer estimates that, during the seven days, he requires 130, 70, 60, 100, 80, 90 and 120 napkins respectively. How many new napkins should he buy and how should he use the laundry service to keep the total costs as low as possible?

Let us identify *sources*. Each napkin used on a given day must either be a new napkin (source 1) or a used napkin from a previous day, which has been laundered in time (sources 2–8).

The *destinations* (1–7) are then the days on which napkins are used, together with a final inventory of napkins when the activities have been completed (8). We then derive a transportation problem of the form shown in Table 3.39.

Table 3.39

		Days on which used j							Final inventory	
		1	2	3	4	5	6	7	8	
New napkins	1	a	a	a	a	a	a	a	0	M
	2			c	c	b	b	b	0	130
	3				c	c	b	b	0	70
	4					c	c	b	0	60
i Used	5						c	c	0	100
napkins	6							c	0	80
	7								0	90
	8								0	120
		130	70	60	100	80	90	120	M	

This labelling is chosen to avoid unnecessary problems which, for example, the north-west corner rule would generate.

Let us assume that $a > c > b$. In Table 3.39, M has to be large enough to give a feasible schedule. We could make $M =$ total requirement, 650. However, it is clear that no optimal solution requires more than the maximal total over any 4 successive days (i.e. slow service), which is 390, and hence we set $M = 390$.

The unit costs in the empty squares are made large enough to ensure they are never used, since feasible solutions, using any of the given starting methods, will exist.

A transhipment problem

Let us suppose we have a standard transportation problem with unit costs, supplies, and requirements as given in Table 3.40, where we use primes to denote the initial destinations.

The optimal solution is $x_{11'} = 1$, $x_{12'} = 1$, $x_{22'} = 2$, $x_{23'} = 4$, $x_{31'} = 2$, $x_{34'} = 5$, with a minimal cost of 196.

Now let us suppose that we *tranship* items so that, for example, we can send items from 1 to 2′ via 2, or via 3′, and so on. Let the unit transportation costs *within* $\{1, 2, 3\}$, and *within* $\{1', 2', 3', 4'\}$ be as shown in Tables 3.41 and 3.42.

To complete the picture we need the reverse costs of Table 3.40, which we assume are not symmetric. These are given in Table 3.43.

We may now formulate the problem, allowing for transhipment, as one large transportation problem as follows. The maximal amount one can tranship into

Table 3.40

		Destinations j'				
		1'	2'	3'	4'	Available supplies
Sources i	1	13	11	15	20	2
	2	17	14	12	13	6
	3	18	18	15	12	7
Requirements		3	3	4	5	

Table 3.41

		Destinations j		
		1	2	3
Sources i	1	0	6	5
	2	5	0	4
	3	4	4	0

Table 3.42

		Destinations j'			
		1'	2'	3'	4'
Sources i'	1'	0	5	4	4
	2'	5	0	2	8
	3'	4	2	0	9
	4'	5	8	9	0

Table 3.43

		Destinations		
		1	2	3
	1′	14	19	20
	2′	10	12	17
Sources i'	3′	17	13	14
	4′	18	12	14

and out of any location is 15 (the total available supplies at $\{1, 2, 3\}$). Hence we add 15 to all initial supplies and requirements, noticing that the original requirements for $\{1, 2, 3\}$ are all 0, and the original supplies for $\{1', 2', 3', 4'\}$ are 0. Table 3.44 gives the final table.

Table 3.44

			New destinations							
			j			j'				
			1	2	3	1′	2′	3′	4′	Available supplies
	i	1	0	6	5	13	11	15	20	17
		2	5	0	4	17	14	12	13	21
		3	4	4	0	18	18	15	12	22
New sources	i'	1′	14	19	20	0	5	4	5	15
		2′	10	12	17	5	0	2	8	15
		3′	17	13	14	4	2	0	9	15
		4′	18	12	14	5	8	9	0	15
Requirements			15	15	15	18	18	19	20	

It is to be noted that the addition to supplies and requirements (which we have chosen to be 15) is arbitrary, providing it is large enough. Any excess is channelled to the diagonal, i.e. unused. The solution is given in Table 3.45.

The diagonal entries may be removed since they merely indicate unused possible transhipments.

Table 3.45

		New destinations							
		j			j'				
		1	2	3	1'	2'	3'	4'	Available supplies
i	1	13			3	1			17
	2		15			2	4		21
	3	2		15				5	22
New sources i'	1'				15				15
	2'					15			15
	3'						15		15
	4'							15	15
Requirements		15	15	15	18	18	19	20	Total cost = 194

There is an alternative method, related to optimal routing, which we will discuss later on in Exercise 3 of Chapter 7. For each (i, j') we calculate the minimal cost for each unit sent from i to j', via intermediate points if need be. Let $c_{ij'}^*$, be this minimal cost. The problem is then reformulated in exactly the same way as in Table 3.40, using the new costs. From the solution in this form we can calculate all the requisite transhipment quantities.

Exercises

1 Solve the following cost minimisation transportation problems, commenting on uniqueness in each case, where i, j, A, R denote supply points, destinations, availabilities and requirements.

(a)

		j				
		1	2	3	4	A
i	1	1	2	3	4	7
	2	4	3	2	0	8
	3	0	2	2	1	11
	R	5	6	9	6	

(b)

		j				
		1	2	3	4	A
i	1	10	5	6	10	15
	2	8	2	7	6	26
	3	12	3	4	8	50
	R	16	10	30	35	

(c)

	j 1	2	3	*A*
1	6	8	4	6
i 2	4	9	3	10
3	1	2	6	15
R	14	12	5	

(d)

	j 1	2	3	4	*A*
1	2	1	4	5	20
2	5	4	3	5	10
i 3	6	2	1	3	35
4	3	6	2	8	16
R	14	20	20	27	

(e)

	j 1	2	3	*A*
1	10	40	20	1
i 2	16	34	28	3
3	20	30	40	3
R	2	1	3	

2 (a) In Exercise 1(a), suppose the requirement at destination 1 increases by two units, and that the supplies may be increased to meet this. What changes in the supply levels give an optimal solution? What would the answer be if the requirement for destination 4 increased by two units?

(b) In Exercise 1(a), suppose that a fifth destination point is added, and a fourth source added to supply exactly the requirement for that destination. If $\{c_{4j}\}$, $\{c_{i5}\}$ are the unit costs for the additional parts of the first problem, determine inequalities between these unit costs for which the original solution will remain optimal.

(c) In Exercise 1(b), suppose that the requirement at destination 1 becomes 15. What is the solution to the problem then, and is it unique?

(d) In Exercise 1(c), suppose that there are penalties q_1, q_2, q_3 respectively for each unit not supplied to destinations 1, 2, 3, and penalties p_1, p_2, p_3 respectively for not using a unit of each supply. Find inequalities between the $\{q_j\}$, $\{p_i\}$ for which it is optimal not to incur any penalties.

3 (a) A company has to supply a product in each of three months. Table 3.46 gives the details. There is also a cost of 1 for each month a unit is kept in stock. Find a supply schedule which will meet the requirements at a minimal total cost. Is your solution unique?

(This problem will be treated in a different manner in Exercise 4 of Chapter 12 on dynamic programming.)

(b) The company knows that the stockholding cost is only an estimate. For what range of the stockholding cost would your solution in (a) still remain optimal?

Table 3.46

Month	1	2	3
Requirements	7	8	10
Maximal amount supplied by normal time operation	6	6	6
Maximal amount supplied by overtime operation	4	4	4
Cost per unit during normal time	2	6	4
Cost per unit during overtime	3	9	6

4 Consider the transportation problem data given in Table 3.47.

Table 3.47

		1	2	3	4	A
	1	2	3	4	5	10
i	2	5	4	3	1	15
	3	1	3	3	2	21
	R	6	11	17	12	

(with j labelling the columns $1, 2, 3, 4$)

(a) Formulate this problem as a linear program in six constraints.
(b) Use the linear programming method of Chapter 2 to show that the solution of Table 3.28 is a unique optimal solution.

5 (a) A company has four warehouses and supplies four customers. The distances involved are small, and the company charges its customers in terms of the charges per unit involved in loading at the warehouses and unloading at the destinations according to Table 3.48. Use the transportation algorithm to find the optimal solution. Is it unique?

Table 3.48

Warehouse	Unit loading charge	Available supplies	Customer	Unit unloading charge	Requirements
1	1	20	1	1	15
2	2	20	2	2	35
3	3	30	3	3	15
4	4	10	4	4	10

   (b) Explain
       (i)   using a linear programming formulation
       (ii) using the transportation algorithm
       why the set of all optimal solutions is the set of all solutions which use up
       completely the supplies from the first three supply points.
6 Explain what modifications you would make to the transportation algorithm
   to convert maximisation problems to minimisation problems, giving reasons.

4
Assignment Problems

4.1 Introduction

Another special linear programming problem is the *assignment problem*. Indeed it is also a very special form of the transportation problem. Although, as such, it may be solved in principle using linear programming, or the transportation stepping-stone algorithm, there is a simpler way of solving the problem, unless it is very large and needs to be computerised, known as the *Hungarian algorithm*, being a development by H. W. Kuhn of some work of the Hungarian E. Egerváry.

As we shall see later on, the linear programming formulation is a very degenerate one which leads to some difficulties, but these can be overcome.

As an example let us suppose that we have a set I of people and a set J of jobs, each set having an equal number of members. Each person in I has to be assigned to exactly one job in J.

If element i in I is assigned to element j in J, there is a cost (or some other measure of performance) c_{ij}. The problem is to determine a total assignment which minimises the sum of the $\{c_{ij}\}$ in the assignment.

The standard assignment problem is in *minimisation* form, in which case c_{ij} must be non-negative. *Maximisation* problems can be handled by using the fact that the maximal value of a function is equal to the negative of the minimal value of its negative, in which case we can cater for negative c_{ij} values.

Let us consider a few examples.

4.2 Some examples

(i) *Medley relay*
A swimming team has 5 members and has to decide which member will swim which leg of a 5 leg relay race. The times in seconds for each swimmer, in excess of a base time for each leg (the base time does not matter since it will be incurred anyhow for any assignment) are given in Table 4.1.

The reader may like to try to solve this. The minimal total time and assignments are given later in the text where this example is needed to illustrate the Hungarian algorithm. Without the aid of the algorithm one might try to solve it using similar procedures to those used to obtain a good starting solution for the transportation problem. Thus one might use the minimal unit cost method: find the smallest c_{ij}, and assign i to j where this occurs, then delete the ith row and jth column,

Table 4.1

		1	2	3	4	5
				Relay leg j		
	1	4	10	3	8	3
	2	7	8	7	6	2
Swimmer i	3	5	6	5	3	2
	4	5	2	7	3	2
	5	6	3	9	5	2

repeating the process until an assignment is obtained. If we do this, beginning with $c_{25} = 2$ as the smallest unit cost, we will accidentally obtain the correct solution, but not if we begin with c_{35}, c_{45} or c_{55} as the smallest unit costs. An alternative approach is to see if the smallest time for each leg is achievable by some assignment since, if so, this must be optimal. For this problem such an assignment would involve swimmer 1 doing both legs 1 and 3, which is not allowed in our problem.

(ii)   *Production scheduling*
A company has n tasks to carry out. It can do only one task in any one day and a task takes exactly one day to complete. Each task, i, has a desired completion time, namely by the end of day t_i. A penalty p_i is paid for each day job i is late in being completed. The problem is to determine which task should be done on each day in order to minimise the total penalty paid.

This sort of problem is tackled in the sequencing and scheduling chapter later on, although the methods given there do not guarantee to give an optimal solution. It may be formulated as an assignment problem simply by setting $c_{ij} = p_i \max \{j - t_i, 0\}$, as is easily checked.

(iii)   *Tendering*
A company has n items to put out for contract, and n contractors. It is company policy to place each item with a different contractor. The cost of placing item i with contractor j is c_{ij}. The problem is to determine which item to place with each contractor in order to minimise the total cost.

(iv)   *Horse jumping*
Consider a problem in which we have n horses and n riders, and an expected number of penalty points for assigning a given rider to a given horse in a horse-

jumping competition. With c_{ij} equal to the penalty for assigning i to j, the problem becomes one of minimising the total expected penalty points.

(v) *Bus crew scheduling*
A company has n bus crews and each has to do a morning route and an afternoon route. A morning route is designated i and an afternoon route j. The morning and afternoon routes are separated by a lunch break. A crew who does a morning route i and an afternoon route j has to travel a distance c_{ij} from the end of the former to the beginning of the latter. The problem is to assign crews to routes to minimise the total distance travelled.

Let us now look briefly at the formulation of the assignment problem as a linear programming problem.

4.3 Linear programming formulation

Let $x_{ij} = 1$ if member i of I is assigned to member j of J, and otherwise let $x_{ij} = 0$. Assuming that we have a balanced assignment problem, with I and J each having n members, numbered from 1 to n, then the linear programming formulation is as follows, where c_{ij} is the cost of assigning i in I to j in J.

$$\text{minimise } M = \sum_i \sum_j c_{ij} x_{ij}$$

subject to

$$\sum_j x_{ij} = 1, \quad \text{for all } i \quad (\text{i.e. } i \text{ is assigned to exactly one } j)$$

$$\sum_i x_{ij} = 1, \quad \text{for all } j \quad (\text{i.e. } j \text{ has exactly one } i \text{ assigned to it})$$

$$x_{ij} = 0 \text{ or } 1 \quad \text{for all } i \text{ and } j.$$

This is actually a transportation problem, with the extra conditions that $x_{ij} = 0$ or 1. The transportation method will, as we know, give whole numbers, and hence 0–1 solutions in any event. Note, however, that the problem is highly degenerate, since we require n positive components for a solution, whereas linear programming requires $2n - 1$ basic variables.

4.4 The Hungarian assignment algorithm

The Hungarian algorithm proceeds by reducing the initial unit cost table to a new unit cost table for which the optimal solutions are identical to those of the initial problem, and for which the optimal solutions are more easily obtainable. The objective is to get as many zeros in the new cost matrix as possible, so that we may easily find n zeros, corresponding to a feasible assignment solution. In this case this assignment is optimal with total cost of zero, and since we keep all the unit cost entries non-negative, we cannot do better than this.

The steps in the algorithm are as follows. We will explain the algorithm as we proceed with the aid of the example of Table 4.1, which we restate as Table 4.2. We will explain the reasons for the steps afterwards.

Table 4.2

		Job j				
		1	2	3	4	5
	1	4	10	3	8	3
	2	7	8	7	6	2
Person i	3	5	6	5	3	2
	4	5	2	7	3	2
	5	6	3	9	5	2

(1) *Reducing the unit cost table to an equivalent one.* Subtract the smallest unit cost in each column from each unit cost in that column. Do the same for the rows. The resulting table tends to have more zeros than the initial one, and no unit costs are negative.

Beginning with Table 4.2 we subtract 4, 2, 3, 3, 2 respectively from each unit cost in columns 1, 2, 3, 4, 5 to obtain Table 4.3. The minimal unit cost in each row is zero and hence no row subtractions take place.

Table 4.3

		Job j				
		1	2	3	4	5
	1	0	8	0	5	1
	2	3	6	4	3	0
Person i	3	1	4	2	0	0
	4	1	0	4	0	0
	5	2	(1)	6	2	0

(2) *Looking for a feasible assignment solution with zero unit costs.* We look for an assignment solution in which each unit cost component is zero. If one exists it is clearly optimal for the unit cost table at this stage. If one does not exist we try to determine whether or not it is possible to draw less than five lines (row and or column lines) so that each zero of the new table lies on at least one such line. If we cannot do this, then an assignment in which each unit cost component is zero must exist, and we look again for one. If we can find less than five lines to cover all the zeros, we move to the next step. In this case we see in Table 4.3 that we can find less than five lines to cover the zeros.

It is best to find the minimal number of lines to cover all the zeros, but it is not essential to do so, and it is sufficient to find less than five lines.

Step (2) of the algorithm is non-trivial in general. Indeed it must be stressed that the Hungarian algorithm is really only suitable for small problems because of the care needed in programming computers to undertake the operations in this step. The best currently available method for solving the assignment problem is a modification of the stepping-stone method of the transportation algorithm.

Returning to step (2), it is useful, when looking for a zero assignment solution at that stage, to look for rows and columns with a single zero, since these zeros must be part of an assignment if one exists. If we need to look for a minimal cover set of lines, a useful heuristic is to find the row or column with most zeros, put a line through this, and proceed in the same way.

(3) *Further modification of the unit cost matrix to an equivalent one.* Find the smallest unit cost entry in Table 4.3 which is not on any of the lines obtained in step (1). This must be positive. Subtract it from all the unit cost entries not on any line and add it to all the unit cost entries on two of the lines. From Table 4.3, the smallest uncovered unit cost is 1 (circled) and we obtain Table 4.4.

Table 4.4

		Job *j*				
		1	2	3	4	5
	1	0	8	0	5	3
	2	2	5	3	2	0
Person *i*	3	(1)	4	2	0	1
	4	1	0	4	0	1
	5	1	0	5	1	0

We now begin the cycle again, starting at (1).

(1)   Each row and column contains a zero, and hence no subtractions can be made without creating negative unit costs.
(2)   We can cover all the zeros in Table 4.4 with four lines as indicated.
(3)   The minimal uncovered unit cost is 1 and we obtain Table 4.5.

Table 4.5

		1	2	3	4	5
				Job j		
	1	0	9	$0*\sqrt{}+$	6	2
	2	1	5	2	2	$0*\sqrt{}+$
Person i	3	0^+	4	1	$0*\sqrt{}$	1
	4	$0\sqrt{}$	$0*$	3	0^+	1
	5	$0*$	$0\sqrt{}+$	4	1	0

At this stage we are able to see that assignments exist each of whose unit cost components is zero. We thus have optimal solutions. There are three—those marked with $*$, $\sqrt{}$, $+$ as indicated in Table 4.5. Returning to Table 4.2, the associated minimal total cost is 16. In $\{x_{ij}\}$ form the solutions are:

$$x_{13} = 1, \quad x_{25} = 1, \quad x_{34} = 1, \quad x_{42} = 1, \quad x_{51} = 1, \quad x_{ij} = 0 \quad \text{otherwise}$$
$$x_{13} = 1, \quad x_{25} = 1, \quad x_{34} = 1, \quad x_{41} = 1, \quad x_{52} = 1, \quad x_{ij} = 0 \quad \text{otherwise}$$
$$x_{13} = 1, \quad x_{25} = 1, \quad x_{31} = 1, \quad x_{44} = 1, \quad x_{52} = 1, \quad x_{ij} = 0 \quad \text{otherwise.}$$

The reasons for the steps in the algorithm

Let us now look at the reasons why the various steps are taken in the algorithm.

The validity of step (1) resides in the fact that if we subtract a constant k from each unit cost in a row or in a column (and hence from any combination of rows and columns), the ranking of the total costs of all the assignments remains the same, since we are in effect subtracting a constant k from all such costs. By using this step we try to get as many zeros as we can in the new, equivalent, unit cost table.

The line covering operation in step (2) results from the fact that an assignment solution, with zero component unit costs, exists *if and only if* the minimal number of row and/or column lines required to ensure that each zero of the whole unit cost table lies on at least one such line is n for an $n \times n$ problem. The fact that this latter condition is necessary arises from the fact that, if we have such an assignment, we may rearrange the rows, or columns, to ensure that the assignment is the diagonal assignment, from which the necessity condition is immediately obvious. We will not prove the sufficiency condition.

It is of interest to note that the actual result we use is known as *Konig's theorem*. A set of cells is called **independent** if each row and column contains one cell or none. The theorem states that the maximal number of independent cells in a given set is equal to the minimal number of lines required to cover all the cells in the set. It is a duality result (see Chapter 2) and is a special case of our transportation problem dual. We construct a new unit cost table with ones in place of the zeros and vice versa and then use the duality theory of Chapter 2, or of Chapter 3 (in transportation form).

The further modification operations in step (3) derive from the following consideration.

First of all, if we subtract a constant from each unit cost entry not on any line and add it to all those unit cost entries on two lines, this is the same as subtracting the same constant from the unit cost entries of each row not having a line through it and adding the same constant to all unit costs in each column having a line through it. This is easily seen by partitioning the unit cost entries into four distinct sets. In set 1, the unit cost entry is not on any line; in set 2 the unit cost entry is on a column line, but not on a row line; in set 3 the unit cost entry is on a row line but not on a column line; in set 4 the unit cost entry is on a row line and on a column line.

For example, let us look at Table 4.4. Using the line set used there (and noting that this set need not be unique), we have the following sets:

set 1: $\{(2,1), (2,3), (3,1), (3,3), (4,1), (4,3), (5,1), (5,3)\}$

set 2: $\{(2,2), (2,4), (2,5), (3,2), (3,4), (3,5), (4,2), (4,4), (4,5), (5,2), (5,4), (5,5)\}$

set 3: $\{(1,1), (1,3)\}$

set 4: $\{(1,2), (1,4), (1,5)\}$.

If $k = 1$ is the constant used in step (3), then it is easily seen that the stipulated operations are equivalent to changing the cost entries in sets $\{1, 2, 3, 4\}$ by quantities $\{-1, 0, 0, 1\}$ respectively, and that this is exactly what is achieved by subtracting from rows and adding to columns as stated. Thus, in line with the basis for step (1), the new problem is equivalent to the old one. The second reason why step (3) is important is that we need to be sure that the algorithm will terminate in a finite number of steps. Now if l rows have no lines through them, and m columns have a line through them, the reduction in cost of any assignment solution, in moving from the old to the new unit cost table, is equal to $(l - m)k$, by virtue of the previous paragraph. Since step (2) has a minimal total number of requisite lines less than n, we have $(n - l) + m < n$, i.e. $l > m$. Hence $(l - m)k > 0$, and we have a positive total cost reduction. We can do this only a finite number of times before the total cost of an optimal assignment is zero. Eventually we must reach a stage when $l = m$.

4.5   Extra aspects

(i)   *Maximisation problems*

Let us suppose that, given Table 4.1, we wished to *maximise* our objective instead of *minimising* it. From a linear programming point of view we may use a straight maximisation algorithm, but for the Hungarian method to work we must work with minimisation problems. Now let $\bar{c}$ be the maximal value of all the $\{c_{ij}\}$. Then from Chapter 2 we see that maximising $\Sigma_i \Sigma_j c_{ij} x_{ij}$ is equivalent to minimising $\Sigma_i \Sigma_j c'_{ij} x_{ij}$ when $c'_{ij} = \bar{c} - c_{ij}$. We thus change Table 4.1 to Table 4.6 and treat the problem as a minimisation problem.

Table 4.6

		Job				
				j		
		1	2	3	4	5
	1	6	0	7	2	7
	2	3	2	3	4	8
Person i	3	5	4	5	7	8
	4	5	8	3	7	8
	5	4	7	1	5	8

To speed up the calculation we may equally well subtract each cost entry in each row, or column, from the maximal cost entry in that row, or column.

(ii)   *Unbalanced problems*

For each problem, I and J may contain different numbers of elements. If J contains n elements and I contains m elements, with $n > m$, and if each element of I is to be assigned to some element of J, with a penalty p_j if element j in J is not used at all, then Table 4.7 gives the equivalent balanced assignment cost unit table.

When I contains more members than J a similar approach is possible. If one wishes to allow for not assigning some i to any j, or vice versa, then a general balanced problem, with dummy rows and columns is possible as for the transportation problem of Chapter 3.

(iii)   *Other assignment objective functions*

The assignment problem we have studied is one in which the objective function is the sum of all the component unit costs of an assignment. There are other problems in which the objective function is different to this. One such problem is

Table 4.7

			Job			
				j		
		1	2 ...	j ...	n	
	1	c_{11}	c_{12} ...	c_{1j} ...	c_{1n}	
	2	c_{21}	c_{22} ...	c_{2j} ...	c_{2n}	
	.	.	.	.	.	
	.	.	.	.	.	
	i	c_{i1}	c_{i2} ...	c_{ij} ...	c_{in}	
Person i	.	.	.	.	.	
	.	.	.	.	.	
	m	c_{m1}	c_{m2} ...	c_{mj} ...	c_{mn}	
	$m+1$	p_1	p_2 ...	p_j ...	p_n	
	.	.	.	.	.	
	.	.	.	.	.	
	n	p_1	p_2 ...	p_j ...	p_n	

known as the **maximin** assignment problem. For this problem the objective function for an assignment is the minimal unit cost component value of the assignment, and this is to be maximised.

As an example consider the following problem. We have n men and n tasks to be performed on a production line. The production rate of man i assigned to task j is a_{ij}. The items produced have to have each of the n tasks carried out on them. Then the production rate is determined by the smallest value of a_{ij} occurring in an assignment. The problem is to determine an assignment to maximise the production rate.

For the assignments *, $\sqrt{}$, + of Table 4.5, for example, the component unit costs are, respectively, from Table 4.1,

$$\{3, 2, 3, 2, 6\}, \{3, 2, 3, 5, 3\}, \{3, 2, 5, 3, 3\}.$$

The minimal component unit costs for assignments *, $\sqrt{}$, + respectively are 2, 2, 2. For the maximin assignment problem, assignments *, $\sqrt{}$, + are equally good, although not optimal. In fact the assignment $x_{14} = x_{24} = x_{33} = x_{41} = x_{52} = 1$ has a minimal component value of 3 and, from this point of view, is better than any of the assignments *, $\sqrt{}$, + referred to. This raises the question of what is the correct formulation of the problem, an issue mentioned briefly at the end of Chapter 2 in the context of multiple objectives and goal programming. Let us now solve the maximin assignment problem of Table 4.1, which we reproduce as Table 4.8.

Table 4.8

		Job j				
		1	2	3	4	5
	1	4	10	3	8	3
	2	7	8	7	6	2
Person i	3	5	6	5	3	2
	4	5	2	7	3	2
	5	6	3	9	5	2

Before doing so, note that we cannot reduce the unit costs in each row, or column, by a constant without changing the problem completely. This is a cautionary point. The reader should check this.

The following algorithm will solve the problem.

Step 1 Choose any assignment solution, e.g. the diagonal assignment.
Step 2 Find the minimal unit cost component for this solution. In this case it is 2.
Step 3 Construct a new table from the original unit cost table of Table 4.8 by putting a 0 where the original unit cost is greater than 2, and otherwise a 1. The reason for this is that a better assignment than in Step 1 exists *if and only if* this assignment has all its costs greater than 2, so that its minimal unit cost component is then greater than 2. Thus such an assignment corresponds to a set of zeros in the new table. We obtain Table 4.9.

Table 4.9

		Job j				
		1	2	3	4	5
	1	0	0	0	0	0*
	2	0	0	0	0*	1
Person i	3	0	0	0*	0	1
	4	0*	1	0	0	1
	5	0	0*	0	0	1

Step 4   Treat the matrix in Table 4.9 as if it were an assignment problem with the specified unit costs and where the problem is to minimise the total costs. A better assignment to that in Step 1 will exist if and only if an assignment with five zeros in Table 4.9 exists. We can easily spot this; thus the assignment * in Table 4.9 is one such assignment. If we had not been able to spot such an assignment, we would have looked for less than five covering lines for all the zeros and, if we had found one, this would have meant that the minimal total cost for Table 4.9 was positive, and hence that the solution for Table 4.8 given in Step 1 was optimal.

We now repeat the procedure beginning at Step 2, and continue until we can no longer get an improvement.

Step 2   The minimal unit cost in Table 4.8, for the solution * of Table 4.9, is 3.
Step 3   The new table corresponding to Table 4.7 is given in Table 4.10.

Table 4.10

		Job j				
		1	2	3	4	5
	1	0	0	1	0	1
	2	0	0	0	0	1
Person i	3	0	0	0	1	1
	4	0	1	0	1	1
	5	0	1	0	0	1

Step 4   We see from Table 4.10 that the minimal total cost for this table is positive (we also see that we can cover all the zeros with less than five lines) and that the solution in Table 4.9 is optimal, with a minimal unit cost component equal to 3.

If we wish to find *all* the optimal solutions, instead of using Step 2 as it is, we put a zero where all the unit costs in Table 4.8 are no less than 3, and otherwise put a 1. We obtain Table 4.11.

Any assignment corresponding to five zeros in Table 4.11 is optimal.

In Chapter 2 mention was made of multiple-objective problems and goal-programming problems, and this is relevant in this context. The original objective function was the sum of all the component costs of an assignment solution, but, as shown with the maximin solution, this need not be the case, and, indeed the solution sets may be quite different. In Exercise 6 we will specifically introduce a

Table 4.11

		1	2	3	4	5
	1	0	0	0	0	0
	2	0	0	0	0	1
Person i	3	0	0	0	0	1
	4	0	1	0	0	1
	5	0	0	0	0	1

Job j

multi-objective type of assignment problem in which we have, in effect, an objective function for each column. This means that, whereas the maximin problem focuses on the worst outcome for each task, we will extend this to a comparison of all tasks, so that it is the performance individually on all tasks which is important.

Exercises

1 Solve the following assignment problems with the objectives as stated.

(a) *Maximise*

	1	2	3	4	5
1	4	2	0	1	5
2	1	3	5	2	7
3	7	4	2	8	9
4	10	0	3	4	5
5	2	8	9	10	1

i, j

(b) *Minimise*

	1	2	3	4	5
1	28	25	35	33	34
2	20	30	23	25	26
3	36	32	36	32	40
4	36	33	37	33	42
5	28	30	33	35	35

i, j

(c) *Maximise*

j

	1	2	3	4	5
1	8	3	7	6	2
2	5	1	4	9	3
i 3	6	0	1	7	4
4	8	3	8	2	8
5	4	1	5	0	1

(d) *Maximin*

j

	1	2	3	4	5
1	4	3	9	6	2
2	3	8	6	6	5
i 3	9	1	7	4	4
4	8	6	7	5	3
5	4	9	5	8	2

(e) *Minimise*

j

	1	2	3	4	5
1	1	6	4	2	8
2	6	3	4	7	2
i 3	4	5	6	3	7
4	6	2	8	6	3
5	2	8	5	2	6

2 After qualifying, medical students must take two six-month jobs in hospital departments, but they cannot take both jobs in the same department. A hospital has four such students and vacancies in four departments; casualty, maternity, medical and surgical. The number of fatal mistakes each student will make in each department is given by

	Casualty	Maternity	Medical	Surgical
Student 1	3	0	2	6
Student 2	2	1	4	5
Student 3	4	2	5	7
Student 4	2	0	2	4

(a) How should they be allotted to departments for the first job so as to minimise total mistakes?

(b) Given that allocation, how should they be allotted for the second six months so no one stays in the same job, and mistakes are minimised?

(c) For this problem, do these two allocations minimise total mistakes over both six-month periods? Explain why or why not.

(d) For any problem, of the above kind, does this method always minimise total number of casualties? Either prove it or give a counter example.

3   A council has three jobs to be done and receives tenders from three firms. The tenders in appropriate units are as follows, where i denotes the firm, and j denotes the job.

		1	2	3
	1	20	35	8
i	2	15	40	7
	3	12	33	6

Firm 1 is capable of doing all jobs at the same time, firm 2 is capable of doing jobs 2 and 3 at the same time, and firm 3 is capable of doing all jobs, but can only do one at a time. Set up the problem of assigning jobs to firms as an assignment problem and find the solution. Is it unique?

4   In the text it was stated that the minimal number of lines required to cover all the zero cells in an assignment table was equal to the maximal number of independent zero cells, and that this could be deduced from duality theory. Use the duality formulation of the transportation problem to deduce this.

5   In a transportation problem if $x_{ij} \neq 0$, there is a time t_{ij} taken to carry out the actual transportation. How would you modify the assignment maximin algorithm to find the min max transportation time?

6   In an assignment problem, let the component unit costs for the n columns be, for solution x,

$c_1(x), c_2(x), \ldots, c_j(x), \ldots, c_n(x)$, where $c_j(x)$ is the jth column unit cost.

Solution x is said to dominate solution y if

$c_j(x) \leqslant c_j(y), \quad j = 1, 2, \ldots, n$

and $c_j(x) < c_j(y)$, for some j.

For example in Table 4.12 the circled assignment dominates the assignment given in squares.

Table 4.12

		Job j				
		1	2	3	4	5
	1	④	[10]	3	8	3
	2	7	8	7	[6]	②
Person i	3	5	⑥	5	3	[2]
	4	[5]	2	⑦	3	2
	5	6	3	[9]	⑤	2

How would you formulate as an assignment problem the problem of determining whether the circled assignment is dominated by some other assignment? Just put down the appropriate unit cost table and explain its entries. Clue: try to find a unit cost table using similar approaches to that of the max min assignment problem.

5

Sequencing and Scheduling

5.1 SPT scheduling

Owing to the inefficiency of his new receptionist, a dentist finds there are six patients in the waiting room, all with the same appointment time. Mrs Antrobus requires 20 minutes treatment; Mr Bagshott, 15 minutes; Mr Cuthbert, 15 minutes; Mrs Dolittle, 10 minutes; Mr Earnshaw, 10 minutes; and Miss Fotherington, 5 minutes. His first impulse is to treat the patients in alphabetical order, but he realises after a moment's thought that this may not be best. Consider the times that he will finish treating each patient. (N.B. he can only treat one patient at a time.)

Mrs A's treatment completed in 20   minutes
Mr B's treatment completed in $(20 + 15)$ minutes
Mr C's treatment completed in $(20 + 15 + 15)$ minutes
Mrs D's treatment completed in $(20 + 15 + 15 + 10)$ minutes
Mr E's treatment completed in $(20 + 15 + 15 + 10 + 10)$ minutes
Miss F's treatment completed in $(20 + 15 + 15 + 10 + 10 + 5)$ minutes

Thus on average each patient's treatment will be completed in

$$(20 + 35 + 50 + 60 + 70 + 75)/6 = 51\tfrac{2}{3} \text{ minutes.}$$

Is it possible, the dentist wonders, to treat the patients in some other order so that the average time is less?

Look again at how the average time to completion of treatment was calculated:

$$\text{average time} = \text{total time}/6$$

$$= (6 \times 20 + 5 \times 15 + 4 \times 15 + 3 \times 10 + 2 \times 10 + 1 \times 5)/6$$

Now calculating the average time for any other order of treating patients will give:

average time = $\tfrac{1}{6}$ [6 × (treatment time of 1st patient)
+ 5 × (treatment time of 2nd patient)
+ 4 × (treatment time of 3rd patient)
+ 3 × (treatment time of 4th patient)
+ 2 × (treatment time of 5th patient)
+ 1 × (treatment time of 6th patient)].

Consider specifically the first and second patients to be treated. Suppose the treatment time of the first is T minutes and that of the second is t minutes, where $T > t$. These two quantities contribute $\frac{1}{6}(6 \times T + 5 \times t)$ minutes to the average time. If the first two patients are treated in the reverse order, $\frac{1}{6}(6 \times t + 5 \times T)$ minutes are contributed to the average time. Because

$$[\tfrac{1}{6}(6 \times t + 5 \times T) - \tfrac{1}{6}(6 \times T + 5 \times t)] = \tfrac{1}{6}(t - T) < 0,$$

the average time is reduced by reversing the order. It follows that the patient to be treated first should be the one with the shortest treatment time. A similar argument shows that the patient treated second should have the second shortest processing time; that the patient treated third should have the third shortest treatment time; etc.

Hence the dentist should treat the patients in the order (Miss F, Mr E, Mrs D, Mr C, Mr B, Mrs A). Equally, of course, he could treat them in the order (Miss F, Mr E, Mrs D, Mr B, Mr C, Mrs A), because Mr B and Mr C require the same treatment time. Moreover, there are two other possible orders, because Mrs D and Mr E require the same time. The average time to the completion of the patients' treatment is now $35\frac{5}{6}$ minutes.

The problem that we have described is known as a **sequencing** (or **scheduling**) **problem**. It is usual to imagine that we have a set of n jobs $\{J_1, J_2, \ldots, J_n\}$, which, for the present, we assume must all be processed on a single machine. Here the jobs are the patients and the machine is the dentist. However, many other examples spring readily to mind: the scheduling of n programs on a computer; n planes queueing up to land at an airport; the processing of n different batches of crude oil at a refinery; etc. We mentioned a particular scheduling problem and its solution in Chapter 4.

We assume that all jobs are ready for processing at time zero. For each job we define the following quantities:

p_i the **processing time** of J_i, i.e. the time that J_i actually requires on the machine.

d_i the **due date** of J_i, i.e. the time by which we should like to have J_i completed.

C_i the **completion time** of J_i, i.e. the time at which the processing of J_i completes.

L_i the **lateness** of J_i: $L_i = C_i - d_i$.

T_i the **tardiness** of J_i: $T_i = \max\{0, C_i - d_i\}$.

Note that the first two quantities, p_i and d_i, are data of the problem; they are fixed whatever the sequence. The other quantities, C_i, L_i and T_i, are dependent on the sequence; the objective functions that we shall consider will be based on these. The distinction between lateness and tardiness will be discussed shortly.

In the example we sought a sequence which minimised the mean completion time: $\bar{C} = (1/n) \sum_{i=1}^{n} C_i$. We learnt that to do this we should use the *shortest processing time (SPT) rule*. To minimise $\bar{C}$ on a single machine sequence the jobs such that J_i is processed before J_j if $p_i < p_j$. If $p_i = p_j$, the ordering of J_i and J_j is immaterial.

Often our primary objective is not to minimise $\overline{C}$; perhaps we are more concerned with whether jobs become overdue. Above we have defined two quantities: the lateness and tardiness of a job. We might wish to minimise the mean lateness due to a sequence:

$$\overline{L} = \frac{1}{n} \sum_{i=1}^{n} L_i = \frac{1}{n} \sum_{i=1}^{n} (C_i - d_i)$$

$$= \frac{1}{n} \sum_{i=1}^{n} C_i - \frac{1}{n} \sum_{i=1}^{n} d_i$$

$$= \overline{C} - \frac{1}{n} \sum_{i=1}^{n} d_i.$$

Now the d_i are fixed quantities independent of the sequence, so $((1/n)\Sigma d_i)$ is a constant. Hence minimising $\overline{C}$ minimises $\overline{L}$; so the SPT rule minimises $\overline{L}$ as well as $\overline{C}$. However, we should note that $L_i = (C_i - d_i)$ is negative when a job is completed before its due date. This implies that in minimising $\overline{L}$ we penalise ourselves for those jobs that are late and reward ourselves for those jobs that are early. However, there may be no advantage in finishing jobs early; indeed, we may have to pay storage costs for holding the completed jobs until they are required. For this reason we often consider the tardiness of a job. This is simply its positive lateness. In this book we shall not consider how to minimise $\overline{T}$; it is, alas, too difficult a problem for us.

Sometimes it is more appropriate to minimise to maximum lateness or tardiness due to a sequence. In fact a sequence which minimises the first of these quantities minimises the other (see Exercise 6). To do this we use the *earliest due date (EDD) rule*. To minimise $L_{max} = \max_{i=1}^{n} \{L_i\}$ on a single machine, sequence the jobs so that J_i is processed before J_j if $d_i < d_j$. If $d_i = d_j$, the ordering of J_i and J_j is immaterial. This EDD rule is a special case of an algorithm developed by Lawler.

5.2   Lawler's algorithm

Consider the following example.

A market research firm has to undertake six surveys for a certain client. Some surveys use the results of other surveys, and therefore the latter must be performed first. In Table 5.1 we list the time needed to undertake each survey (p_i), the due date of each survey (d_i) and any other surveys which must be completed first. We suppose that the current date is 1 January and ignore the difference in lengths of the months. The firm has only enough staff to undertake one survey at a time and, since the total survey time is 15 months, it is clear that some surveys must be late. Moreover, some surveys are more important than others. To take account of this the firm wishes to sequence the surveys to minimise:

$$T^w_{max} = \max\{1 \times T_1, 1 \times T_2, 1 \times T_3, 2 \times T_4, 2 \times T_5, 2 \times T_6\}.$$

Table 5.1

Survey J_i	Time to perform J_i p_i (months)	Required by the end of d_i	Surveys which must be completed before J_i can start
J_1	2	March	—
J_2	3	June	J_1
J_3	4	August	J_2
J_4	3	July	—
J_5	2	December	J_4
J_6	1	July	J_4

This example has introduced two further concepts into our standard sequencing problem. First, there are **precedence constraints**, which restrict the order in which jobs may be performed. These constraints may be given in tabular form as in Table 5.1, but they can also be given in a convenient pictorial form. Figure 5.1 gives that appropriate to the example.

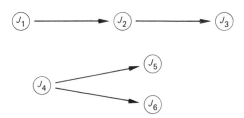

Fig. 5.1 The precedence constraints for the marketing research example

Second, **weighting factors**, w_i, have been introduced to represent the relative importance of jobs. Here we wish to minimise the maximum weighted tardiness, $T^w_{max} = \max^n_{i=1}\{w_i T_i\}$. **Lawler's algorithm** is a method for solving this problem. It begins by finding the job that should be sequenced last. Then it finds the job that should be second to last; then third to last; etc.

Let V be the set of jobs that the precedence constraints permit us to perform last. Let $\tau = \Sigma^n_{i=1} p_i$; τ is the completion time of the last job whatever the sequence. Choose a job in V which minimises $w_i \max\{\tau - d_i, 0\}$ and suppose that this job is J_k; put J_k last.

Now remove J_k completely from the problem to obtain a new problem with $(n-1)$ jobs and repeat the procedure. This finds the job that should be last in the reduced problem and hence penultimate in the original problem. By repeating this $n-2$ times we eventually sequence all the jobs.

Table 5.2

τ	J_i: p_i: d_i: w_i:	J_1 2 3 1	J_2 3 6 1	J_3 4 8 1	J_4 3 7 2	J_5 2 12 2	J_6 1 7 2	Scheduled job
15		*	*	7	*	⑥	16	J_5
13		*	*	⑤	*	S	12	J_3
9		*	③	S	*	S	4	J_2
6		3	S	S	*	S	⓪	J_6
5		2	S	S	⓪	S	S	J_4
2		⓪	S	S	S	S	S	J_1

In Table 5.2 we have solved the marketing research example. In the headings we have summarised all the data for the problem, namely the quantities $\{p_i, d_i, w_i\}$. The entries in column J_i are respectively:

*	if J_i cannot be scheduled in the current last position; or
$w_i \max\{\tau - d_i, 0\}$	if it is possible to schedule J_i in the current last position; or
S	if J_i has already been scheduled.

The scheduled job at each τ minimises $w_i \max\{\tau - d_i, 0\}$. The final schedule is found by reading *up* the final column and the resulting $T^w_{\max}$ found by taking the largest of the circled quantities.

To check the construction of the table consider the first row. τ, the completion time of the last job, is 15. The precedence constraints do not permit J_1 to be processed last, for then J_2 would have to be processed before J_1. Similarly neither J_2 nor J_4 can be last. So $V = \{J_3, J_5, J_6\}$. The quantities $w_i \max\{\tau - d_i, 0\}$ are respectively:

$$w_3 \max\{\tau - d_3, 0\} = 1 \times \max\{15-8, 0\} = 7;$$
$$w_5 \max\{\tau - d_5, 0\} = 2 \times \max\{15-12,0\} = 6;$$
$$w_6 \max\{\tau - d_6, 0\} = 2 \times \max\{15-7,0\} = 16.$$

The minimum is 6, so J_5 is scheduled last and the minimum, 6, is circled. It follows that the penultimate job must complete at $(15 - p_5) = (15 - 2) = 13$, so τ for the next row is 13 and the procedure continues.

The procedure for selecting the last job works because, if J_k is chosen from V to minimise $w_i \max \{\tau - d_i, 0\}$, then there is a sequence minimising T^w_{max} which has J_k as its last job. This is not hard to prove. If any sequence S, satisfying the precedence requirements, has as its last job $J_l \neq J_k$, we have only to show that, if S' is constructed from S by moving J_k to last job and J_l to penultimate job and leaving all other jobs in the same order, then

(1) S' satisfies the precedence requirements, and
(2) $[T^w_{max}$ for $S'] \leqslant [T^w_{max}$ for $S]$.

But (1) is true because J_k is allowed to be last, and (2) is true because in going from S to S' all jobs except J_k move forward or stay in the same position, so that the corresponding $w_i T_i$ do not increase, and for the last job

$$w_k T_k \leqslant w_l T_l \qquad \text{(by our procedure)}$$

and hence T_{max} cannot increase. Taking S to be an optimal schedule gives the result.

To extend the analysis to the full iterative procedure we need only realise that, if J_k is last in some optimal sequence, then sequencing the first $n-1$ jobs optimally and putting J_k at the end gives an overall optimal sequence.

The method still works if instead of T_{max} we seek to minimise

$$\max_{i=1}^{n} \gamma_i(C_i),$$

where γ_i is any non-decreasing function of C_i; by non-decreasing we mean that $x \geqslant y$ implies $\gamma_i(x) \geqslant \gamma_i(y)$ (see Fig. 5.2).

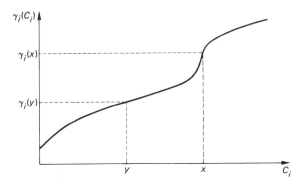

Fig. 5.2 A general non-decreasing function

In our case we have

$$\gamma_i(x) = w_i \max \{x - d_i, 0\}.$$

In the general case we choose as the last job one in V which minimises $\gamma_i(\tau)$, but otherwise the algorithm is the same.

5.3   Smith's algorithm

A natural objective in scheduling might be to minimise $\overline{C}$ subject to no job being late, i.e. subject to $T_{max} = 0$. **Smith's algorithm** accomplishes this on a single machine. Like Lawler's algorithm it constructs the schedule beginning at the last job and working forward to the first job in the sequence.

Again let $\tau = \Sigma_{i=1}^{n} p_i$, the completion time of the last job whatever the sequence. Let V be the set of jobs that can be scheduled last without being late, i.e. those jobs with $d_i \geqslant \tau$. From V select a job, say J_k, with the longest processing time. Put this job last. Delete J_k completely from the problem and repeat the procedure on the reduced problem to find the job to be sequenced in the penultimate position. Delete this job and continue in the obvious fashion.

Without providing a complete justification of the algorithm we can see intuitively why it works. The SPT rule can be stated alternatively as 'put the longest job last'. Smith's algorithm simply modifies this to 'of the jobs that will not be late put the longest last'. We work through an example in Table 5.3. The data are given in the headings. The entries in column J_i are respectively

* if J_i cannot be scheduled in the current last position without being late; or
p_i if it is possible to schedule J_i in the current last position; or
S if J_i has already been scheduled.

In each row we schedule the job with the largest value of p_i for those without an * or an S. The optimal value of $\overline{C}$ is simply the sum of the τ column divided by the number of jobs, and an optimal schedule is given by reading *up* the final column.

Table 5.3

τ	J_i:	J_1	J_2	J_3	J_4	J_5	J_6	
	p_i:	2	1	4	3	2	1	Scheduled
	d_i:	10	15	7	14	9	11	job
13		*	1	*	3	*	*	J_4
10		2	1	*	S	*	1	J_1
8		S	1	*	S	2	1	J_5
6		S	1	4	S	S	1	J_3
2		S	1	S	S	S	1	J_2
1		S	S	S	S	S	1	J_6

Note that for the schedule $(J_6, J_2, J_3, J_5, J_1, J_4)$, $\overline{C} = 40/6$. Another schedule which meets the due dates is given by the EDD rule (*why?*). However, this schedule is $(J_3, J_5, J_1, J_6, J_4, J_2)$, for which $\overline{C} = 52/6$. Thus Smith's algorithm brings a significant improvement in terms of $\overline{C}$ over the EDD sequence, which simply tries to meet the due dates.

5.4 Johnson's algorithm for the two-machine flow-shop

Many scheduling problems involve more than one machine. Here we consider a simple case with two machines, M_1 and M_2. We assume that each job requires processing first on M_1 then on M_2. Because all the jobs flow between the machines in the order (M_1, M_2), the problem is said to be a flow-shop problem. The processing time of J_i on M_1 will be denoted by α_i, and that on M_2 by β_i. In this problem we shall not consider objectives such as $\overline{C}, T^w_{max}$, etc. They are very difficult to minimise and no simple algorithm exists. Instead we seek merely to minimise the overall time to complete all the jobs, $C_{max} = \max^n_{i=1} \{C_i\}$, which is known as the **makespan** of the schedule.

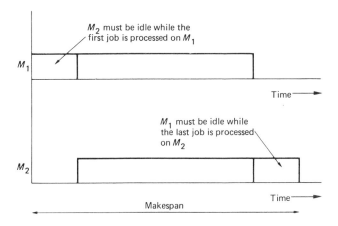

Fig. 5.3 The idle time that must occur for any schedule

To see how we might proceed, look at Fig. 5.3. Processing on each machine is indicated by blocks positioned along a time axis. Processing on M_2 cannot begin until the first job has been processed on M_1. Similarly all processing on M_1 must have finished before the processing of the last job begins on M_2. Intuitively, therefore, we need to minimise these two periods when one of the machines must be idle. Johnson has shown that his algorithm, which does precisely this, does indeed minimise makespan.

The steps in **Johnson's algorithm** are as follows.

Step 1 Select the smallest time in the list

$$\alpha_1, \alpha_2, \ldots, \alpha_n, \quad \beta_1, \beta_2, \ldots, \beta_n.$$

If there is a tie, select any of the smallest times.

Step 2 If the smallest time is α_k, do kth job first. If it is β_k, do kth job last.

Step 3 Now repeat procedure on remaining $n-1$ jobs.

To see the application of this algorithm consider the example in Table 5.4.

Table 5.4

Job J_i	Processing times	
	α_1	β_1
J_1	25	15
J_2	10	12
J_3	12	11
J_4	8	10
J_5	9	15
J_6	15	12

Smallest time   is $\alpha_4 = 8$ so schedule J_4 first: $(J_4, -, -, -, -, -,)$
Next smallest time is $\alpha_5 = 9$ so schedule J_5 second: $(J_4, J_5, -, -, -, -,)$
Next smallest time is $\alpha_2 = 10$ so schedule J_2 third: $(J_4, J_5, J_2, -, -, -,)$
Next smallest time is $\beta_3 = 11$ so schedule J_3 sixth: $(J_4, J_5, J_2, -, -, J_3)$
Next smallest time is $\beta_6 = 12$ so schedule J_6 fifth: $(J_4, J_5, J_2,-, J_6, J_3)$
So job J_1 goes in last remaining position and best schedule is $(J_4, J_5, J_2, J_1, J_6, J_3)$.

To find the makespan resulting from this schedule we draw a **Gantt diagram**, which has a separate time axis for each machine and displays the processing of a job by a machine by an appropriate use of blocks (see Fig. 5.4). From the diagram it can be seen that the total time to complete all six jobs is 90. Notice the idle time on machine M_2 between 45 and 52.

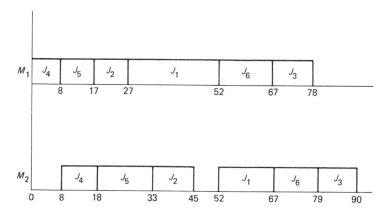

Fig. 5.4 The Gantt diagram for the schedule produced by Johnson's algorithm

5.5 Johnson's algorithm for the two-machine job-shop

In this section we consider a two-machine job-shop problem. The difference between this and the flow-shop problem is that the jobs do not all require processing first on M_1 then on M_2. Typically the jobs may be divided into four classes:

N_1 – those with processing order M_1 then M_2;
N_2 – those with processing order M_2 then M_1;
N_3 – those requiring processing only on M_1;
N_4 – those requiring processing only on M_2.

Again our objective is to minimise makespan. Now that we know how to solve the flow-shop problem, it is straightforward to solve this problem.

To find an optimal schedule, the steps are as follows.

Step 1   Schedule the jobs in N_1 with the flow-shop algorithm to get the sequence S_1.
Step 2   Schedule the jobs in N_2 with the flow-shop algorithm to get the sequence S_2, *but remember that for this group M_2 is the first machine.*
Step 3   Schedule the jobs in N_3 in any order to get the sequence S_3.
Step 4   Schedule the jobs in N_4 in any order to get the sequence S_4.

An optimal schedule for this problem is:

process the jobs on M_1 in the order (S_1, S_3, S_2);
process the jobs on M_2 in the order: (S_2, S_4, S_1).

Notice that this schedule has a different order on each machine.

To see that this generates an optimal schedule, we need only realise that C_{max} is increased unnecessarily if M_2 is kept idle waiting for jobs of type N_1 to complete on M_1 when there are still jobs of types N_2 and N_4 to be processed on M_2. Similarly C_{max} is increased unnecessarily if M_1 is kept idle waiting for jobs of type N_2 to complete on M_2 when there are still jobs of types N_1 and N_3 to be processed on M_1.

A simple example illustrates the application of the algorithm (see Table 5.5).

Here we have $N_1 = \{J_1, J_2, J_3\}$, $N_2 = \{J_4, J_5, J_6\}$, $N_3 = \{J_7\}$ and
$N_4 = \{J_8\}$.

It is easy to find

$$S_1 = (J_1, J_3, J_2), \qquad S_2 = (J_6, J_4, J_5), \qquad S_3 = (J_7), \qquad S_4 = (J_8).$$

So machine M_1 processes jobs in the order: $(J_1, J_3, J_2, J_7, J_6, J_4, J_5)$ and machine M_2 processes jobs in the order: $(J_6, J_4, J_5, J_8, J_1, J_3, J_2)$. The Gantt diagram is given in Fig. 5.5, and shows that the total time to complete all the jobs is 46.

Table 5.5

Job	First machine		Second machine	
	Machine	Processing time	Machine	Processing time
J_1	M_1	12	M_2	13
J_2	M_1	4	M_2	3
J_3	M_1	11	M_2	10
J_4	M_2	4	M_1	6
J_5	M_2	4	M_1	2
J_6	M_2	1	M_1	3
J_7	M_1	8		
J_8	M_2	2		

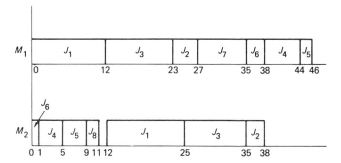

Fig. 5.5 The Gantt diagram for the job shop example

5.6 Johnson's algorithm for the three-machine flow-shop

Here we consider the processing of n jobs through three machines, M_1, M_2, M_3. Each job must be processed first on M_1, then on M_2, and finally on M_3. The jobs 'flow' between the machines in the same order. The processing times of job J_i are a_i, b_i, and c_i on M_1, M_2, and M_3 respectively. Our aim again is to minimise the makespan.

In general this problem is intractable: however, there is a simple, special case that we can solve. From now on, we assume that the processing times on the second machine are dominated in the following sense:

$$\text{either} \quad \min_{i=1}^{n} \{a_i\} \geqslant \max_{i=1}^{n} \{b_i\} \quad \text{or} \quad \min_{i=1}^{n} \{c_i\} \geqslant \max_{i=1}^{n} \{b_i\} \quad \text{or both.}$$

Johnson showed—but we shall not, because the proof is difficult—that a sequence that is optimal for this three-machine problem is also optimal for a two-machine problem constructed from the three-machine processing times, and vice versa. The two-machine flow shop is simply constructed with processing times:

$\alpha_i = a_i + b_i$, $\beta_i = b_i + c_i$. This constructed problem is solved by Johnson's algorithm as given in Section 5.4. The resulting schedule is optimal for the original three-machine problem. Again, a simple example will illustrate the idea (see Table 5.6).

Table 5.6

Job	Processing times			Constructed processing times	
	a_1	b_1	c_1	$\alpha_i = a_i + b_i$	$\beta_i = b_i + c_i$
J_1	5	2	6	7	8
J_2	7	4	5	11	9
J_3	9	1	6	10	7
J_4	6	4	8	10	12
J_5	12	3	9	15	12
J_2	5	2	7	7	9

The two-machine algorithm builds up the sequence in the following order:

$$(J_1, -, -, -, -, -), \qquad (J_1, -, -, -, -, J_3), \qquad (J_1, J_6, -, -, -, J_3),$$
$$(J_1, J_6, -, -, J_2, J_3), \qquad (J_1, J_6, J_4, -, J_2, J_3).$$

Thus an optimal sequence for the original problem is $(J_1, J_6, J_4, J_5, J_2, J_3)$. Figure 5.6 gives the Gantt diagram for this schedule. Note that it has been drawn for the original three-machine problem.

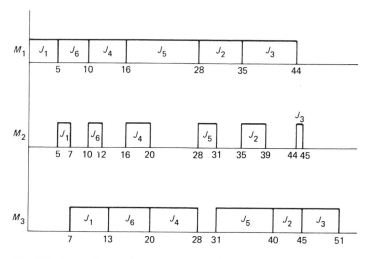

Fig. 5.6 Gantt diagram for the three-machine problem

5.7   Easy problems, hard problems and NP-completeness

At first sight it would seem that scheduling problems should be relatively easy to solve. Certainly the ones that we have studied were, although we did sound warnings that flow-shop and job-shop problems are difficult to solve with objective functions other than C_{max} or in the general case with more than two machines. Why might the apparent simplicity of scheduling problems hide difficulties which make them very hard to solve?

Scheduling problems are members of a class of problems known under the general heading of combinatorial optimisation problems. The distinguishing feature of these is that they seek to optimise a function over a *finite* set. For instance, in the scheduling problems that we have studied each possible schedule corresponds to a permutation of the n jobs. Since there are $n!$ possible permutations, there are $n!$ possible schedules. $n!$ is finite for any n, so finding a schedule which optimises an objective function is a combinatorial problem. Other examples of combinatorial optimisation problems are the assignment problems of Chapter 4 and the critical path and network routing problems that we shall examine in the coming chapters.

The solution of combinatorial optimisation problems should be easy. The set of alternatives is finite; so simply calculate the objective function value for each member and pick the optimal value. The finite size of the set means that this can be achieved in finite time. Unfortunately, this process of exhaustive search, known as **complete enumeration**, is easier said than done.

The set of alternatives may be finite, but that does not mean it is small. It is usually very large indeed. For instance, there are $20! = 2.4 \times 10^{18}$ possible sequences of 20 jobs. Even with the fastest of modern computers which could search through, say, 100 million schedules per second, using the complete enumeration algorithm it would take nearly eight centuries to find an optimal schedule. Such figures are the rule, not the exception. While in principle complete enumeration will solve any combinatorial optimisation problem, in practice it is usually computationally intractable to use the algorithm. Other more construct-ive methods, which do not search through the entire set, are needed. Unfortunately, it is only in a very few classes of combinatorial problem that they have been found.

One of the great conjectures of modern mathematics (and computer science) is that for the majority of combinatorial problems no method other than complete enumeration—or a more subtle implementation of exhaustive search, known as **implicit enumeration**—will guarantee to find an optimal solution. Thus, if this conjecture is correct, and there is much evidence that it is, the majority of combinatorial optimisation problems will take centuries to solve. For reasons that we shall not discuss here, this majority is known as the family of **NP-complete** problems. Perhaps the best known of these is the **travelling salesman problem**. A salesman must visit n cities. He is given the inter-city distances. What route should he adopt to visit each city (at least) once in the shortest possible total travelling? Sounds easy, doesn't it: try it!

Not all combinatorial problems are hard; some are easy. For them there exist constructive algorithms that generate an optimal solution without searching through all the alternatives. This chapter has concerned easy scheduling problems. Assignment problems are easy too, as are the critical path and network routing problems that follow.

Exercises

1   Find the sequence of the eight jobs given in Table 5.7 which minimises $\max_{i=1}^{n} \{\alpha_i T_i\}$ on a single machine and which satisfies the precedence requirements. Use Lawler's algorithm.

Table 5.7

Job	Due date	Processing time	α_i	Jobs to be completed first
J_1	6	3	2	6
J_2	7	4	2	—
J_3	9	2	1	6
J_4	16	1	3	1
J_5	9	4	2	2, 8
J_6	4	3	1	—
J_7	15	3	2	1, 3
J_8	3	4	1	—

How would the sequence change if your objective was to minimise $\max_{i=1}^{m} \{\alpha_i T_i^2\}$?

2   Define $W_i = C_i - p_i$ to be the waiting time of the ith job for a single machine problem. Show that minimising $\overline{W} = 1/n \sum_{i=1}^{n} W_i$ is equivalent to minimising $\overline{C}$.

Table 5.8

Job	J_1	J_2	J_3	J_4	J_5	J_6	J_7
Processing time	6	2	1	9	3	1	8
Due date	33	13	6	22	31	38	14

What sequence of the following seven jobs (Table 5.8) on a single machine minimises the total waiting time, whilst ensuring that all due dates are met?

3   Using Lawler's algorithm, prove that the EDD rule minimises both L_{max} and T_{max} on a single machine when there are no precedence constraints.

4   (a)   A computer compiles and runs programs. Each program must be compiled on the computer before it can be run, and the computer can compile one program and run another at the same time. The time to compile and run seven different programs is given in Table 5.9.

Table 5.9

Program	Compiling time	Running time
ANOV	6	12
SQUARE	4	8
LINPROG	9	6
DYPROG	7	8
QUEUE	14	5
INVENTORY	8	13
NETWORK	16	10

Find the optimal order to compile and run the program so as to minimise the total time. What is this minimum time?

(b)   Assume that the computer is modified so that it may compile one program, run another, and print out the results of a third. The running times given in part (a), in fact, include the printing times, which are 8, 4, 3, 5, 2, 11, 9 respectively. What is the minimum time to process all the programs on the modified computer?

Draw the Gantt diagrams for (a) and (b).

5   In the three-machine flow-shop problem given in Table 5.10, apply Johnson's algorithm of Section 5.6 *regardless of the fact that the dominance condition on the second machine is not satisfied*. Draw a Gantt diagram of this schedule and from inspection of this find a schedule with a shorter makespan.

Table 5.10

Job	Processing time		
	M_1	M_2	M_3
J_i	a_i	b_i	c_i
J_1	5	1	7
J_2	3	6	2
J_3	4	3	1
J_4	5	5	2

6   Show that a schedule which minimises L_{max} also minimises T_{max}.

6
Critical Path Analysis

6.1 Introduction

Critical path analysis—CPA, for short—is a technique for solving a class of scheduling problems that are so common and so important that it deserves a chapter to itself. The aim of CPA is to schedule the component activities of a complex project so that it may be completed as soon as possible; i.e. CPA seeks to minimise makespan. To be more specific, a complete project may usually be analysed into a number, often a very large number, of distinct activities. Some of these activities may be undertaken simultaneously. In other cases, one activity may start only after certain others have completed; there are precedence constraints between the activities. Our problem is to schedule the processing of activities so that the overall project is completed as soon as it may be. A simple example should make these ideas clear.

Example: Building a house (Note that this is obviously a great simplification of the real problem of scheduling the various phases of house building.)

Table 6.1

Activity	Description	Duration (Days)	Activities that must be completed before current activity commences
A	Dig and pour foundations	21	—
B	Make window and door frames	7	—
C	Build walls	10	A, B
D	Build roof	6	C
E	Install plumbing	3	C
F	Install electrical wiring	2	D
G	Plaster walls	4	E, F
H	Decorate	6	G
I	Landscape garden	8	D

This example has 9 activities (see Table 6.1). Real life examples have hundreds, perhaps thousands, of activities. However, 9 activities will be quite enough for us; we have no computer. In fact, this example has enough subtleties (to do with things called 'dummy activities') to make us prefer to delay consideration of its solution. We shall look at some simpler examples first.

6.2   Project networks

Consider the project given by Table 6.2. In this table we have used the conventional expression 'depends on' to mean that one activity cannot commence until the other activities have been completed. Thus activity D cannot begin until B has completed; its commencement depends on the completion of B.

Table 6.2

Activity	A	B	C	D	E	F	G	H
Duration	5	3	2	9	1	6	4	8
Depends on	—	A	A	B	B	C	D	E, F, G

Suppose we draw the **project network** shown in Fig. 6.1. Each activity has been associated with a directed line or **arc** in the network. The direction here clearly indicates the direction of time. Notice that we cannot start (say) activity E until activity B has been completed, as required by our table.

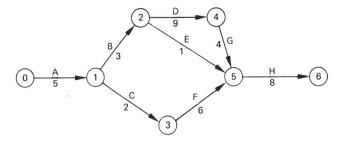

Fig. 6.1

Each activity (arc) joins two vertices or points called **events**. An activity $i \rightarrow j$ is said to have **start event** i and **finish event** j. A **path** between any two events i and j is any set of consecutive arcs starting at i and finishing at j. Thus B–D–G is a path between 1 and 5. Not all pairs of vertices have paths between them e.g. 3 and 4, or 5 and 2. *Note*. There is a path between 2 and 5 but not one in the opposite direction between 5 and 2.

Each arc or activity has a duration associated with it. The duration or length of a path is the sum of the durations of its activities. It is clear that the length of a path corresponds to the time necessary to complete those activities. Now the length of the *longest* path between 0 and 6 gives the *shortest* time in which we may complete the whole job. We shall call any longest path a **critical path** (hence CPA), and any activity on a critical path a **critical activity**. Here we see clearly that A–B–D–G–H is the longest path, with length $5 + 3 + 9 + 4 + 8 = 29$. Note that if the completion of any critical activity is delayed, then the critical path becomes longer and completion of the whole project is delayed. It is for this reason that they are known as critical activities.

In general we have two problems.

(1) How do we draw the project network given the (duration and) dependencies of activities?
(2) How do we determine the critical path(s)?

6.3 Drawing project networks

Note that a project network

(1) possesses a unique initial event, from which all activities which depend on no others start;
(2) possesses a unique terminal event, at which all activities upon which no other depends finish;
(3) has at least one activity starting from each event except the terminal event;
(4) has at least one activity finishing at each event except the initial event;
(5) has no closed loops.

So let us try and draw the simple example given in Table 6.3.

Table 6.3

Activity	A	B	C	D	E	F	G	H	I
depends on	—	A	A	B	B	C, D	B	G	E, F, H
from i	0	1	1	2	2	3	2	4	5
to j	1	2	3	3	5	5	4	5	6

We start with the 'from i' and 'to j' rows blank. Clearly A can start immediately. So the start event of A is 0, the initial event for the project. Hence 0 is entered under A in the from i row. Next we try to start B. This cannot begin until A has been completed. Thus we give A the finish event 1 by entering 1 appropriately in the 'to j' row. Obviously we start B at 1 as well; hence 1 is entered in the 'from i' row. C also starts on A's completion and so shares the start event 1. D cannot start until B completes. So we give B's finish event the next available event number, 2. Thus D starts from 2. E starts from 2 as well. F cannot start until C and D have been completed. So we complete both these at 3 and start F from there. And so on.

Generally we proceed along the 'from i' row, filling in start events consecutively and returning to the 'to j' row to complete activities as dictated by the dependencies. Notice that we have made an implicit assumption in doing this. We have assumed that the table is arranged so that dependent activities must always be to the right of those activities on which they are dependent. Thus we shall always arrange the table in this way.

Returning to our example we find that the project network in Fig. 6.2 results.

Unfortunately, this simple method of assigning start and finish events can lead to difficulties. Consider Table 6.4. This gives two activities between events 1 and 2

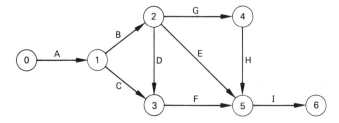

Fig. 6.2

Table 6.4

Activity	A	B	C	D
depends on	—	A	A	B, C
from *i*	0	1	1	2
to *j*	1	2	2	3

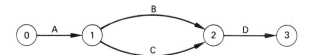

Fig. 6.3

(Fig. 6.3). It is a convention in CPA that we allow at most one activity between any two events. This convention has its roots in the early computer programs designed to implement CPA. Strictly it is no longer necessary; computer programming is now more sophisticated. However, tradition lingers on and we shall not be radical. Thus we shall insist that at most one activity joins any two events. So we introduce **dummy activities** which have zero duration (see Table 6.5 and Fig. 6.4). We shall explain shortly how the event numbering is generated. Note that conventionally dummies are shown as dotted arcs in the networks.

Table 6.5

Activity	A	B	C	D	Dummies	
depends on	—	A	A	B, C		
from *i*	0	1	1	4	2	3
to *j*	1	2	3	5	4	4

Next consider Table 6.6. If we generate event numbers as before, we arrive at the situation shown. This is clearly unsatisfactory as the event numbers imply that

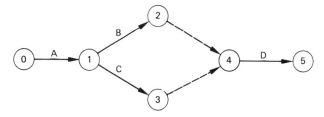

Fig. 6.4

Table 6.6

Activity depends on from *i* to *j*	A	B	C	D	E	F
	—	—	B	A, C	C	D, E
	0	0	1	2	2	
	2	1	2			

E depends upon A, which is not so. There is no simple way of avoiding this, so again we introduce dummies (see Table 6.7 and Fig. 6.5).

Table 6.7

Activity depends on from *i* to *j*	A	B	C	D	E	F	Dummies			
	—	—	B	A, C	C	D, E				
	0	0	1	4	3	7	2	3	5	6
	2	1	3	5	6	8	4	4	7	7

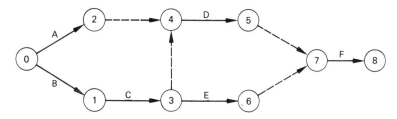

Fig. 6.5

Notice that in both cases where it was necessary to introduce dummies, we had an activity that depended on at least two activities. Not all multiple dependencies cause problems; in Table 6.3 activities F and I depend on more than one other, yet no difficulty results. Nonetheless, it is true that, when difficulties occur, they do occur because of multiple dependencies. Thus, in generating node numbers we use multiple dependencies as a cue to introduce dummies and avoid possible difficulties. This means that we may introduce more dummies than are strictly necessary, but we shall certainly avoid any problems that might otherwise arise.

Hence we modify our method of generating node numbers. Whenever we encounter a multiple dependence we return and ensure that those activities are completed by assigning *distinct* finish events. Thus in Table 6.6 the dependency of D in both A and C leads to A finishing at 2 and C finishing at 3. Next we assign a distinct node number to the start event of the dependent activity. Here D starts at 4. Finally we create dummies to the start event of the dependent activities from the finish events of those activities on which it depends. Thus we create dummies $(2 \to 4)$ and $(3 \to 4)$ here. You may check that dummies $(5 \to 7)$ and $(6 \to 7)$ are introduced similarly. Notice that this latter pair of dummies are unnecessary; no problem occurs if they are not introduced. Nonetheless, we shall adopt the ultra-safe policy of introducing dummies whenever problems may arise. Having said that, there is no reason why we should not remove unnecessary dummies at a later stage. Doing so makes the network neater and allows faster calculation of the critical path on a computer.

There are two simple rules which enable us to remove dummies.

(a)   *The addition rule*

Suppose $(i \to j)$ is a dummy activity. If we add the reverse dummy activity $(j \to i)$ to the network and do not invalidate its logic (i.e. introduce false dependencies), then events i and j can be amalgamated. This will always, but not only, happen if the activity which ends at event i occurs only once in the 'depends on' row (equivalently, the dummy activity $(i \to j)$ is the *only* exit from event i).

For instance, consider the project given in Table 6.8, which leads to the network shown in Fig. 6.6.

Table 6.8

Activity	A	B	C	D	E	F	G	H
depends on	—	—	A	B, C	C	E, D	A	G, F
from i	0	0	1	4	3	7	1	10
to j	1	2	3	5	6	8	9	11
Dummies								
from i	2	3	5	6	8	9		
to j	4	4	7	7	10	10		

Applying the addition rule we find

events 8,   9   and   10   can be amalgamated;
events 6,   7   and   5   can be amalgamated;
events 2   and   4   can be amalgamated.

Hence we get the network in Fig. 6.7.

As an exercise use the addition rule to check that 5, 6, and 7 may be amalgamated in Fig. 6.5.

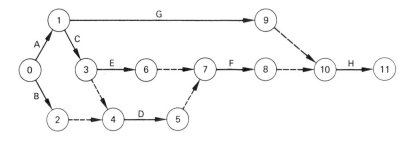

Fig. 6.6

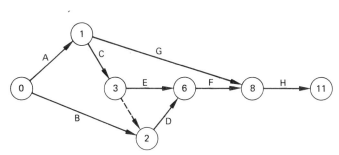

Fig. 6.7

(b) *The substitution rule*
If we substitute $(j \rightarrow i)$ for the dummy activity $(i \rightarrow j)$ and in doing so create a closed loop, $(i \rightarrow j)$ is redundant and can be removed (but events i and j cannot usually be amalgamated). Essentially this rule identifies superfluous dummy activities for which the logical dependence of activities starting at j on activities finishing at i is ensured by a path without the need for $(i \rightarrow j)$.

For example, consider the project given in Table 6.9, which gives rise to Fig. 6.8. By the addition rule events 2 and 5 may be amalgamated. Hence we obtain the network shown in Fig. 6.9. Now note that the substitution rule allows dummy activity $(1 \rightarrow 4)$ to be removed (since its reversal completes a closed loop).

Table 6.9

Activity depends on from i to j	A	B	C	D	E
	—	—	—	A, B, C	A, B
	0	0	0	4	5
	1	2	3		
Dummies from i to j	1	2	3	1	2
	4	4	4	5	5

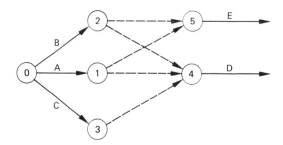

Fig. 6.8

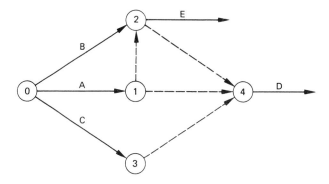

Fig. 6.9

Notes

(1)   The use of the addition rule did not correspond to an activity appearing only once in the 'depends on' row.
(2) $(1 \to 4)$ could not be removed initially. Thus we must repeatedly check each dummy during elimination.
(3)   The addition rule also shows that events 3 and 4 may be amalgamated.

Finally, one general point should be noted about the addition and substitution rules. Both are concerned only with whether a dummy activity is necessary to preserve the correct dependencies of activities within the network. Neither pay any heed to the convention that two distinct activities cannot join the same pair of nodes. Thus before a dummy activity is removed, it must be checked to see if it is required by the convention. For instance, application of the addition rule to the network in Fig. 6.4 removes both dummy activities despite the fact that one must be kept to maintain the convention.

6.4 Finding the critical path

Early date

We begin by considering the earliest that we can arrive at each event. Let

e_i = earliest time that we can arrive at event i with all the incoming activities completed

a_{ij} = duration of activity $(i \rightarrow j)$. Remember that for a dummy $a_{ij} = 0$.

Assume $e_0 = 0$.

Clearly $e_j = \max_i (e_i + a_{ij})$, where the maximum is taken over those i with an arc to j.

Let us return to the example given in Fig. 6.1.

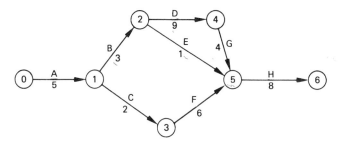

Fig. 6.1 (repeated)

Here we find

$$e_0 = 0$$
$$e_1 = e_0 + a_{01} = 0 + 5 = 5$$
$$e_2 = e_1 + a_{12} = 5 + 2 = 7$$
$$e_3 = e_1 + a_{13} = 5 + 3 = 8$$
$$e_4 = e_3 + a_{34} = 8 + 9 = 17$$
$$e_5 = \max \{e_3 + a_{35}, e_4 + a_{45}, e_2 + a_{25}\}$$
$$= \max \{17 + 4, 8 + 1, 7 + 6\} = 21$$
$$e_6 = e_5 + a_{56} = 21 + 8 = 29.$$

Clearly, if n is the terminal event,

e_n = length of critical path = completion time of project.

In this example $e_6 = 29$ = length of longest (critical) path, as may be checked by inspection.

Late date

Next we consider the latest that we can start an activity without delaying any activity on the critical path and hence delaying the completion of the project. Let

l_i = latest time we can leave event i without extending the length of the critical path, i.e. l_i is the latest time that we can start all activities which begin at i without falling behind schedule.

Clearly for the finish event $l_n = e_n$.
   Generally, we see that

$l_i = \min_j (l_j - a_{ij})$, where the minimum is taken over those j with an arc from i.

In the example:

$$l_6 = 29 = e_6$$

$$l_5 = l_6 - a_{56} = 29 - 8 = 21$$

$$l_4 = l_5 - a_{45} = 21 - 4 = 17$$

$$l_3 = \min \{l_5 - a_{35}, l_4 - a_{34}\} = \min \{21 - 1, 17 - 9\} = 8$$

$$l_2 = l_5 - a_{25} = 21 - 6 = 15$$

$$l_1 = \min \{l_3 - a_{13}, l_2 - a_{12}\} = \min \{8 - 3, 15 - 2\} = 5$$

$$l_0 = l_1 - a_{01} = 5 - 5 = 0.$$

Critical path

On the critical path(s) there can be no leeway; any delay delays the completion of the entire project. Hence $e_i = l_i$ for all events on critical paths. Such events are known as **critical events**. In the example 0, 1, 3, 4, 5 and 6 are critical; only 2 is non-critical.
   For any critical activity, $a_{ij} = l_j - e_i$; for any delay a critical activity will increase the length of the critical path.
   For any non-critical activity $a_{ij} < l_j - e_i$. The quantity $(l_j - a_{ij} - e_i)$ is called the **total float of activity** $(i \rightarrow j)$. It represents the maximum possible delay that can be incurred in the processing of this activity without increasing the critical path length, providing that there are no delays elsewhere. Occasionally it is of interest to know how much delay can be incurred on an activity without the condition that there are no delays elsewhere. Here two concepts are useful. The **independent float of an activity** $(i \rightarrow j)$ is the maximum delay that can be incurred on the activity without placing any constraints whatsoever on any other activity. It is the quantity $(e_j - a_{ij} - l_i)$. The **free float at an activity** $(i \rightarrow j)$ is the maximum delay that may be incurred on an activity without placing any constraints on the processing of activities later in the network. It is defined to be $(e_j - a_{ij} - e_i)$. These three floats are shown in Fig. 6.10.

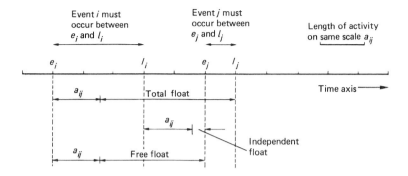

Fig. 6.10 The definitions of the various floats associated with an activity

Table 6.10

Activity	Joins	Total float $l_j - e_i - a_{ij}$	
A	0 → 1	5 − 0 − 5 = 0	critical
B	1 → 3	8 − 5 − 3 = 0	critical
C	1 → 2	15 − 5 − 2 = 8	total float of 8
D	3 → 4	17 − 8 − 9 = 0	critical
E	3 → 5	21 − 8 − 1 = 12	total float of 12
F	2 → 5	21 − 7 − 6 = 8	total float of 8
G	4 → 5	21 − 17 − 4 = 0	critical
H	5 → 6	29 − 21 − 8 = 0	critical

Table 6.10 shows the situation for the example, and shows that the critical path is A → B → D → G → H. The independent and free floats of the non-critical activities are shown in Table 6.11.

Table 6.11

Activity	Joins	Independent float $e_j - a_{ij} - l_i$	Free float $e_j - a_{ij} - e_i$
C	1 → 2	7 − 2 − 5 = 0	7 − 2 − 5 = 0
E	3 → 5	21 − 1 − 8 = 12	21 − 1 − 8 = 12
F	2 → 5	21 − 6 − 15 = 0	21 − 6 − 7 = 8

These values can be simply understood in the context of the project network. Consider first activities C and F. These together form a path joining the critical events 1 and 5. The total time allowed for processing on this path is $e_5 - e_1 = 21 - 5 = 16$. (Remember that early date = late date at critical events.) The total processing time for C and F together is $2 + 6 = 8$. Thus in total a delay of

$16 - 8 = 8$ can be accommodated without any change in the critical path length. Thus the total floats for C and F are both 8, as indeed we have found them to be. Any delay on C means that less can be allowed on the later activity F. Thus C has a free float of 0. However, any delay of 8 or less on F does not constrain further any later activity. Thus F has a free float of 8. Finally, any delay on either C or F reduces the allowable delay on the other. So both have zero independent float. On the other hand consider activity E. This joins the critical events 3 and 5. Any float on E is available to E alone. Thus for E total float = free float = independent float = 12.

While we are considering activity E, note that it joins two critical events, *but that it is not a critical activity*. In general, critical activities must join critical events, but not every activity that joins two critical events need be critical. Thus the critical path must be determined by checking for activities with zero total floats, and not simply by joining critical events.

Finally, we note that it is conventional to combine the display of the project network and the early and late dates. The nodes are drawn larger and include timing information, perhaps thus:

Because the early and late date calculations are so easy, it is a simple matter to pass through the network from the initial to terminal events filling in early dates, then from the terminal to the initial event filling in late dates.

Figure 6.11 shows the project network and critical path for the house-building example given in Table 6.1.

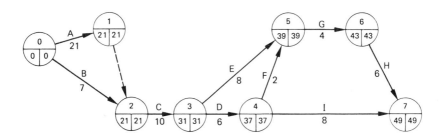

Fig. 6.11   The project network for the house building example

The critical path is A–C–D–F–G–H. Note that in this example *every* event is critical, but activities B, E and I are non-critical.

6.5 Cost considerations in CPA

So far we have been taking the activity durations as given, fixed quantities. However, in real life this is seldom so. By employing more men and machines, and generally by spending money, it is usually possible to hasten the processing of some, if not all activities. In this section we shall consider CPA in which we can control the duration of some of the activities at a cost. We shall assume the cost structure given in Fig. 6.12. Each activity has a maximum duration, the **normal time**, and a minimum duration, the **crash time**. Any duration between these limits is possible. Moreover, the cost is assumed to be a linear function of the time.

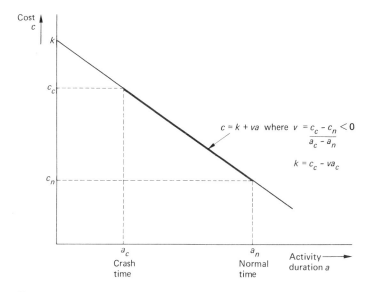

Fig. 6.12

Costs relating to the duration of an activity are known as **direct costs**. There are also other costs, which relate to the project's final completion date or, equivalently, the length of the critical path. Such costs are called **indirect**. Spending more on direct costs usually reduces indirect costs. Our problem is to find the balance which gives the minimum total cost.

One method for doing this is to formulate the problem as a linear program. Solving this linear program guarantees that one finds the minimum total cost. However, the linear program is complex and not at all suitable for hand calculation. For small project networks there is a simple, heuristic procedure well suited to hand calculation, which usually finds a solution with minimum total cost, although in some cases it may find only a very good, but not optimal, solution (see Exercise 4).

Example   Suppose that the direct costs, activity, durations and dependencies in a project are as given in Table 6.12. Suppose further that the indirect costs are £5000 per week of critical path length.

Table 6.12

Activity:	A	B	C	D	E	F	G	H
Depends on:	—	—	A	B	B	C, D	E	F, G
Normal duration in weeks, a_n:	2	8	4	1	2	5	6	1
Crash duration in weeks, a_c:	1	5	3	1	2	5	2	1
Normal cost in £1000s, c_n:	10	15	20	7	8	10	12	1
Crash cost in £1000s c_c:	15	21	24	7	8	10	36	1

Note that activities D, E, F and H have been given fixed durations. Only the durations of A, B, C and G can be controlled.

We begin by drawing the project network and calculating the critical path when all the activities take their normal duration. Note how we plot the network against a horizontal time axis. This is shown in Fig. 6.13.

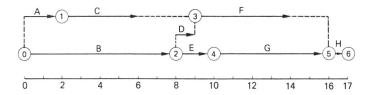

Fig. 6.13

In the network the solid lines indicate the actual processing assumed to start as early as possible; horizontal dotted lines indicate the free floats of activities (and, were there any, dummy activities). Events are plotted at their early dates.

Here the critical path is clearly B–E–G–H, with length 17 weeks. The total cost when all activities are at their normal times is therefore as given in Table 6.13.

Now consider the extra cost per week's reduction for each of the four activities whose durations we can reduce or **crash** (Table 6.14). Clearly crashing a non-

Table 6.13

		£1000s
Direct cost	A	10
	B	15
	C	20
	D	7
	E	8
	F	10
	G	12
	H	1
Indirect cost 17 × 5	=	85
		168

Table 6.14

Activity	Cost/week's reduction in £1000s
A	$(15-10)/(2-1) = 5$
B	$(21-15)/(8-5) = 2$
C	$(24-20)/(4-3) = 4$
G	$(36-12)/(6-2) = 6$

critical activity is a waste of money; it does not reduce the critical path length by a millisecond. Of the four activities only B and G are critical. It is cheapest to crash B. Moreover, crashing B costs £2000 per week, which will be more than saved in indirect costs. So let us crash B. We can crash B by up to 3 weeks. In Fig. 6.13 we see that reducing B pulls the network which is to the right of event 2 towards the left. We can crash B until this shifting of part of a network closes up a free float completely. When this happens the critical path may change and we should stop and check. Nothing happens until the third week is crashed, when the network plotted against time becomes that in Fig. 6.14.

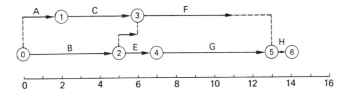

Fig. 6.14

This crashing has cost $£3 \times 2000$ in direct costs and saved $£3 \times 5000$ in indirect costs. Thus the total cost becomes

$$\text{Total cost in } £1000\text{s} = 168 + 3 \times 2 - 3 \times 5$$
$$= 159.$$

Here we see that, although C now has no free float, the critical path is still B–E–G–H. This is because the only activity immediately depending on C, namely F, has free float itself. With B fully crashed only A, C, and G can be crashed. A and C are non-critical, so there is no point in crashing these. Consider crashing G. For each week it will cost $£6000$ in direct costs but save only $£5000$ in indirect costs. Clearly to crash G would, on balance, waste money. So we have reached a solution; it is, in fact, an optimal solution.

Suppose, however, that it had only cost $£2500$ per week to crash G and also that it was possible to crash F by one week at a cost of $£2000$. Then first we would have crashed B by three weeks as before, and then crashed G by two weeks, whereupon we would have absorbed all F's free float. Thus the network would be as in Fig. 6.15. *All* the activities would be critical now. Crashing any one of A, C, F and G alone will not reduce the critical path. However, crashing more than one simultaneously might do so. Since B and D cannot be crashed, there is no point in considering crashing either A or C: doing so would only open up free float before event 3. Crashing F and G together costs $£(2500 + 2000)$ per week, which is less than the indirect costs and, moreover, it reduces the critical path. So we would crash both F and G by 1 week. No further crashing of any combination of activities reduces the critical path.

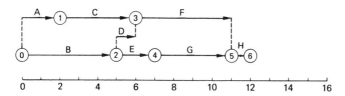

Fig. 6.15

To summarise: the first step in this heuristic procedure is to draw the network to a time scale with all activities set at their normal durations and scheduled to start as early as possible. Free floats are indicated by dotted lines. The cheapest way of reducing the critical path length by one unit (in the example, a week) is found. This may involve crashing just one critical activity or it may involve the simultaneous crashing of two or more critical activities. It is never worth considering the crashing of non-critical activities. If the cheapest cost of reducing the critical path length by one unit is less than the indirect cost for one unit of critical path length, the appropriate activities are crashed. This process is iterated, care being taken at each stage to note whether any further activities become critical. The process terminates when the cost of reducing the critical path length exceeds the indirect costs.

Let us turn now to the linear programming formulation of our problem. As before, let e_i be the early time of event i and let n be the finish event in the project network. Thus e_n is the length of the critical path. Next let a_{ij} be the actual processing time of each activity $(i \rightarrow j)$. Then $e_1, e_2, \ldots, e_n$ and all the a_{ij} will be the decision variables in our linear program.

The indirect costs are easy to evaluate. If C is the indirect cost/unit time for the critical path, the indirect costs are Ce_n. The direct costs are almost as easy to evaluate. Look back to Fig. 6.12. Subscript the intercept k and gradient v of the cost curve with ij to associate each with its activity. Then the direct cost is

$$\sum_{\text{all activities}} (k_{ij} + v_{ij}a_{ij}).$$

Thus our task is to minimise the total cost

$$\sum_{\text{all activities}} (k_{ij} + v_{ij}a_{ij}) + Ce_n.$$

We may ignore the constants k_{ij}, so our objective function in the linear program is

minimise $\sum_{\text{all activities}} v_{ij}a_{ij} + Ce_n.$

over all

e_i, a_{ij}

The constraints are of two types.

First, the a_{ij} and the e_i must be compatible. Thus for all activities $(i \rightarrow j)$ we must have $e_j \geqslant e_i + a_{ij}$ from the definition of early dates (see Section 5.4) or, equivalently, $e_j - e_i - a_{ij} \geqslant 0$.

Second, the a_{ij} must lie between the normal and crash times. Thus for all $(i \rightarrow j)$ we must have

$a_{ij} \geqslant a_{c,ij},$ the crash time of $(i \rightarrow j)$:

and $a_{ij} \leqslant a_{n,ij},$ the normal time of $(i \rightarrow j)$.

Finally, we must have the usual non-negativity constraints on e_i and a_{ij}. However, most of these are implicit in the main constraints of the problem. Although this linear program is large, it has a special structure and may be solved fairly rapidly on a computer.

6.6 Resource levelling

Let us suppose that we have settled on the durations of all the activities and that now all we have to do is schedule the actual start times of the non-critical activities. We can, of course, choose to start them at any times that are compatible with both the early and late dates at their start and finish events and with the dependencies of the project network. However, there may be some advantage in choosing the start times more carefully.

For instance, we may wish to minimise the maximum daily manpower required, subject, of course, to not extending the length of the critical path. In other words, minimising the maximum daily manpower is a sub-objective in the problem; minimising the length of the critical path remains the prime objective. (Here we have another example of a multi-objective optimisation problem: see Section 2.18.) Let us consider an example based upon the network shown in Fig. 6.13. We shall now assume that no activity can be crashed. So our problem is to schedule the non-critical activities to minimise the manpower requirements. Suppose that each activity requires the manpower given by Table 6.15.

Table 6.15

Activity	Men needed
A	1
B	1
C	2
D	2
E	3
F	2
G	1
H	2

Thus, if C, D, and E were all processed on the same day (as they might be), we should need 7 men. The problem is to schedule the non-critical activities so that the maximum number of men required at any time is minimised. Although this problem is remarkably easy to state, it is in general very difficult to solve. Here we shall find the optimal schedule simply by using our nous. We shall approach the problem as if it were a jig-saw. First we draw a graph against time indicating the manpower requirements of the critical activities (see Fig. 6.16). Each activity is represented by a block. The blocks for the non-critical activities A, C, D, F must be located between the early and late dates of their start and finish events. As an exercise you should confirm that the early and late dates are those indicated in the diagram.

The first thing to note from Fig. 6.16 is that at least 3 men are needed because E requires 3 for two weeks. Our problem is to add the blocks for the non-critical activities to the graph so that:

(1)   the maximum increases as little as possible; and
(2)   the processing obeys all the dependencies.

The range of possible weeks in which each non-critical activity can be processed is shown in Fig. 6.16. On top of these we must remember that, for example, A

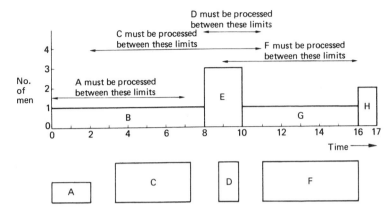

Fig. 6.16

must precede D. Now in this case it is clear that we may add all the blocks without increasing the maximum manpower above 3 (see Fig. 6.17).

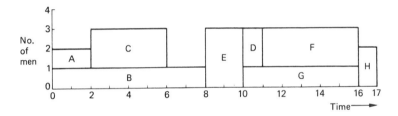

Fig. 6.17

This type of problem is called resource levelling, because we aim to 'spread out' or 'level' the processing of activities; doing this, of course, minimises the daily demands on resources and manpower. Resource levelling is one of the few NP-complete or hard combinatorial problems (see Section 5.7) that we discuss in this book. The method that we give here for solving it is clearly only suitable for small problems. Other methods must be used for large problems. We shall not discuss these other methods, but we do note that the majority of them are heuristic. They seek to find a good solution, although perhaps not an optimal solution, quickly. Being NP-complete this type of problem is such that algorithms for finding an optimal solution may take a prohibitively long time.

Exercises

1 For the project shown in Table 6.16 find the earliest completion date and critical path.

Table 6.16

Activity	A	B	C	D	E	F	G	H
Depends on	—	—	A	A, B	B	D, E	E	G, H
Duration	3	2	5	4	3	4	3	1

In finding the earliest that this project can be finished, it is assumed that there is unlimited manpower. Suppose that each activity can only be done by one man (i.e. if we put two men on the same activity it does not get done more quickly). However, two or more men may be working on different activities at the same time. Show that the quickest the project can be done if there is only one man available throughout is 25. How quickly can it be done if there are two men available?

2   The Choo-Chew Restaurants wish to convert old railway carriages into restaurants. The activities involved in the conversion were as shown in Table 6.17. Find the critical path and earliest opening date. By shifting the non-critical activities, minimise the maximum number of men required.

Table 6.17

		Depends on	Duration (weeks)	No. of men
A	Purchase and renovate coaches	—	10	4
B	Purchase restaurant equipment	—	3	2
C	Hire personnel	—	1	1
D	Select and purchase site	—	2	2
E	Obtain licences	D	7	1
F	Site preparation	E	3	3
G	Move coaches onto site	A, F	5	2
H	Install gas, electricity, water	G	4	4
I	Install equipment	D, H	4	5
J	Decorate	B, H	3	2
K	Stock bar and kitchen	I, J	6	3
L	Advertise	G	3	1
M	Train personnel	C, I	4	2
N	Undertake pilot operation	K, L	7	2
O	Start operating fully	M, N	—	—

3   Table 6.18 gives details of eight activities, which together form a project. Draw a project network and find the early dates, late dates and critical activities, given that all activities take their normal time. Given that the indirect costs amount to £500 per week, use the heuristic algorithm given in Section 6.5 to determine which activities should be crashed and by how much. What is the final cost of your network?

Table 6.18

Activity	Depends on	Durations Normal time (weeks)	Crash time (weeks)	Direct costs Normal (£)	Crash (£)
A	—	4	2	800	1800
B	A	3	2	400	500
C	A	7	4	800	1100
D	B	3	2	500	700
E	C, D	4	4	1000	1000
F	—	6	4	800	1000
G	F	7	3	400	1200
H	E, G	5	4	1000	1600

4 Draw a project network from the details given in Table 6.19. Find the critical path when all activities take their normal time. Given that the indirect costs amount to £600 per week, use the heuristic algorithm given in Section 6.5 to determine which activities should be crashed and by how much. Is the solution optimal? (*Hint*: Consider crashing B, C, and G by 1 week and simultaneously uncrashing F by 1 week.)

Table 6.19

Activity	Depends on	Duration Normal (weeks)	Crash time (weeks)	Direct costs Normal (£)	Crash (£)
A	—	3	3	600	600
B	A	15	13	2000	2300
C	A	7	4	1100	2000
D	A	10	9	800	900
E	C	8	8	1300	1300
F	C	4	3	800	1000
G	F, D	5	4	750	1000

5 In manufacturing a watch, each of 7 cogs have to be processed on two machines. If all cogs are to be processed in the order machine M_1 then machine M_2 and if the processing times in minutes for each operation are as in the table, what is the shortest time to make all the cogs?

Cog n:	1	2	3	4	5	6	7
Machine M_1:	3	2	1	2	3	2	1
Machine M_2:	1	2	1	1	2	1	1

Manufacturing the 5 spindles requires 3 machines, all in the order M_3, M_4, M_5.

If the processing times in minutes are as given in Tables 6.20 and 6.21, what is the shortest time to make all the spindles?

Table 6.20

Spindle no:	1	2	3	4	5
Machine M_3:	3	3	3	4	3
Machine M_4:	2	1	2	2	1
Machine M_5:	4	4	6	3	4

Table 6.21

Activities required to make a watch:

		Depends on	Duration (min.)
A	Make cogs	—	see above
B	Make spindles	—	see above
C	Temper and make main springs	—	5
D	Assemble clockwork	A, B, C	2
E	make face	—	3
F	Fix face to works	D, E	1
G	Make case	—	7
H	Put works in case	F, G	1
I	Make strap	—	1
J	Fix strap to watch	H, I	1

Draw a project network for making a watch, determine the critical activities and find the shortest time to make a watch.

Given that it requires one man to operate each machine when making cogs and spindles and one man to complete each other activity, what is the minimum number of men required to make a watch in the shortest time? Assume any man can do any job and that no man may leave a machine to rejoin it later (but he need not wait until his fellow machine operators have finished).

7
Optimal Routing

7.1 The basic problem—Dijkstra's algorithm

A certain small island has 7 towns joined by roads which are so narrow that only one-way traffic is allowed, the permitted directions being indicated by the arrows on the map shown in Fig. 7.1. The distance in miles between each pair of towns connected by a road is also shown. The map is, of course, schematic and does not represent real geographic positions of towns or roads (cf. London underground map).

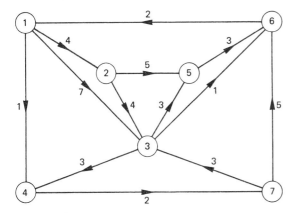

Fig. 7.1

The only fire station on the island is in town 1 and the fire authorities would like to know the shortest route from 1 to every other town. In our solution of this problem we shall use graph-theoretic terminology by referring to the towns as **vertices** and to the lines (roads, in the example) joining vertices as **arcs**. A sequence of vertices joined by arcs is called a **path** and all vertices of the path except the first and last are called **intermediate**. As an example, in Fig. 7.1, P: 1 $\rightarrow 4 \rightarrow 7 \rightarrow 3 \rightarrow 5$ is a path and 3, 4 and 7 are intermediate vertices. A path P can also be thought of as a sequence of arcs and it has length $l(P)$ equal to the sum of its arc lengths (which, we assume, are positive). Thus, the length of P is $1 + 2 + 3 + 3 = 9$. A path is **elementary** if no vertex appears twice. All shortest paths must be elementary since, for example, $2 \to 3 \to 4 \to 7 \to 3 \to 5$ must have greater length than $2 \to 3 \to 5$.

The virtue of graph-theoretic terminology is that it frees us from the tyranny of a particular interpretation (road networks, in our case). For example, in the CPA project networks described in Chapter 5 we had vertex = event and arc = activity. In that chapter, we sought *longest* paths and this made sense because the networks were acyclic (no paths existed which started and finished at the same vertex). For acyclic networks the longest and shortest path problems are essentially the same; we can just multiply arc lengths by -1. However, Fig. 7.1 is *not* acyclic, for $1 \to 3 \to 6 \to 1$ is a path, for example. This makes the optimal routing problem considerably more challenging. It is possible to generalise the method of Chapter 5 and this is outlined in Chapter 12 as part of the general approach of dynamic programming. Instead, we will describe a procedure which is more efficient under our restriction of positive arc lengths, although invalid if this is relaxed.

Most methods of solving shortest path problems find not only the shortest path from 1 to any other vertex j but also the length of that path, $\theta(j)$. The particular approach of Dijkstra described here generates the vertices in increasing order of $\theta(j)$. Conventionally, we can set $\theta(1) = 0$ and then we obtain vertices $j_1, j_2, \ldots, j_{n-1}$ (assuming n vertices) where $\theta(1) \leqslant \theta(j_1) \leqslant \cdots \leqslant \theta(j_{n-1})$. The approach rests upon the fact that the shortest path from 1 to j_k can only have $j_1, \ldots, j_{k-1}$ as intermediate vertices. This result is an immediate consequence of the observations that any subpath of a shortest path is also a shortest path and that arc lengths are positive. At the kth iteration ($2 \leqslant k \leqslant n-1$) let $d(j)$ be the length of the shortest amongst those paths from 1 to j for which the intermediate vertices are restricted to $j_1, \ldots, j_{k-1}$. Then, it follows from our result that j_k will minimise $d(j)$ over all vertices except $1, j_1, \ldots, j_{k-1}$. In order to update $d(j)$ for the next iteration, note that if $d(j)$ changes when j_k is added to the previously permissible intermediate vertices, then j_k must be the penultimate vertex in the new restricted shortest path from 1 to j because of the ordering of vertices. This means that $d(j)$ is changed to $d(j_k) + l(j_k, j)$, where $l(i, j)$ is the length of the arc from i to j. This says that, if there is an arc from j_k to j and

$$d(j_k) + l(j_k, j) < d(j), \tag{7.1}$$

then $d(j)$ is changed as above. Initially, i.e. when $k = 1$, we can take $d(j) = l(1, j)$ if there is an arc from 1 to j, and $d(j) = \infty$ (which we interpret as an 'infinite length' and thus greater than any finite length), otherwise. This is obviously the shortest path length when no intermediate vertices are allowed.

Returning to Fig. 7.1, we start with

$$d(2) = l(1, 2) = 4, \qquad d(3) = 7, \qquad d(4) = 1, \qquad d(5) = d(6) = d(7) = \infty.$$

The least of these is $d(4) = 1$. So we may conclude that $\theta(4) = 1$. We must now update d to permit paths to pass through 4. From Fig. 7.1 the only arc starting at 4 goes to 7 and

$$d(7) = \infty > d(4) + l(4, 7) = 1 + 2 = 3$$

so we change $d(7)$ to 3. The values of d (omitting vertex 4) are now

$$d(2) = 4, \qquad d(3) = 7, \qquad d(5) = d(6) = \infty, \qquad d(7) = 3.$$

The smallest of these is $d(7)$, so $\theta(7) = 3$.

This procedure is repeated, dropping vertices as they are chosen when minimising the ds. At the next iteration we observe that arcs go from 7 to 3 and 6 and

$$d(3) = 7 > d(7) + l(7, 3) = 3 + 3 = 6,$$

$$d(6) = \infty > d(7) + l(7, 6) = 3 + 5 = 8,$$

so we change $d(3)$ to 6 and $d(6)$ to 8. This gives

$$d(2) = 4, \qquad d(3) = 6, \qquad d(5) = \infty, \qquad d(6) = 8.$$

Since $d(2)$ is smallest, we put $\theta(2) = 4$ and observe that

$$d(3) = 6 < d(2) + l(2, 3) = 4 + 4 = 8,$$

so do not change $d(3)$ and

$$d(5) = \infty > d(2) + l(2, 5) = 4 + 5 = 9,$$

so put $d(5) = 9$.

We can summarise the computation to date and complete the method in Table 7.1, which displays $d(j)$.

Table 7.1

Iteration \ j	2	3	4	5	6	7	Minimising j
1	4	7	1	∞	∞	∞	4
2	4	7	—	∞	∞	3*	7
3	4	6*	—	∞	8*	—	2
4	—	6	—	9*	8	—	3
5	—	—	—	9	7*	—	6
6	—	—	—	9	—	—	5

Once a vertex has been picked as a minimiser it is ignored for the rest of the method except for updating the values of d in the immediately following iteration. Furthermore, we have indicated with an asterisk any place where $d(j)$ is decreased. The lengths of the shortest paths are just the lowest numbers in each column. Thus, we have

j	2	3	4	5	6	7
θ	4	6	1	9	7	3

We are really at least as interested in the shortest paths themselves as their lengths. To find these we must produce paths from 1 to j of length $\theta(j)$ for each j. This is done as follows. We first find the lowest asterisk in the jth column and put $\pi(j)$ equal to the minimising j in the row just above. If there is no asterisk put $\pi(j) = 1$. Thus we get

$$\pi(2) = 1, \qquad \pi(3) = 7, \qquad \pi(4) = 1, \qquad \pi(5) = 2,$$
$$\pi(6) = 3, \qquad \pi(7) = 4.$$

Note that the convention for including asterisks means that

$$\theta(j) = \theta(\pi(j)) + l(\pi(j), j). \tag{7.2}$$

So, if P' is a path from 1 to $\pi(j)$ with $l(P') = \theta(\pi(j))$ and P is the path obtained by adding arc $(\pi(j), j)$ to P', then $\theta(j) = l(P)$. This says that $\pi(j)$ is the penultimate vertex of a shortest path from 1 to j.

From this result, it follows that we can find the shortest path from 1 to j in reverse order by calculating $j, \pi(j), \pi(\pi(j))$ and so on until we reach 1. As an example, for $j = 3$ we get 3, $\pi(3) = 7$, $\pi(7) = 4$, $\pi(4) = 1$ and so the shortest path is $1 \to 4 \to 7 \to 3$ which has length $1 + 2 + 3 = 6 = d(3)$. Similarly, for $j = 5$ we get $1 \to 2 \to 5$, which has length $4 + 5 = 9 = d(5)$. We can do this for every vertex to find all the shortest paths, and one convenient way of displaying all these paths simultaneously is to draw those arcs of Fig. 7.1 which go from $\pi(j)$ to j for $j = 2, \ldots, n$. This has been done in Fig. 7.2.

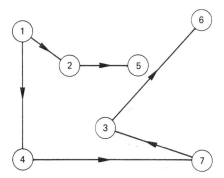

Fig. 7.2

Figure 7.2 is called the *shortest path tree rooted at* l, and for any vertex j there is exactly one path from 1 to j in the tree and it is a shortest path.

If our problem had been simply to find the shortest route between 1 and any specified vertex, say 3, we could have stopped as soon as that vertex was found to minimise some row. In the example we would have stopped at row 4 of Table 7.1.

Our method also applies equally well if the roads are not one-way. We simply imagine that each two-way road is replaced by a pair of one-way roads in opposite directions, each of length equal to the original road length. Thus

(We denote two-way roads by a line without an arrow.) Thus the algorithm can still be applied. There is no need to write down the two opposite arcs explicitly provided we remember the convention.

As an example let us imagine that all the arrows have been erased in Fig. 7.1. The calculations proceed as in Table 7.2.

Table 7.2

Iteration	j 2	3	4	5	6	7	Minimising j
1	4	7	1	∞	2	∞	4
2	4	3*	—	∞	2	3*	6
3	4	3	—	5*	—	3	3
4	4	—	—	5	—	3	7
5	4	—	—	5	—	—	2
6	—	—	—	5	—	—	5
d	4	3	1	5	2	3	
π	1	4	1	6	1	4	

The corresponding shortest path tree (which still has directions indicating which way the arc is traversed) is shown in Fig. 7.3.

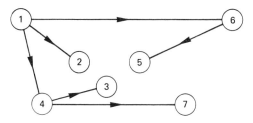

Fig. 7.3

7.2   Finding all shortest paths—Floyd's algorithm

Suppose now that a motoring organisation on our island of the previous section wishes to determine the least distance between *every* pair of towns. This could be achieved by applying Dijkstra's algorithm starting from each vertex in turn. An alternative method due to Floyd shares some features of Dijkstra's method. At the kth iteration ($1 \leqslant k \leqslant n$), let $d(i, j)$ be the length of the shortest path from i to j with intermediate vertices restricted to $1, 2, \ldots, k$. The updating at the kth iteration changes $d(i, j)$ if

$$d(i, j) > d(i, k) + d(k, j),$$

in which case $d(i, j)$ is replaced by $d(i, k) + d(k, j)$. To initialise the procedure, $d(i, j)$ is set to $l(i, j)$ for all i and j for which there is an arc from i to j ($d(i, i) = 0$). Otherwise, $d(i, j)$ is set to ∞. In Fig. 7.1, this means starting with Table 7.3.

Table 7.3

	1	2	3	4	5	6	7
1	0	4	7	1	∞	∞	∞
2	∞	0	4	∞	5	∞	∞
3	∞	∞	0	2	3	1	∞
4	∞	∞	∞	0	∞	∞	2
5	∞	∞	∞	∞	0	3	∞
6	2	∞	∞	∞	∞	0	∞
7	∞	∞	3	∞	∞	5	0

The remaining calculations are set out in Tables 7.4–7.9. In each table we have indicated the row and column used to calculate the next table by printing the figures in bold type. In tabular terms, the updating rule compares the entry in row i and column j, assuming $i, j \neq k$, with the sum of the entry in row i and the indicated column and entry in column j and the indicated row. If the sum is smaller than the entry, the entry is reduced to the sum. We have marked each such reduction with an asterisk. No table appears for $k = 5$ because no changes occur from $k = 4$.

Table 7.4   ($k = 1$)

	1	2	3	4	5	6	7
1	0	4	7	1	∞	∞	∞
2	∞	0	4	∞	5	∞	∞
3	∞	∞	0	2	3	1	∞
4	∞	∞	∞	0	∞	∞	2
5	∞	∞	∞	∞	0	3	∞
6	2	6*	9*	3*	∞	0	∞
7	∞	∞	3	∞	∞	5	0

Table 7.5 ($k = 2$)

	1	2	3	4	5	6	7
1	0	4	**7**	1	9*	∞	∞
2	∞	0	**4**	∞	5	∞	∞
3	∞	∞	0	2	3	1	∞
4	∞	∞	∞	0	∞	∞	2
5	∞	∞	∞	∞	0	3	∞
6	2	6	**9**	3	11*	0	∞
7	∞	∞	**3**	∞	∞	5	0

Table 7.6 ($k = 3$)

	1	2	3	4	5	6	7
1	0	4	7	**1**	9	8*	∞
2	∞	0	4	**6***	5	5*	∞
3	∞	∞	0	**2**	3	1	∞
4	∞	∞	∞	**0**	∞	∞	2
5	∞	∞	∞	∞	0	3	∞
6	2	6	9	**3**	11	0	∞
7	∞	∞	3	**5***	6*	4*	0

Table 7.7 ($k = 4$)

	1	2	3	4	5	6	7
1	0	4	7	1	**9**	8	3*
2	∞	0	4	6	**5**	5	8*
3	∞	∞	0	2	**3**	1	4*
4	∞	∞	∞	0	∞	∞	2
5	∞	∞	∞	∞	**0**	3	∞
6	2	6	9	3	**11**	0	5*
7	∞	∞	3	5	**6**	4	0

Table 7.8 ($k = 6$)

	1	2	3	4	5	6	7
1	0	4	7	1	9	8	**3**
2	7*	0	4	6	5	5	**8**
3	3*	7*	0	2	3	1	**4**
4	∞	∞	∞	0	∞	∞	**2**
5	5*	9*	12*	6*	0	3	**8***
6	2	6	9	3	11	0	**5**
7	6*	10*	3	5	6	4	0

Table 7.9 $(k = 7)$

	1	2	3	4	5	6	7
1	0	4	6*	1	9	7*	3
2	7	0	4	6	5	5	8
3	3	7	0	2	3	1	4
4	8*	12*	5*	0	8*	6*	2
5	5	9	11*	6	0	3	8
6	2	6	8*	3	11	0	5
7	6	10	3	5	6	4	0

Table 7.9 represents the final table of distances (why?). If we also wish to determine an optimal route between any pair of towns we must derive an extra table of values of $k(i, j)$, where $k(i, j)$ is the largest value of k for which there is an asterisk in position (i, j), i.e. row i and column j. If no asterisk has appeared in this position we will conventionally put $k(i, j) = 0$.

We have displayed $k(i, j)$ in Table 7.10.

Table 7.10

	1	2	3	4	5	6	7
1	—	0	7	0	2	7	4
2	6	—	0	3	0	3	4
3	6	6	—	0	0	0	4
4	7	7	7	—	7	7	0
5	6	6	7	6	—	0	6
6	0	1	7	1	2	—	4
7	6	6	0	3	3	3	—

Now, if $k(i, j) = \kappa \geqslant 1$, then in the $d(i, j)$ table for $k = \kappa$ we have

$$d(i, j) = d(i, \kappa) + d(\kappa, j)$$

and $d(i, j) = \theta(i, j)$. Consequently,

$$\theta(i, \kappa) + \theta(\kappa, j) \leqslant d(i, \kappa) + d(\kappa, j)$$
$$= d(i, j)$$
$$= \theta(i, j)$$
$$\leqslant \theta(i, \kappa) + \theta(\kappa, j).$$

The second inequality follows from the fact that $\theta(i, \kappa) + \theta(\kappa, j)$ is the length of some path from i to j. Thus,

$$\theta(i, j) = \theta(i, \kappa) + \theta(\kappa, j).$$

If $k(i, j) = 0$, then, by definition, $\theta(i, j) = l(i, j)$. Using these results, a shortest path between any pair of vertices can be constructed from the $k(i, j)$ table.

As an example consider $(1, 6)$. Then $k(1, 6) = 7$ and therefore

$$\theta(1, 6) = \theta(1, 7) + \theta(7, 6)$$
$$= \theta(1, 4) + \theta(4, 7) + \theta(7, 3) + \theta(3, 6) \quad [k(1, 7) = 4, k(7, 6) = 3]$$
$$= l(1, 4) + l(4, 7) + l(7, 3) + l(3, 6) \quad [\text{All } k(i, j) = 0].$$

So $1 \to 4 \to 7 \to 3 \to 6$ is a shortest path, in agreement with Fig. 7.2. Similarly, for $(5, 7)$ we get

$$5 -- \to 7 \quad (-- \to \text{denotes a path which is not an arc})$$
$$5 -- \to 6 -- \to 7$$
$$5 \to 6 -- \to 4 -- \to 7 \quad (\to \text{denotes an arc})$$
$$5 \to 6 -- \to 1 -- \to 4 \to 7$$
$$5 \to 6 \to 1 \to 4 \to 7.$$

This procedure can never repeat a vertex since shortest paths are elementary. An alternative method (widely used in computer routines) for obtaining the shortest routes is described in Exercise 2.

The undirected case is even easier to solve since we know that $\theta(i, j) = \theta(j, i)$ (why?) and so once we have completed any of the tables for $i > j$ we can fill in (or even omit) the rest by using the symmetry.

7.3 The minimum height problem

We could reinterpret the numbers on the map of Fig. 7.1 as heights (in thousands of feet, say) of mountain passes which must be crossed in order to traverse any particular road. If the mountains are subject to heavy winter snow cover, it becomes appropriate to find a route between a specified pair of towns whose maximum height is as small as possible. Formally, we can measure the 'height' of any path as the maximum of the numbers on that route. Thus, in Fig. 7.1 the path $1 \to 2 \to 3$ has height $\max\{4, 4\} = 4$. The heights of $1 \to 3$ and $1 \to 4 \to 7 \to 3 \to 6$ are 7 and 3 respectively.

This problem is similar to the ones we have considered, except that we replace the sum of a pair of numbers by the maximum. This means we can still use Dijkstra's and Floyd's algorithms provided they are modified by replacing '+' by 'max'. We will solve the minimum height problem from vertex 1 to all other vertices in Fig. 7.1. The modified version of Dijkstra's method replaces inequality (1) with

$$d(j) > \max\{d(k), l(k, j)\}$$

or equivalently

$$d(k) < d(j) \quad \text{and} \quad l(k, j) < d(j)$$

and changes $d(j)$ to $\max\{d(k), l(k, j)\}$. The calculations are set out in Table 7.11.

Table 7.11

Iteration \ j	2	3	4	5	6	7	Minimising j
1	4	7	1	∞	∞	∞	4
2	4	7	—	∞	∞	2*	7
3	4	3*	—	∞	5*	—	3
4	4	—	—	3*	3*	—	5
5	4	—	—	—	3	—	6
6	4	—	—	—	—	—	2
d	4	3	1	3	3	2	
π	1	7	1	3	3	4	

We have left the problem of drawing the minimum height tree, which is defined analogously to the shortest path tree, to the reader.

(Similar modifications can be made to Floyd's algorithm if the minimum height paths between all pairs of vertices are required.)

7.4 A generalisation

Suppose that we wish to travel between two of the towns on Fig. 7.1 in minimum time and that the time required to traverse the road from i to j depends not only on i and j but also on the time we arrive at i, say t. We will write $\phi_{ij}(t)$ for the time we arrive at j. We can then calculate the time required to get from 1 to 4 via the path $1 \to 2 \to 3 \to 4$, assuming we start at time 0, by writing t_i for the time we reach i, so $t_i = 0$ and

$$t_2 = \phi_{12}(t_1)$$
$$t_3 = \phi_{23}(t_2)$$
$$t_4 = \phi_{34}(t_3).$$

Although we have referred to t as a 'time' this format encompasses both the previous cases. The length of the path (Sections 7.1 and 7.2) arises if we take

$$\phi_{ij}(t) = t + l(i, j)$$

whilst the height of the path (Section 7.3) is generated by

$$\phi_{ij}(t) = \max\{t, l(i, j)\}.$$

However, for any $\phi_{ij}(t)$ satisfying $\phi_{ij}(t) \geqslant t$ a modified version of Dijkstra's algorithm is available, which specialises to the previous versions in the cases we have already met.

To apply the general algorithm we start by putting

$$d(j) = \phi_{ij}(0)$$

where we take the starting time to be 0. We then pick that vertex k which minimises $d(j)$. For all j which have not been picked, if

$$d(j) > \phi_{kj}(d(k))$$

we replace $d(j)$ with $\phi_{kj}(d(k))$. This procedure is repeated until all vertices have been picked.

This generalisation enables us to solve, for example, the problem of travelling as quickly as possible between two locations, given a set of timetables for journeys between intermediate locations. This example requires a very large amount of data, and so we will illustrate the method by solving Fig. 7.1 in the case when

$$\phi_{ij}(t) = 2t + l(i, j)$$

This means that the 'time' of the path $1 \rightarrow 2 \rightarrow 3 \rightarrow 4$ is found from

$$t_2 = 2 \times \ 0 + 4 = \ \ 4$$
$$t_3 = 2 \times \ 4 + 4 = 12$$
$$t_4 = 2 \times 12 + 3 = 27$$

so that $1 \rightarrow 2 \rightarrow 3 \rightarrow 4$ has 'time' 27.

The calculations are set out in Table 7.12. We will leave to the reader the task of drawing the *minimum time tree* rooted at 1.

Table 7.12

	2	3	4	5	6	7	Minimising
1	4	7	1	∞	∞	∞	4
2	4	7	—	∞	∞	4*	2
3	—	7	—	13*	∞	4	7
4	—	7	—	13	13*	—	3
5	—	—	—	13	13	—	5
6	—	—	—	—	13	—	6
d	4	7	1	13	13	4	
π	1	1	1	2	7	4	

Exercises

1 Consider the network shown in Fig. 7.4, which represents the road system connecting the seven towns on an island.

(a) Use Dijkstra's algorithm to find the shortest paths from 1 to all other vertices. Draw the shortest path tree rooted at 1.

(b) Repeat (a) for the undirected case, i.e. assume all arrows have been erased. In this case, find the shortest path from 1 to a point x, $2\frac{1}{2}$ miles from vertex 3 on the road from 3 to 6 (assuming all distances are in miles). What would your answer be if x were $3\frac{1}{2}$ miles from vertex 3?

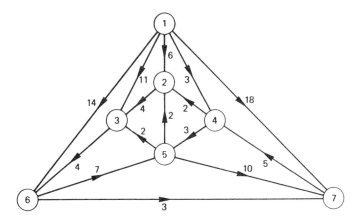

Fig. 7.4

(c)   Use a suitable version of Dijkstra's algorithm to find minimum height paths from 1 to each other vertex in the undirected case. Draw the minimum height tree rooted at 1.

(d)   Use Floyd's algorithm to find the length of the shortest path between each pair of vertices in the undirected case. Use the results of this algorithm to find shortest paths between 6 and 2 and between 6 and 1.

In parts (e) and (f) assume the network is undirected.

(e)   The population of the seven towns is as shown in Table 7.13. A hospital is to be built in one of the towns. Assuming that each member of the population will pay one visit per year on average to the hospital, where should it be located to minimise the total distance travelled?

Table 7.13

Town	1	2	3	4	5	6	7
Population in 1000s	41	28	30	26	27	40	38

(f)   Two schools are to be built and towns 1, 3, 4, 6 and 7 offer suitable sites. Assuming the size of the schools can be adjusted so that any child can attend its nearest school, where should the schools be built in order to minimise the maximum distance any child must travel to school?

(g)   If the numbers in the network are times and on reaching any vertex you wait for 30 % of the time you have spent travelling so far before setting out for the next vertex, find the earliest time at which you can arrive at each vertex starting from 1 and the paths which will achieve these times.

2 Suppose that when using Floyd's method a table of $K(i, j)$ for all i, j with $i \neq j$ is constructed as follows.

> Initially put $K(i, j) = j$.
>
> If at the kth iteration $d(i, j) > d(i, k) + d(k, j)$

(so $d(i, j)$ is reduced), then $K(i, j)$ is changed to $K(i, k)$.

Show that when the method is completed, if $K(i, j) = k$, then (i, k) is the first arc of a shortest path from i to j and explain how the complete shortest path can be found. Apply this method to Exercise 1(d).

3 Solve the transhipment problem of Section 3.4 by
  (a) applying Floyd's algorithm,
  (b) setting the transportation cost $c_{ij'}^*$ from source i to destination j' equal to the minimal cost found via Floyd's method and
  (c) solving the resulting transportation problem.

8
Deterministic Inventory Control

8.1 A simple model

The owner of a small clothes shop sells, on average, d shirts of a particular size per week. Realistically, the actual number sold per week and the time between sales is subject to seasonal variation and random fluctuation, amongst other factors. However, for the time being we will assume that sales are completely uniform, i.e. a time of exactly $1/d$ weeks elapses between successive sales. Suppose the owner repeatedly orders q shirts. Having an order arrive before it is absolutely necessary only increases costs. This means that he should arrange for the order to arrive when the stock is zero and the next demand for a shirt is due. If he does this, then a graph of the number of shirts in stock, or inventory level, I, against time is as shown in Fig. 8.1 for $q = 6$. Note that when an order arrives I jumps from 0 to q and then drops immediately to $q - 1$ because of the next sale. The **ordering cost** is $A + cq$ where A is a fixed cost, reflecting transport, administrative or other costs which are independent of the order size, and c is a unit cost per item ordered. In addition, the owner needs to tie up his capital or borrow money to purchase the shirts and this will not be available to him while the goods remain unsold. Also, costs of storage may be incurred so that it is appropriate to assume a **holding cost**, h, per item for each week it is stored.

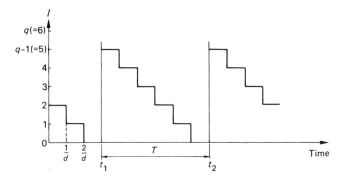

Fig. 8.1

From the graph in Fig. 8.1 we see that I is a **cyclic** or periodic function of time. This means that the graph consists of the same portion repeated over and over again. In Fig. 8.1, this portion (running from t_1 to t_2) takes time T, the **cycle time**. T is also, of course, the time between successive orders. Let us calculate the total holding cost in a cycle. Since we have $q - 1$ items in stock for time $1/d$, $q - 2$ items for time $1/d$, $q - 3$ items for time $1/d$ etc. the total cost is

$$h[(q-1)+(q-2)+ \cdots +1](1/d)$$

$$= hq(q-1)/2d \qquad (= h \times \text{area under the graph in a cycle}).$$

To this we must also add the order cost $A + cq$ for one cycle.

Since T will vary with q, it is more helpful to convert the result to a cost per week. Assuming T is measured in weeks, this is achieved by dividing the cost per cycle by T since, clearly, cost per week = cost per cycle/length of cycle (in weeks).

From Fig. 8.1, we see that T is made up of q intervals of length $1/d$, so that $T = q/d$ and the cost per week is given by κ_I (I for 'integer'), where

$$\kappa_I(q) = (A + cq + hq(q-1)/2d)/(q/d)$$

$$= \frac{dA}{q} + cd + \tfrac{1}{2}h(q-1) \qquad (q \geqslant 1). \tag{8.1}$$

In some cases it may be more appropriate or at least a useful approximation (e.g. a large clothes shop) to treat the demand as continuous. Thus, at a time t ($< T$) after the order for q items arrives, we assume that dt have been sold, and therefore the inventory level is $q - dt$. Then Fig. 8.1 is replaced by Fig. 8.2.

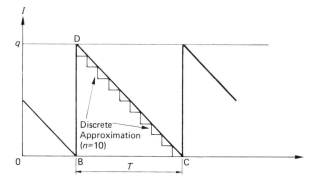

Fig. 8.2

To evaluate the holding cost in this case we could replace the continuous model by a discrete approximation in which an order for q items is replaced by an order for n items of size q/n and the time between sales of each batch of q/n is T/n, where T is still the cycle time. This is illustrated in Fig. 8.2 for $n = 10$. Then, the holding cost is h multiplied by the area under the staircase graph. As n gets larger, the discrete approximation approaches the continuous case and the area under the staircase approaches the area of the triangle BCD. We conclude that the exact holding cost is

$$h \times \text{area BCD} = h(\tfrac{1}{2}qT).$$

Since the amount sold in time T is dT and this must equal the amount ordered, i.e. q, we must have $T = q/d$, and the cost per week in the continuous case is given by

$$\kappa(q) = (A + cq + \tfrac{1}{2}hqT)/T = \frac{dA}{q} + cd + \tfrac{1}{2}hq. \tag{8.2}$$

We have taken one week as the unit of time in this example, but in other contexts a day, month, year or some other time interval may be appropriate. For this reason we will use the non-specific expression 'cost per unit time' in future. When solving exercises the reader should take care that the same unit is used to measure all times.

If the shop owner wishes to make his costs as small as possible he will choose q to minimise $\kappa(q)$. This involves using expression (8.1) and minimising over integer q or using (8.2) and minimising over continuous q. We will solve the latter case first since the technique involved (setting the derivative equal to zero) is likely to be more familiar to the reader. The graph of $\kappa(q)$ is shown in Fig. 8.3. Note that $\kappa(q)$ becomes large for small q and large q, and therefore the minimising q^* is the unique positive q at which $d\kappa/dq = 0$.

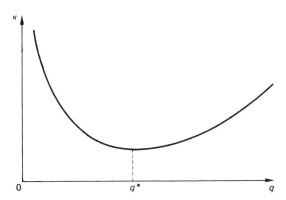

Fig. 8.3

Since

$$\frac{d\kappa(q)}{dq} = \frac{-dA}{q^2} + \tfrac{1}{2}h$$

this gives

$$q^* = \sqrt{\left(\frac{2dA}{h}\right)}.$$

It may be more useful to know the optimal T, i.e. T^*. We have

$$T^* = q^*/d = \sqrt{\left(\frac{2A}{hd}\right)} \quad \text{and} \quad \kappa(q^*) = \sqrt{(2Ahd)} + cd.$$

For example, if $d = 7.6$, $A = 5.3$, $h = 3.0$, then

$$q^* = 5.18, \quad T^* = 0.68, \quad \kappa(q^*) = 15.55 + 7.6c.$$

To find the minimum of (8.1) over positive integer values of q we use the following technique. For a function $\phi(q)$, where q is integer-valued and ϕ has the general shape of κ in Fig. 8.3 (convex) we calculate $\Delta\phi(q) = \phi(q+1) - \phi(q)$. This is illustrated in Fig. 8.4.

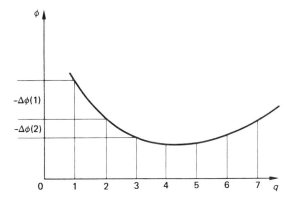

Fig. 8.4

It follows by looking at Fig. 8.4 that, if q^* is the minimum value of f, then

$$\Delta\phi(q) < 0 \quad \text{for } q < q^*$$
$$\Delta\phi(q) \geqslant 0 \quad \text{for } q \geqslant q^*$$

(in fact this defines the smallest minimiser of ϕ, if there is more than one). Thus the procedure is as follows.

Take q^* to be the smallest (positive integer) value of q which makes $\Delta\kappa(q)$ non-negative. Then q^* minimises ϕ.

Applying this to expression (8.1) (which differs from (8.2) only by a constant term), we have

$$\Delta\frac{dA}{q} = \frac{dA}{q+1} - \frac{dA}{q} = \frac{-dA}{q(q+1)}$$

$$\Delta[\tfrac{1}{2}h(q-1)] = \tfrac{1}{2}hq - \tfrac{1}{2}h(q-1) = \tfrac{1}{2}h,$$

and adding these together gives

$$\Delta \kappa_I(q) = -\frac{dA}{q(q+1)} + \tfrac{1}{2}h.$$

So $\Delta \kappa(q) \geqslant 0$ means

$$q(q+1) \geqslant 2dA/h. \tag{8.3}$$

We can 'complete the square' by adding $\tfrac{1}{4}$ to each side of (8.3), giving

$$q^2 + q + \tfrac{1}{4} = (q + \tfrac{1}{2})^2 \geqslant \frac{2dA}{h} + \tfrac{1}{4}$$

or

$$q \geqslant \sqrt{\left(\frac{2dA}{h} + \tfrac{1}{4}\right)} - \tfrac{1}{2} \qquad \text{(taking the positive root).}$$

Thus, if we write $\lceil a \rceil$ for the least integer greater than or equal to a (e.g. $\lceil 5\tfrac{3}{4} \rceil = 6$, $\lceil 2 \rceil = 2$), then

$$q^* = \lceil \sqrt{[(2dA/h) + \tfrac{1}{4}]} - \tfrac{1}{2} \rceil.$$

With the numerical values used earlier we find

$$\sqrt{\left(\frac{2dA}{h} + \tfrac{1}{4}\right)} - \tfrac{1}{2} = 4.71$$

so that $q^* = 5$, $T^* = 0.66$, $\kappa(q^*) = 14.06 + 7.6c$.

The reader should check that if h is changed to 4, then $q^* = 4.49$ in the continuous case and $q^* = \lceil 4.02 \rceil = 5$ in the integer case. As the discussion so far shows, the continuous case is less messy than the integer case and so we will concentrate on the former in the remainder of the chapter. However, we will return to the latter case in the next chapter.

8.2   Lost sales

We now turn to the question of whether it is worthwhile always to order enough stock to meet the demand in each cycle. Suppose to the contrary that q is ordered but $T > q/d$. Then the shop will be out of stock for part of each cycle and we will assume that potential customers make their purchases elsewhere if the stock level is zero. As a result, the shopkeeper will suffer a reduced profit as a consequence of losing sales. We will therefore look for the values of T and q which *maximise* profits. Clearly, this is also the appropriate criterion for the model of Section 8.1, but when no sales are lost, the quantity of sales per cycle of length T is equal to the demand per cycle, dT. Hence the quantity of sales per unit time is just a constant and so the same will be true of the sales revenue. Consequently, maximising profits (= sales revenue − costs) gives identical answers to minimising costs in the original model.

Returning to the lost-sales problem, in the continuous case (see Exercise 2 for the discrete case) the graph of inventory against time is shown in Fig. 8.5. Note that $T - t$ is the length of time in each cycle during which sales are being lost. It is also the time interval between stock running out and receipt of the next order.

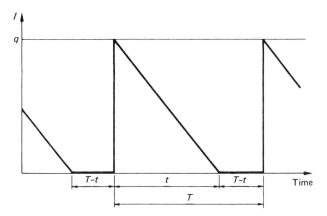

Fig. 8.5

The cost per cycle is the same as the simple model of the preceding section, i.e.

$A + cq + \frac{1}{2}hqt$.

If the selling price per item is k, the total revenue per cycle is kq. Noting that $td = q$ and that the cycle length is T, we see that the profit (= revenue − cost) per unit time, $\Pi(q, T)$, is

$$\Pi(q, T) = (kq - A - cq - \tfrac{1}{2}hq^2/d)/T.$$

To maximise Π, we will start by fixing q and maximising Π with respect to T. If the numerator is positive, Π increases as T decreases. However, from Fig. 8.5, we see that $T \geqslant q/d$, so that the maximising value of T is $T = q/d$. If the numerator is negative, Π increases (approaches 0) as T increases. There is no upper limit on T but $T = \infty$ can be effectively achieved by never reordering, giving a profit per unit time of 0. Substituting these maximising values for T into Π, we see that the maximum value of Π is given by

$$\Pi_M(q) = \max\left\{(k-c)d - \frac{dA}{q} - \tfrac{1}{2}hq, 0\right\}. \tag{8.4}$$

(If the numerator of Π is zero, the value of T is irrelevant but (8.4) still applies.) A graph of Π_M vs. q is drawn in Fig. 8.6, and we have distinguished two cases:

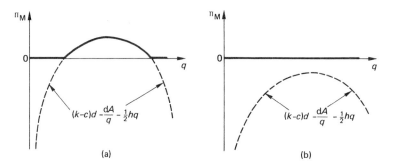

Fig. 8.6

(a) the maximum of

$$(k - c)d - \frac{dA}{q} - \tfrac{1}{2}hq$$

is positive and (b) the maximum is non-positive.
    Since

$$(k - c)d - \frac{dA}{q} - \tfrac{1}{2}hq$$

is maximal when $dA/q + \tfrac{1}{2}hq$ is minimised, i.e. when $q = \sqrt{(2dA/h)}$ by the results of Section 8.1, we see that the two cases of Fig. 8.5 are defined by

$$\text{(a)} \ kd - cd - \sqrt{(2Ahd)} > 0 \qquad \text{and} \qquad \text{(b)} \ kd - cd - \sqrt{(2Ahd)} \leqslant 0.$$

In case (a) we choose $q^* = \sqrt{(2dA/h)}$ and $T^* = q^*/d$, which says that we operate without lost sales. In case (b) we choose $T^* = \infty$, so that q^* is irrelevant. This says that we do not operate at all. These results can be expressed in the following prescription: calculate q^* and the resulting optimal profit assuming no sales are lost. If this profit is positive, use q^*. Otherwise do not operate. Thus there is no real lost sales problem in the deterministic model. (In the special case where the optimal profit is zero, any T will do and so it *is* optimal to operate with lost sales, but it is also optimal not to operate at all or to operate without lost sales.)
    For example, if $d = 7.6$, $A = 5.3$, $h = 3.0$, $c = 1.7$, $k = 3.7$, then $kd - cd - \sqrt{(2Ahd)} = -0.37$, a negative profit, so don't operate. But, if k is changed to 3.8, the optimal profit becomes $0.41 > 0$, so we use $q^* = 5.18$ (cf. the example of Section 8.1) and $T^* = q^*/d = 0.68$. Indeed, this solution is optimal for any k giving a positive profit, i.e. for $k > 28.47/d = 3.75$.

8.3 Backlogging

In this section we will assume that, if a customer arrives when the stock level is zero, the sale is **backlogged**. This means that he will receive his goods when the shopkeeper's next order arrives. Consequently backlogged sales accrue at the rate d from the point at which the inventory level becomes 0. The quantity of sales backlogged at any instant is called the **shortage** and we will define the net inventory, NI, at any instant to be

NI = inventory level (I) − shortage.

Thus $NI = I$ if the stock level is positive and $NI = -$ shortage if the stock level is 0. We will write s for the maximum level of shortage, which occurs just before an order is fulfilled. A graph of NI against time is shown in Fig. 8.7. When an order arrives, q items are added to the stock but s are immediately taken out to meet the s backlogged orders. Hence, the maximum NI is $q - s$.

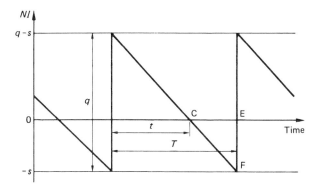

Fig. 8.7

We shall introduce an additional cost to represent penalties, such as loss of goodwill, arising from backlogging. Since some customers will have to wait longer than others we will make this cost proportional to the length of time an item is backlogged. So let b be the cost per item, per unit time in shortage. Thus, ordering plus holding costs per cycle are, from Fig. 8.6,

$$A + cq + \tfrac{1}{2}h(q-s)t,$$

where t is the length of time by which NI exceeds 0 in each cycle. The shortage cost per cycle, by an argument similar to that used to find the holding cost, is

$$b \times \text{area of CEF} = \tfrac{1}{2}bs(T-t).$$

We could have also included a cost proportional to s (i.e. the penalty cost p of the last section) but this makes the subsequent analysis much more complicated in general and so we have excluded it in order to simplify the exposition (but see Exercise 3).

By familiar arguments, $T = q/d$, $T - t = s/d$ and $t = (q - s)/d$ and so the cost per cycle is

$$A + cq + [h(q - s)^2 + bs^2]/2d$$

and the cost per unit time, obtained by dividing this by T, can be written

$$\kappa(q, s) = \frac{dA}{q} + cd + [h(q - s)^2 + bs^2]/2q.$$

Note that $0 \leqslant s \leqslant q$, so that $\kappa(q, s)$ must be minimised subject to this constraint.

In some cases, external constraints may fix T and thus q (e.g. a supplier delivers on a certain date each month). Therefore, the only variable the shopkeeper can vary is s. Since

$$bs^2 + h(q - s)^2 = (h + b)s^2 - 2hqs + hq^2$$

$$= (h + b)\left[s - \frac{hq}{h + b} \right]^2 + \frac{hb}{h + b} q^2,$$

this is minimised at

$$s = \frac{hq}{h + b} \tag{8.5}$$

and this value of s satisfies $0 \leqslant s \leqslant q$. Hence the minimal cost is

$$\frac{dA}{q} + cd + \frac{hbq}{2(h + b)}.$$

Note that this is the same as expression (8.2) with h replaced by $hb/(h + b)$, and so we can deduce that, if q *can* be varied, q^* minimises costs, where

$$q^* = \sqrt{\left(\frac{2dA(h + b)}{hb} \right)}, \tag{8.6}$$

$$s^* = \sqrt{\left(\frac{2dhA}{(h + b)b} \right)} \quad \text{from (8.5)},$$

and

$$\kappa(q^*, s^*) = \sqrt{\left(\frac{2dAhb}{(h + b)} \right)} + cd.$$

As $b \to \infty$, then $s^* \to 0$ and q^* and κ approach the standard expressions of Section 8.1, where no backlogging is allowed.

If $d = 7.6$, $A = 5.3$, $h = 3.0$ and $b = 5.2$, then $q^* = 6.51$, $s^* = 2.38$ and $T^* - t^* = s^*/d = 0.31$. The optimal policy is perhaps most easily described by saying that the order quantity is 6.51 timed to arrive 0.31 weeks after the stock level drops to 0.

8.4 Discounting

Suppliers often allow quantity discounts. This means that the unit cost is reduced if more than a given quantity is ordered. More generally, let us imagine a series of m critical levels $q_1, q_2, \ldots, q_m$, where

$$0 = q_1 < q_2 < \cdots < q_m$$

and suppose that the unit cost is c_1 if $q_1 \leqslant q < q_2$, c_2 if $q_2 \leqslant q < q_3, \ldots, c_{m-1}$ if $q_{m-1} \leqslant q \leqslant q_m$ and c_m for $q \geqslant q_m$. For example, Table 8.1 displays q_i and c_i for $m = 5$.

Table 8.1

i	1	2	3	4	5
q_i	0	20	40	100	200
c_i	4.1	3.9	3.6	3.4	3.3

Such a discount structure can lead to the anomaly that the cost is not necessarily an increasing function of the number ordered. For example, the cost of 39 items is 152.1 whereas 40 items can be purchased for 144. Such anomalies are often avoided by requiring, say, purchases over 20 items to be a multiple of 5, but the anomaly does not affect the analysis so we shall ignore it.

Under our discount structure, the cost of ordering q items is

$$A + c_i q \qquad \text{for } q_i \leqslant q < q_{i+1}$$

where $q_{m+1} = \infty$. If backlogging is excluded, the cost per unit time is

$$\kappa(q) = \kappa_i(q) = \frac{dA}{q} + c_i d + \tfrac{1}{2} hq \quad \text{for} \quad q_i \leqslant q < q_{i+1} (q > 0),$$

$$i = 1, \ldots, m.$$

A graph of κ against q is shown in Fig. 8.8.

The heavy line in Fig. 8.8 is the graph of κ. Notice that $\kappa_i(q)$ is minimised at $\bar{q} = \sqrt{(2dA/h)}$ for all $i = 1, \ldots, m$. It is clear from Fig. 8.8 that the minimiser of κ can be found by the following procedure.

Choose r so that

$$q_r \leqslant \bar{q} < q_{r+1}.$$

This means that q_r is the highest critical level which does not exceed $\bar{q}$. We set q^* equal to whichever of $\bar{q}, q_{r+1}, \ldots, q_m$ gives the least value of κ. In other words, we look for the minimiser of

$$\kappa_r(\bar{q}), \kappa_{r+1}(q_{r+1}), \ldots, \kappa_m(q_m).$$

(If $r = m$ the minimiser is $\bar{q}$.)

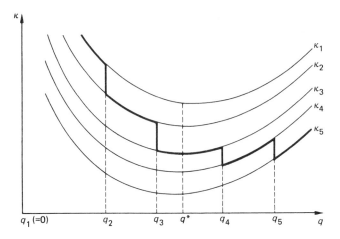

Fig. 8.8

If $d = 76$, $A = 5.3$, $h = 0.3$ and q_i, c_i are as given in Table 8.1, then $\bar{q} = 51.8$, so $r = 3$ and

$$\kappa(51.8) = 15.55 + 76 \times 3.6 = 289.15$$
$$\kappa(100) = 402.8/100 + 0.15 \times 100 + 76 \times 3.4 = 277.4$$
$$\kappa(200) = 402.8/200 + 0.15 \times 200 + 76 \times 3.3 = 282.8.$$

Hence $q^* = 100$. If c_3 alone is changed to 3.44, $\kappa(51.8)$ changes to 277.0 and therefore q^* changes to 51.8.

8.5   An inventory–production problem

We have assumed so far that inventory is replenished instantaneously by an external supplier. However, production processes also accumulate inventories and this gives rise to models in which inventory is replenished gradually. As a simple example, suppose that a manufacturer has contracted to supply diesel engines to a tractor manufacturer at an average rate of d per week. The manufacturer decides to produce the engines in production runs of q engines, incurring a cost of $A + cq$ per run, where A represents a fixed set-up cost which must be paid for each run and c is the cost per engine.

The rate of production is r engines per week during any run. We can only expect a feasible solution if $r \geqslant d$ and thus inventory (or net inventory, if backlogging is allowed) will accumulate during a production run and holding costs will be incurred. We will let h be the holding cost per engine, per week in storage. We will assume that the tractor manufacturer is prepared to permit backlogging provided a penalty cost of b per engine per week delayed is paid. The basic problem for this model is how often should the engine manufacturer set up a production run and how many engines should he produce?

We will solve the continuous version of this model, for which the graph of net inventory vs. time is shown in **Fig. 8.9**.

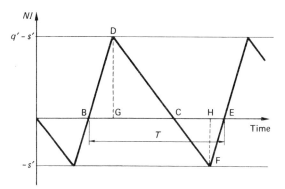

Fig. 8.9

The manufacturing cost per cycle is $A + cq$ and the holding cost per cycle is

$$h \times \text{area BCD} = \tfrac{1}{2}h \times \text{DG} \times \text{BC} = \tfrac{1}{2}h(q' - s') \times (\text{BG} + \text{GC}).$$

The section of the graph from B to D is part of a production run during which tractors are being produced at a rate r and supplied at a rate d, so inventory is accumulating at a net rate of $r - d$. Since, in time BG, the total accumulated is $\text{DG} = q' - s'$, we have

$$(r - d)\text{BG} = q' - s' = d \times \text{GC}.$$

Hence

$$\text{BG} + \text{GC} = (q' - s')\left(\frac{1}{r - d} + \frac{1}{d}\right) = (q' - s')r/(r - d)d$$

and the holding cost per cycle is

$$\tfrac{1}{2}h(q' - s')^2/d'$$

where

$$d' = (r - d)d/r.$$

By a similar argument, the shortage cost per cycle is

$$b \times \text{area CEF} = \tfrac{1}{2}bs' \times (\text{CH} + \text{HE}) = \tfrac{1}{2}bs'\left(\frac{s'}{d} + \frac{s'}{r - d}\right) = \tfrac{1}{2}b(s')^2/d'.$$

Notice that the length of a production run is

$$\text{BG} + \text{HE} = \frac{q' - s'}{r - d} + \frac{s'}{r - d} = \frac{q'}{r - d}$$

and since q engines are produced at a rate r, we have

$$q = \frac{q'r}{r-d} \quad (= q'd/d').$$ (8.7)

Adding together all components of the cost per cycle, we obtain

$$A + \frac{cr}{r-d}q' + \tfrac{1}{2}[h(q'-s')^2 + b(s')^2]/d'.$$

The cycle length is given by

$$T = \text{BC} + \text{CE} = \frac{q'-s'}{d'} + \frac{s'}{d'} = \frac{q'}{d'}\left(=\frac{q}{d}\right)$$

and so the cost per unit time can be written

$$\kappa'(q', s') = \frac{Ad'}{q'} + c'd' + \tfrac{1}{2}[h(q'-s')^2 + b(s')^2]/q',$$

where

$$c' = cr/(r-d).$$

By comparing $\kappa'(q', s')$ with $\kappa(q, s)$ of Section 8.3 we see that these are essentially the same functions, hence the optimal $q*$ is given, from (8.6) and (8.7), by

$$q* = \sqrt{\left(\frac{2d' A(h+b)}{hb}\right)}\frac{d}{d'} = d\sqrt{\left(\frac{2A(h+b)}{hbd'}\right)} = dT*$$

where

$$T* = \sqrt{\left(\frac{2A(h+b)}{hbd'}\right)}.$$

For example, if $d = 25$, $r = 75$, $A = 10\,000$, $h = 0.5$, $b = 10$, then $d' = 50/3$. Hence $T* = 50.2$, $q* = 1255$. So a new production run should be initiated every 50.2 weeks with 1255 engines produced in each run. The run will last $q*/r = 16.7$ weeks.

The case when backlogging is not permitted can also be analysed (see Exercise 5) and it is easy to see that as $b \to \infty$ our solution tends to the non-backlogging solution.

Exercises

1 (a) Solve the simple model when $c = £10$, $d = 2000$, $A = £20$, $h = £2$.
   (b) What would be the optimal solution if the maximal storage space was
        (i) 100 units?
        (ii) 300 units?
        Explain why.

(c) Suppose now you have 100 units of capacity and you could rent additional storage space at a cost of £1 per unit per week, what would be the optimal solution for order quantity and hired storage space? Consider the cases

  (i) when you pay for only those items you have in stock at any one time,

  (ii) when you hire a fixed storage space for the whole year. Assume that the full holding cost h is always payable in addition to storage cost, for every unit held at any time.

2 Show that, in the lost-sales problem, even if the demand is discrete it is optimal either to operate without lost sales or not to operate at all. Hence solve the discrete case when $A = 23$, $c = 8$, $h = 32$, $d = 19$ for all values of k.

3 (a) What is the optimal policy for the continuous demand problem if backlogging is allowed and $A = 23$, $h = 32$, $b = 2$, and $d = 19$?

  (b) Suppose that an additional penalty of k per item backlogged (giving a penalty of $k \times$ the maximum shortage in each cycle) is imposed. What is the optimal policy as a function of k?

4 (a) You are operating a warehouse and your supplier charges 24.3 per item if you purchase fewer than 5 items, 20.1 per item if you purchase at least 5 but fewer than 10, and otherwise 17.4 per item. If there is a fixed cost of 3.2 and storage cost of 1.2 per item, per week, and a demand of 3 per week, how frequently should you order if backlogging is not allowed and demand is continuous?

  (b) Now suppose that these unit costs apply only to the items purchased between the critical levels; so that 9 items would mean 5 items at 24.3 and 4 items at 20.1, giving a total cost of 201.9, whilst 12 items would mean 5 at 24.3, 5 at 20.1 and 2 at 17.4, with a total of 256.8. How does this affect your solution?

5 A factory produces items in runs at a rate r per day, where there is a set-up cost of £1800 for each run. The demand for items is 40 per day and the holding cost is £1 per unit per day held. The cost of producing each item is £5, and shortages are not permitted. Let $r = 400$ and find the optimal q and minimum daily cost. If you could set the production rate r at any value, which would you choose to minimise costs?

9
Probabilistic Inventory

9.1 Introduction

The assumption, made in the preceding chapter, that demand in inventory problems is completely predictable in advance and exactly proportional to time elapsed may often be so unrealistic as to render the results from the model unreliable. In this chapter we shall relax this assumption, assuming instead that the demand in a given time period is a (known) probability distribution. For smooth reading we shall take the 'given time period' to be a week, but the reader should bear in mind that any other fixed time interval may be used instead. A full treatment of this model in complete generality becomes mathematically highly sophisticated. Consequently we will consider only a few aspects of the problem in order to illustrate some of the methods which can be used. In particular, several technical difficulties can be avoided by assuming that the demand is discrete (integer-valued). This is not usually a severe restriction, since in many problems the discrete model is the natural one to choose and the continuous case can often be treated as a limiting case of a sequence of discrete models. Even with the discrete model, a full analysis is beyond the level of this book and we will resort to approximation at several points in the development. Such approximate methods give adequate results in most cases.

We will write p_X for the probability that the demand in a week is X, where X is a non-negative integer. The notation for costs is the same as the preceding chapter. To recall these costs we have

$A + cq$: cost of ordering q items (for $q \geqslant 1$)
h : holding cost/unit/week
k : penalty cost/unit of shortage
b : backlogging cost/item/week in shortage.

The demand per week is now a random quantity, but we shall write d for the expected demand per week, i.e.

$$d = \sum_{X=0}^{\infty} X p_X.$$

Since the total cost per week depends on the (random) demand it is a random quantity and we will take as our objective the minimisation of the expected cost per week.

9.2 Periodic review

To start our investigation we will look at problems in which institutional constraints force the shopkeeper of Chapter 8 to have his order delivered at fixed time intervals. Thus we shall assume that the cycle length T is fixed, which means that minimising expected cost per week is equivalent to minimising expected cost per cycle. To simplify the development we will take $T = 1$ week so that p_X is the probability that the demand per cycle is X.

Since the demand is random, it is not generally possible to guarantee that there will be sufficient stock to meet the demand, so shortages cannot be ruled out. Therefore, one is forced to consider lost sales or backlogging. In this chapter we will deal only with backlogging, but similar techniques may be applied to the lost-sales case. Notice, however, that we have included costs b per item per week in shortage *and* k per item of shortage. (This is the same as Exercise 8.3.) For the same reason it is not necessarily sensible to order the same amount for each cycle independently of how much is in stock at the time of ordering. Instead we will assume that the size of the order (which arrives instantaneously) is chosen so that the inventory level rises to S at the beginning of each cycle. A couple of typical cycles are illustrated in Fig. 9.1. Note that the amounts ordered in successive cycles q, q', q'' vary from one cycle to another.

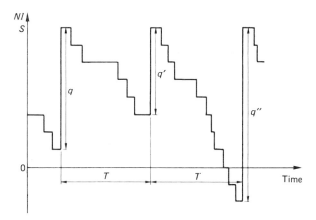

Fig. 9.1

Let us start by calculating the cost per cycle under the assumption that demand not immediately fulfilled is backlogged.

Each cycle starts with $NI = S$ and, if the demand in the cycle is X, the cycle terminates with $NI = S - X$ immediately before the next order arrives, and then NI jumps back to S. This means that the amount ordered is X at the start of the next cycle. Thus the expected order cost is

$$\sum_{X=0}^{\infty} (\text{cost of ordering } X \text{ items}) \times p_X$$

$$= 0p_0 + \sum_{X=1}^{\infty} (A + cX)p_X$$

$$= A \sum_{X=1}^{\infty} p_X + c \sum_{X=1}^{\infty} Xp_X$$

$$= A \left(\sum_{X=0}^{\infty} p_X - p_0 \right) + c \left(\sum_{X=0}^{\infty} Xp_X - 0p_0 \right)$$

$$= A(1 - p_0) + cd.$$

The expected storage and shortage costs depend on the behaviour of the demand within a cycle and this information is not provided by the distribution of X. We will therefore adopt an approximate method. We will calculate, for each demand level X, the storage and shortage costs which would occur assuming a deterministic demand per week of X. Then we will take the expectation over all possible demand levels. When $X \leqslant S$, there is no shortage and the deterministic approximation is shown in Fig. 9.2.

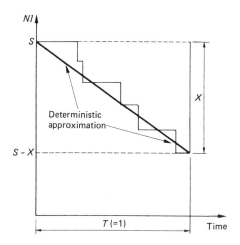

Fig. 9.2

The random nature of the demand means that we cannot guarantee that the order arrives at the exact moment of a sale, so we have assumed that, on average, its arrival is half-way between orders. This means that the area under the graph and thus the holding cost is the same as if we had regarded demand as continuous, as shown in Fig. 9.2. Hence the holding cost is

$$h\tfrac{1}{2}[S +(S - X)] = \tfrac{1}{2}hS + \tfrac{1}{2}h(S - X) \qquad \text{for } X \leqslant S,$$

and the shortage cost is 0.

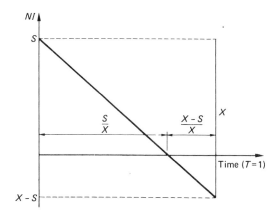

Fig. 9.3

When $X > S$ the picture is rather more complicated, as shown in Fig. 9.3. We have drawn the graph for continuous demand since, as in the case $X \leqslant S$, it gives the same costs as discrete demand. By an argument similar to that of Section 8.3, we see that $NI \geqslant 0$ for a time S/X, so that the holding cost is

$$\tfrac{1}{2}hS(S/X) = \tfrac{1}{2}hS^2/X \qquad \text{for } X > S \tag{9.1}$$

and the shortage cost is

$$k(X - S) + \tfrac{1}{2}b(X - S)[(X - S)/X] = k(X - S) + \tfrac{1}{2}b(X - S)^2/X$$
$$\text{for } X > S.$$

Taking the expectation of these expressions with respect to X and adding the ordering cost gives a total expected cost per cycle

$$\kappa(S) = A(1 - p_0) + cd + \tfrac{1}{2}hS \sum_{X = 0}^{S} p_X + \tfrac{1}{2}h \sum_{X = 0}^{S} (S - X)p_X +$$

$$\tfrac{1}{2}hS^2 \sum_{X = S+1}^{\infty} p_X/X + k \sum_{X = S+1}^{\infty} (X - S)p_X + \tfrac{1}{2}b \sum_{X = S+1}^{\infty} (X - S)^2 p_X/X.$$

For computational purposes it is easier to rewrite this. We can use

$$\sum_{S+1}^{\infty} p_X = \sum_{X = 0}^{\infty} p_X - \sum_{X = 0}^{S} p_X = 1 - \sum_{X = 0}^{S} p_X$$

and

$$\sum_{S+1}^{\infty} Xp_X = \sum_{X=0}^{\infty} Xp_X - \sum_{X=0}^{S} Xp_X = d - \sum_{X=0}^{S} Xp_X,$$

to rewrite κ as

$$\kappa(S) = A(1-p_0) + cd + kd + \tfrac{1}{2}bd - kS - bS + (h + k + b)S \sum_{X=0}^{S} p_X$$

$$- (\tfrac{1}{2}h + k + \tfrac{1}{2}b) \sum_{X=0}^{S} Xp_X + \tfrac{1}{2}(h + b)S^2 \sum_{X=S+1}^{\infty} p_X / X. \qquad (9.2)$$

We have imposed no *a priori* upper bound on the distribution of X, so the sums run to ∞. In practice, there is usually an upper limit, and then all the sums are finite. For example, if $A = 2$, $c = 1$, $h = 5$, $k = 10$, $b = 10$ and the distribution of X is given in Table 9.1, we have

$$d = 0 \times 0.05 + 1 \times 0.1 + \cdots + 6 \times 0.05 = 3,$$

Table 9.1

X	0	1	2	3	4	5	6
p_X	0.05	0.1	0.2	0.3	0.2	0.1	0.05

so that

$$A(1-p_0) + cd + kd + \tfrac{1}{2}bd = 49.9,$$

and κ is calculated in Table 9.2. We see that the optimal value of S is $S = 3$. (There is no need to consider $S > 6$. Why?)

Table 9.2

S	$\sum_{X=0}^{S} p_X$	$\sum_{X=0}^{S} Xp_X$	$\sum_{X=S+1}^{6} p_X/X$	κ
0	0.05	0	0.3783	49.9
1	0.15	0.1	0.2783	34.0
2	0.35	0.5	0.1783	24.0
3	0.65	1.4	0.0783	19.4
4	0.85	2.2	0.0283	19.8
5	0.95	2.7	0.0083	23.0
6	1	3	0	27.4

The rather complicated expression for κ can be replaced by a simpler approximation when $b = 0$ and the proportion of each cycle spent in shortage is small ('small shortage' approximation). This means we can replace S/X by 1 in the formula (9.1) for the holding cost when $X > S$, which now becomes $\frac{1}{2}hS$. As a result $\kappa(S)$ as given by (9.2) is replaced, after a little rearrangement, by

$$\kappa_a(S) = A(1 - p_0) + cd + kd - (k - \tfrac{1}{2}h)S + (k + \tfrac{1}{2}h)\sum_{X=0}^{S}(S - X)p_X.$$

In the last chapter we saw that κ_a is minimised at S^*, where S^* is the smallest value of S for which $\Delta\kappa_a(S) \geqslant 0$. To calculate $\Delta\kappa_a$ note that, if

$$\psi(S) = \sum_{X=0}^{S}(S - X)p_X,$$

then $\Delta\psi(S) = \displaystyle\sum_{X=0}^{S+1}(S + 1 - X)p_X - \sum_{X=0}^{S}(S - X)p_X$

$$= 0p_{S+1} + \sum_{X=0}^{S}(S + 1 - X)p_X - \sum_{X=0}^{S}(S - X)p_X$$

$$= \sum_{X=0}^{S}p_X = \text{Prob}\,(X \leqslant S).$$

Consequently

$$\Delta\kappa_a(S) = \tfrac{1}{2}h - k + (\tfrac{1}{2}h + k)\sum_{X=0}^{S}P_X$$

and $\Delta\kappa_a(S) \geqslant 0$ can be rewritten as

$$\text{Prob}\,(X \leqslant S) = \sum_{X=0}^{S}p_X \geqslant \frac{k - \tfrac{1}{2}h}{k + \tfrac{1}{2}h}. \tag{9.3}$$

Then S^* is the smallest S satisfying (9.3). For example, with the data given above,

$$(k - \tfrac{1}{2}h)/(k + \tfrac{1}{2}h) = 0.6$$

and Prob $(X \leqslant S)$ is given in the first column of Table 9.2, from which we see that $S^* = 3$.

9.3 Two-bin policies

The policy described in the last section, with a fixed time interval between orders, is known as a **periodic review** policy. It has the advantage that the administrative work associated with ordering occurs at regular intervals and can be allowed for in advance. Additionally deliveries may only be made at specified times. It carries the disadvantage that the expected cost of a policy is independent of the fixed cost A. However, if, in some week, the demand is small (though positive) and the stock level has consequently suffered little depletion, then the policy still specifies a positive order so that the fixed cost A is incurred. It seems plausible that, in such a case, it may be worth postponing a (positive) order until the next week (or even later possibly) in order to spread the fixed cost over a longer time interval. A more sophisticated periodic policy involves two integer parameters S and r, with $S > r$. If the net inventory at the end of a cycle is Y, then nothing is ordered if $Y \geqslant r + 1$, whilst $S - Y$ is ordered if $Y \leqslant r$. Equivalently, order only if the inventory level does not exceed r and then choose the order quantity to bring the inventory level up to S.

The analysis of this policy is complicated and we will, instead, drop the periodicity requirement. However, we will also add another element to make the model more realistic, by allowing a time interval L to elapse between ordering and receipt of the order. In deterministic problems such as those analysed in the last chapter, such a *lead time* is easily incorporated by ordering a time L before the instant at which we desire the order to arrive. Since, in such a problem, the quantity required can be predicted exactly, the order size is known. However, when demand is known only as a probability distribution, there is no way in which the net inventory at the time the order arrives can be predicted exactly. We will therefore require two parameters: the amount ordered q and the re-order level r. A **two-bin** policy says that an order for q items is made when the inventory level falls to r. Such a policy requires monitoring of the inventory system in order to spot the instant at which I drops to r (or less). A simple form of monitoring, involving transferring cards from one bin to another, explains the name of the policy. If administrative, monitoring and similar extraneous costs are ignored it can be shown that the optimal two-bin policy is cheaper to operate than any periodic review policy.

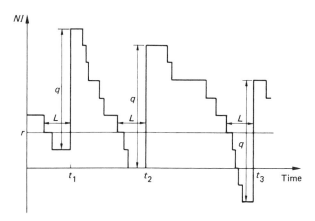

Fig. 9.4

A couple of typical cycles (running from t_1 to t_2 and from t_2 to t_3) are shown in Fig. 9.4. Note that, when q items arrive at the end of the second complete cycle (time t_3), there are two items backlogged, so the net inventory level becomes $q - 2$.

We will write p_X for the probability that X items are demanded in time L and start by calculating the expected cost per cycle of ordering plus shortage. The cost of ordering is $A + cq$. Since $NI = r$ when the order is placed and X items are sold during the lead time,

$$\text{shortage} = \begin{cases} 0 & \text{if } 0 \leqslant X \leqslant r \\ X - r & \text{if } X \geqslant r+1 \end{cases}$$

so that the expected shortage cost is

$$k \sum_{X = r+1}^{\infty} (X - r)p_X = k \left[d - r + \sum_{X = 0}^{r} (r - X)p_X \right].$$

(To keep the analysis as simple as possible, we will put $b = 0$ in this section.)
Adding these costs gives

$$A + kd + cq - kr + k \sum_{X = 0}^{r} (r - X)p_X.$$

To convert this into a cost per week runs into the difficulty that the cycle length is random. However, it can be proved that

$$\text{expected cost/unit time} = \frac{\text{expected cost/cycle}}{\text{expected cycle time}}.$$

We have already used the deterministic version of this result in Chapter 8, but when demand is random the relationship requires proof. (It is not, in general, true that the expectation of the ratio of random variables is the ratio of their expectations.)

To find the expected cycle time ET, we can use the idea that expected demand in a given time interval should be proportional to the length of that time interval. This result may be exactly true, for example if the demand is a Poisson process (see Chapter 10). In general, it holds approximately. Thus we will use

$$\frac{\text{expected demand per cycle}}{\text{expected cycle time}} = \frac{\text{expected demand in lead time } L}{L}.$$

Since backlogging is being used, the demand in any cycle is q, so that

$$ET = Lq/d$$

and we can conclude that expected ordering plus shortage costs per week are

$$\frac{dA}{Lq} + \frac{cd}{L} + \frac{kd}{Lq} \left[d - r + \sum_{X = 0}^{r} (r - X)p_X \right].$$

To obtain the holding cost we will use the same as in our approximate analysis of periodic review policies.

More specifically, the following holds approximately.

Expected holding cost/week

$$= \tfrac{1}{2}h \times [\text{expected initial inventory} + \text{expected final inventory}]$$

where 'initial' and 'final' refer to a cycle. At the time of ordering $I = r$, and by the time the order arrives X further items have been demanded, so that

$$\text{final inventory} = \begin{cases} r - X & \text{if } 0 \leqslant X \leqslant r \\ 0 & \text{if } X \geqslant r + 1 \end{cases}$$

and thus

$$\text{expected final inventory} = \sum_{X=0}^{r} (r - X)p_X .$$

Since, for any X, the final net inventory is $r - X$ and the order size is q, the next cycle must start with

$$\text{initial inventory} = r - X + q,$$

which enables us to conclude that

$$\text{expected initial inventory} = \sum_{X=0}^{\infty} (r - X + q)p_X = r - d + q.$$

(We have ignored, as having small probability, the possibility that $r - X + q < 0$.) Thus expected holding cost per week is

$$\tfrac{1}{2}h \left[r - d + q + \sum_{X=0}^{r} (r - X)p_X \right].$$

Adding all the cost terms we find that expected total costs per week $\kappa_a(q, r)$ are given by

$$\kappa_a(q, r) = \tfrac{1}{2}hq + h\alpha(r) + d\beta(r)/Lq + \text{constant},$$

where

$$\alpha(r) = \tfrac{1}{2}r + \tfrac{1}{2} \sum_{X=0}^{r} (r - X)p_X \tag{9.4a}$$

$$\beta(r) = A + kd - kr + k \sum_{X=0}^{r} (r - X)p_X \tag{9.4b}$$

constant $= cd/L - \tfrac{1}{2}hd.$

It is not possible, in general, to write down analytic expressions for (q^*, r^*), the minimisers of $\kappa_a(q, r)$. However, it is clear that q^* must minimise $\kappa_a(q, r^*)$ and r^* must minimise $\kappa_a(q^*, r)$ and we will develop an iterative procedure based on this observation. We shall start by choosing an r_1 arbitrarily (usually $r_1 = 0$). Then we look for q minimising $\kappa_a(q, r_1)$, say $q = q_1$. Now turn to r and find r_2 which minimises $\kappa_a(q_1, r)$. We continue in this way, alternately minimising with respect to q and r, until some minimiser is repeated, i.e. we find $r_m = r_{m-1}$ or $q_m = q_{m-1}$.

When we terminate, the final minimisers generated must satisfy the property that each minimises κ_a if the other is fixed. Assuming there is a unique q and r with this property we can conclude that q^* and r^* have been found. Careful analysis of α and β shows that, under suitable conditions, if $r_1 = 0$, then

(1) $q_1, q_2, \ldots$ is a non-increasing sequence
(2) $r_1, r_2, \ldots$ is a non-decreasing sequence
(3) $q_i \geqslant q^*$ for all i
(4) $r_i \leqslant r^*$ for all i.

Consequently the iterative method must find the optimal solution in a finite number of steps.

To carry out the procedure, we must be able to perform single-variable minimisations of κ. Notice first that

$$\kappa_a(q, r) = \frac{d\beta(r)}{Lq} + \tfrac{1}{2}hq + \text{terms only depending on } r.$$

We saw how to minimise an expression of this type with respect to q in Section 8.1. Thus the minimum is

$$q = \left[\sqrt{\left(\frac{2d}{hL}\beta(r) + \tfrac{1}{4} \right)} - \tfrac{1}{2} \right]. \tag{9.5}$$

We also have

$$\kappa_a(q, r) = h\alpha(r) + d\beta(r)/Lq + \text{terms only depending on } q.$$

We need to calculate

$$\Delta_r\kappa_a(q, r) = \kappa_a(q, r+1) - \kappa_a(q, r).$$

This is facilitated by noting that

$$\Delta\alpha(r) = \tfrac{1}{2} + \tfrac{1}{2}\text{Prob}(X \leqslant r)$$

and $\Delta\beta(r) = -k + k\text{Prob}(X \leqslant r)$

using a result from the previous section. Hence

$$\Delta_r\kappa_a = \left(\tfrac{1}{2}h - \frac{kd}{Lq} \right) + \left(\tfrac{1}{2}h + \frac{kd}{Lq} \right)\text{Prob}(X \leqslant r)$$

so that $\Delta_r\kappa_a \geqslant 0$ can be written

$$\text{Prob}(X \leqslant r) = \sum_{X=0}^{r} p_X \geqslant \left(k\frac{2d}{hL} - q \right) \Big/ \left(k\frac{2d}{hL} + q \right) \tag{9.6}$$

and so the minimiser is the smallest r satisfying (9.6).

As an example we will find (q^*, r^*) when $A = 15$, $h = 2$, $k = 10$, $L = 4$ and p_X is as given in Table 9.1. To avoid recalculating them at each iteration, we note that

$$d = 3 \qquad 2d/hL = 0.75$$

$$2kd/hL = 7.5 \qquad A + kd = 45.$$

Then, putting $r_1 = 0$, we find

$$\beta(r_1) = \beta(0) = 45.$$

Hence from (9.6)

$$q_1 = \lceil \sqrt{(0.75 \times 45 + \tfrac{1}{4})} - \tfrac{1}{2} \rceil = \lceil 5.33 \rceil = 6.$$

Then

$$\left(k\frac{2d}{hL} - q \right) \Big/ \left(k\frac{2d}{hL} + q \right) = 1.5/13.5 = 0.11$$

and $P(X \leqslant 1) = 0.15$, $P(X = 0) = 0.05$, so $r_2 = 1$,

$$\beta(1) = 45 - 10 + 10(1 \times 0.05) = 35.5.$$

Hence

$$q_2 = \lceil \sqrt{(0.75 \times 35.5 + \tfrac{1}{4})} - \tfrac{1}{2} \rceil = 5.$$

So $(7.5 - 5)/(7.5 + 5) = 0.2$ and $r_3 = 2$

and $\beta(2) = 45 - 20 + 10(2 \times 0.05 + 1 \times 0.1) = 27.$

So $q_3 = 5 = q_2 = q^*, r^* = r_3 = 2.$

Exercises

1   Find the optimal value of S in the periodic review model, when $A = 3$, $c = 0.5$, $h = 1.5$, $k = 1$, $b = 3.5$ and p_X is as given in Table 9.3.

Table 9.3

X	0	1	2	3	4	5
p_X	0	0.1	0.2	0.3	0.2	0.2

2   A shopkeeper orders items monthly, incurring a fixed cost for each positive order of £40. It costs £6 per month to store each item and unfulfilled demand

Table 9.4

X	0	1	2	3
p_X	0.15	0.25	0.3	0.3

is backlogged at a cost to the shopkeeper of £100 per item irrespective of the time the customer has to wait. The demand p_X per month is given in Table 9.4.

Use the approximate analysis of Section 9.2 to ascertain the value of S which the shopkeeper should use.

The shopkeeper is offered the option of having deliveries every two months. Should he accept?

3 Solve the two-bin problem with $A = 25, h = 2, k = 10, L = 2$ and the same p_X as Exercise 1.

10
Queueing Theory

10.1 Introduction

Most people queue at least once a day, and if we believe the saying 'time is money', this is an expensive activity. In this chapter, we model how queues form and how they should be controlled. A queue occurs when 'customers' arrive who require a 'service' from 'servers' where the service will take time to perform. Examples of queues are as follows.

(1) Customers arriving at a supermarket check-out, where the servers are the check-out operators, who serve the customer by calculating the bill. The arrivals of the customers and the time it takes to serve them are random and usually there are several servers, who operate on a 'first-come–first-served' basis.

(2) Patients arrive at a hospital casualty unit randomly to await treatment. The time the doctor takes to deal with each patient is random, but the service is not on a first-come–first-served basis, as the very ill patients are given priority.

(3) Items come off a production line at regular intervals and are stored in a warehouse while waiting for dispatch. The waiting time for the items—the 'customers'—is random depending on demand, and usually several items are dispatched together. In many cases, since the items which are most conveniently placed are dispatched first, this means that the service is on a 'last-in–first-out' basis.

(4) Cars arrive at traffic lights at random times and have to wait until the lights indicate they may proceed. Here the queue builds up, not because the traffic lights (the server) take long to perform the service, but because there are periods of time when the lights are red and they are not doing any 'serving'.

(5) Messages transmitted from peripherals and terminals wait to be served by the central processing unit in a computer system. There are sophisticated rules governing the order in which these messages are served built into the computer system. These include interrupting the service on a given message if it is taking too long, and returning to it later.

10.2 Deterministic example

Consider washing machines which come off the production line at a rate of one every four minutes. It takes exactly three minutes to box the machine. The 'customers' in this case are the washing machines and the service is their boxing. The graph of the number in the queue against time looks like Fig. 10.1. (We still consider the 'customer' who is being served as part of the queue. A queue consists of all the people who are being served or waiting to be served.)

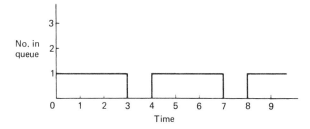

Fig. 10.1

For three-quarters of the time, there is one customer, the one being served in the queue and for one-quarter of the time there is no one in the queue. If we let p_n be the probability that if we look at the queue at some randomly chosen time, we will find n in the queue, then $p_1 = \frac{3}{4}$ and $p_0 = \frac{1}{4}$. Alternatively, if we define p_i to be the proportion of time for which there are i in the queue, the result is the same. In fact this is always the case, even when the times of arrival and the times of service are random, though the proof of this result is a 'deep' (i.e. hard) theorem. Once we have calculated the probabilities p_n of there being n in the queue, we can find out other properties of the queue. For example, the average number of people waiting at any one time is $0.p_0 + 1.p_1 = \frac{3}{4}$ in this case; while the proportion of time the server is 'idle' (i.e. no washing machines are being boxed) is $p_0 = \frac{1}{4}$.

10.3 Steady state situation

With random arrivals and random service times, the number in the queue in its early stages is dependent on the starting conditions of the queue (see Fig. 10.2). After some time this effect wears off and the queue size either settles down to some steady state random fluctuations, which do not depend on the initial queue size, or else the queue 'explodes' towards infinity. (Just imagine what would happen if it took 5 minutes to box each machine in the example of Section 10.2.) In most queueing problems it is assumed that the queue is in its steady state and is not exploding. This makes the mathematics easier, but means that we have always to be careful about applying the results to cases where the queue will be in operation for only a short time or when we are interested in the start-up of the queue.

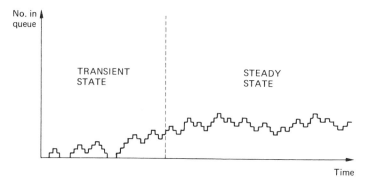

Fig. 10.2

10.4   Factors affecting a queue

There are four factors which affect the way a queue operates.

(1)   *The arrival pattern of customers.* Customers may arrive at regular intervals like items off a production line, or completely at random like supermarket customers, or with some variation about a regular pattern, as in an appointment system. If there is only a finite population of possible customers, then the rate at which they arrive depends on the number queueing already.

(2)   *Service times.* The time it takes to serve a customer can be fixed or random depending on circumstances. Thus the time for a car to go through an automatic car wash is essentially fixed, while the time to fill it up with petrol varies and depends on how much petrol is required.

(3)   *The number of servers.* There can be many or no servers to deal with the customers. The traffic lights are an example of where, for certain periods of time, there is no server available. In the case of more than one server, for a queue, we are thinking of the situation where only one queue forms and a customer goes to whichever server becomes available next. This describes the situation when cars queue for the first available petrol pump as opposed to supermarket customers at check-outs where essentially several independent one-server queues form.

(4)   *Queue discipline.* This describes how the server decides who he will serve next when he finishes the previous service. We concentrate on the 'first-in–first-out' or FIFO rule, so that the server serves the customer who has been waiting the longest. As described in an earlier example some queues, consisting of stored items in a warehouse, might use 'last-in–first-out' (LIFO) so the customer who joined last will be served next. Other queueing disciplines, especially of jobs in a computer system, assign different priorities to the customers, and it is the highest-priority customer who has waited longest who is served next.

When we model random arrival patterns and random service times, the most common distributions to use are the Poisson process and the negative exponential distribution respectively. These two distributions are closely related, and before dealing with them in the context of queues we will look at some of their properties.

10.5 The Poisson process

The arrival pattern is a Poisson process with rate λ, if the probability that n customers arrive between time s and time $s + t$ is

$$\frac{(\lambda t)^n}{n!} e^{-\lambda t} \qquad \text{for } n = 0, 1, 2, 3, \ldots.$$

Thus the probability that no customers arrive in this time is $e^{-\lambda t}$; the probability that one arrives is $\lambda t e^{-\lambda t}$, and the probability of two arrivals is $(\lambda t)^2 e^{\lambda t}/2$. We can work out the expected number N of customers to arrive between s and $s + t$ by saying

$$\exp(N) = \sum_{n=0}^{\infty} n \operatorname{Prob}(N = n) = \sum_{n=0}^{\infty} \frac{n(\lambda t)^n}{n!} e^{-\lambda t},$$

$$\sum_{n=0}^{\infty} \frac{(\lambda t)^n}{n-1!} e^{-\lambda t} = (\lambda t) \sum_{r=0}^{\infty} \frac{(\lambda t)^r}{r!} e^{-\lambda t} \qquad \text{(where we write } r = n - 1\text{)}.$$

Using the fact that $e^x = \sum_{r=0}^{\infty} x^r/r!$, this gives

$$\exp(N) = \lambda t \, e^{\lambda t} \, e^{-\lambda t} = \lambda t.$$

So λ is the average rate at which customers arrive at the queue.

One disadvantage of the Poisson process is that the number of customers arriving between s and $s + t$ does not depend on s. Thus it is not very good for modelling arrival processes which vary in time, like traffic with its 'rush hours'.

One other useful property of Poisson arrival processes is that the combination of two Poisson processes is still a Poisson process. Thus if there are two types of customers who arrive at a queue, the first type arrive in a Poisson process with rate λ_1, and the second type arrive in a Poisson process with rate λ_2, then the overall arrival process of any type of customer is still Poisson but with rate $\lambda_1 + \lambda_2$.

10.6 The negative exponential distribution

The commonest way of modelling random service times is by the negative exponential distribution. If the service time T has negative exponential distribution with rate μ, then

$$\text{Prob}\{T \leqslant t\} = 1 - e^{-\mu t}, \qquad t \geqslant 0. \tag{10.1}$$

The service time T can take any value from 0 up to infinity. This is the first occasion in the book that we have had to deal with such a continuous random variable. So it is worth recalling some of the definitions for such variables.

The distribution function $F_T(t)$ is the probability $\{T \leqslant t\}$, while the density function $f_T(t)$ is the derivative of $F_T(t)$ with respect to t. The function $f_T(t)$ plays the same role as the probability $X = x$ does for finite-valued random variables. Although, for the continuous variable T, the probability that $T = t$ is zero for almost all values of t, it is true that

$$\text{Prob}\{t \leqslant T \leqslant t + h\} = F_T(t + h) - F_T(t) \approx \int_t^{t+h} f_T(s)\,ds.$$

In the discrete case

$$\text{Prob}\{x \leqslant X \leqslant x + h\} = \sum_{k=x}^{x+h} P_X(k).$$

The expectation or mean of a random variable T with continuous distribution is given by

$$E[T] = \int_0^\infty t f_T(t)\,dt.$$

For the negative exponential distribution, the density function is $f_T(t) = \mu e^{-\mu t}$, since by (10.1) $F_T(t) = 1 - e^{-\mu t}$. So

$$E[T] = \int_0^\infty t f_T(t)\,dt = \int_0^\infty t \mu e^{-\mu t}\,dt$$

$$= [-te^{-\mu t}]_0^\infty + \int_0^\infty e^{-\mu t}\,dt = 0 + [e^{-\mu t}/\mu]_0^\infty = \frac{1}{\mu},$$

where we have used integration by parts to solve the integral. Hence the average service time is $1/\mu$, which explains why we call μ the service rate, since in a time t on average $t/(1/\mu) = \mu t$ customers are served. If we look at the time between arrivals in a Poisson process we find that the inter-arrival times also have negative exponential distribution.

Another property of the negative exponential distribution is that it has no memory. Suppose you have already been served for a time s, what is the probability you will have to wait at least another time t before the service is finished? Recall that we write $\text{Prob}\,(A|B)$ as the probability A occurs given that B has occurred, and this conditional probability satisfies

$$\text{Prob}\,(A|B) = \frac{\text{Prob}\,(A \text{ and } B \text{ occur})}{\text{Prob}\,(B \text{ occurs})},$$

so we are interested in $\text{Prob}(T \geqslant t + s | T \geqslant s)$, where T is service time. Hence

$$\text{Prob}(T \geqslant t + s | T \geqslant s) = \text{Prob}\{T \geqslant t + s \text{ and } T \geqslant s\}/\text{Prob}\{T \geqslant s\}$$
$$= \text{Prob}\{T \geqslant t + s\}/\text{Prob}\{T \geqslant s\}$$
$$= e^{-\mu(t+s)}/e^{-\mu s} = e^{-\mu t}$$
$$= \text{Prob}\{T \geqslant t\}.$$

Thus the probability of being served in the next t units of time is independent of how long you have already been served or even if you have been served at all yet. This seems a strange property, but it is surprising in how many types of service it occurs.

We mentioned that the Poisson process and the negative exponential distribution are related. To see this, consider A, the distribution of time between arrivals in a Poisson process. If the last arrival was at time s, then if there has been no further arrival by $s + t$, we know $A \geqslant t$. Thus

$$\text{Prob}\{A \geqslant t\} = \text{Prob}\{0 \text{ arrivals between } s \text{ and } s + t\} = e^{-\lambda t}$$

so $\text{Prob}\{A \leqslant t\} = 1 - e^{-\lambda t}$, and A has negative exponential distribution with parameter λ.

The Poisson process also then has this 'memoryless' property—the chance of someone not arriving in the next t time units does not depend on how many arrived in the recent past. This property is called the Markov property after A. A. Markov, who first looked at such processes.

10.7 Types of queue

To obtain the properties of a queue, you can either use simulation or analytic technique. On complicated cases you need to use simulation (see Chapter 13) on a computer to see what will happen (but remember you need to do lots of simulations to get a feel for the queue), but for simple queues their properties can be calculated exactly, and we can determine how best to control them. Queues are denoted by three parameters, $X/Y/c$, where X describes the arrival pattern, so

$X = M$ means the arrivals are a Poisson process
        (because such processes have the Markov property)
$X = D$ means arrivals at deterministic (regular) times
$X = G$ means a general arrival pattern
$X = M_n$ means Poisson process arrivals, but the rate depends on the number
        in the queue at that time

Y describes the service times, where

$Y = M$ means negative exponential service times, since they have the
        Markov properties
$Y = D$ means constant service times

$Y = G$ means a general service time

$Y = M_n$ means negative exponential service times with a rate depending on
the number in the queue

c is the number of servers in the queue.

10.8 M/M/1 queue

The simplest queue we will investigate is that in which there is one server, whose
service times are negative exponential with rate μ, and the customers arrive in a
Poisson process with rate λ.

Recall that p_n is the probability that there are n people in the queue, i.e. being
served or waiting to be served at any random time when it is in its steady state. In
this steady state, the probability that there are n people in the queue does not
change in time. Thus we would expect that the rate at which the queue changes
from having n in the queue to having some other number in the queue should
equal the rate at which it changes from having some other number of customers in
the queue to having n in the queue. The only way the queue can change from
having no customers is for someone to arrive. So the rate at which it changes is the
probability there are no customers in the queue (p_0) multiplied by the rate at
which customers arrive (λ). Similarly, the only way the queue can change to
having none in the queue, is if there is only one in the queue and that customer's
service is completed. Thus the rate at which it will change to no customers is p_1,
the probability there is one customer in the queue times μ, the rate at which the
service ends. Thus we would expect

$$\lambda p_0 = \mu p_1 \qquad \text{or} \qquad p_1 = (\lambda/\mu)p_0.$$

Similarly, the rate at which the queue changes from having n customers in the
queue to some other number is p_n, the probability that there are n in the queue,
multiplied by $(\lambda + \mu)$, the sum of the rate at which another customer arrives plus
the rate at which one leaves because his service is completed. The queue can
change to having n customers, either by having $n - 1$ customers and a new one
arrives or by having $n + 1$ customers and a customer completes its service. This
leads to

$$(\lambda + \mu)p_n = \lambda p_{n-1} + \mu p_{n+1}.$$

In particular we have

$$\lambda p_1 + \mu p_1 = \mu p_2 + \lambda p_0.$$

Using $\lambda p_0 = \mu p_1$ gives

$$\mu p_2 = \lambda p_1 \qquad \text{or} \qquad p_2 = (\lambda/\mu)p_1.$$

We can repeat this for all values of n and continue to get

$$\mu p_n = \lambda p_{n-1} \qquad \text{or} \qquad p_n = (\lambda/\mu)p_{n-1}.$$

Thus

$$p_n = (\lambda/\mu)p_{n-1} = (\lambda/\mu)^n p_0$$

can be proved. Obviously we require $\lambda \leqslant \mu$ (the rate at which people arrive is less than the rate at which they can be served); otherwise the queue will grow to infinity. We call $\rho = \lambda/\mu$, the traffic intensity and notice that $\rho < 1$ if the queue is not to explode.

Since $p_n = \rho^n p_0$ and we must have

$$\sum_{n=0}^{\infty} p_n = 1,$$

then

$$\sum_{n=0}^{\infty} \rho^n p_0 = 1 = p_0 (1 + \rho + \rho^2 + \rho^3 + \cdots).$$

Since $\rho < 1$, if we multiply both sides by $(1 - \rho)$ we get $p_0 = 1 - \rho$. Hence

$$p_n = (1 - \rho)\rho^n.$$

The expected number in the queue, N, can now be calculated:

$$\begin{aligned}
\text{Exp}\{N\} &= \sum_{n=0}^{\infty} np_n = \sum_{n=0}^{\infty} n\rho^n(1 - \rho) \\
&= 0 + (\rho - \rho^2) + 2(\rho^2 - \rho^3) + 3(\rho^3 - \rho^4) + \cdots \\
&= \rho + \rho^2 + \rho^3 + \cdots \\
&= \rho(1 + \rho + \rho^2 + \cdots)
\end{aligned}$$

which using the same idea as in calculating p_0 becomes $\rho/(1 - \rho)$.

If we recall that the average service time is $1/\mu$, then when someone joins the queue he expects to find $\exp(N)$ there already, and so he expects to wait a time $(\exp(N) + 1) \times 1/\mu$ until he has been served. So expected waiting time

$$\begin{aligned}
\exp\{W\} &= (\exp[N] + 1)/\mu \\
&= \left(\frac{\rho}{1 - \rho} + 1\right) \times \frac{1}{\mu} = \frac{1}{\mu(1 - \rho)} = \frac{1}{\mu - \lambda}.
\end{aligned}$$

Petrol station problem I

In a one-pump petrol station, cars wishing to fill up arrive in a Poisson process with rate 48α per hour, where α is the average fraction of a tank of petrol they have left when they decide to fill up. The time taken to fill a tank completely is 2 minutes on average, and it takes another 2 minutes on average to pay, the overall distribution being negative exponential. Find the expected length of the queue and the average waiting time per car, if on average people fill up when they have one-eighth of a tank of petrol left.

There is a rumour that petrol will soon be more expensive, so now on average people fill up when their tank is half full. What happens now?

This is an M/M/1 queue, where, since $\alpha = \frac{1}{8}$ cars arrive in a Poisson process rate $48 \times \frac{1}{8} = 6$ per hour. So $\lambda = 6$ and the service time is negative exponential, with mean $2 + 2(1 - \alpha)$ minutes. As $\alpha = \frac{1}{8}$ the service rate is

$$\mu = \frac{60}{2 + 2(1 - \frac{1}{8})} \text{ per hour} = \frac{60}{3\frac{3}{4}} = 16.$$

Thus $\rho = \lambda/\mu = \frac{6}{16} = \frac{3}{8}$ and so $p_n = (\frac{3}{8})^n \frac{5}{8}$.
Expected (number in queue) $= \rho/(1 - \rho) = \frac{3}{8}/(1 - \frac{3}{8}) = \frac{3}{5}$.
Average waiting time $= 1/(\mu - \lambda) = 1/(16 - 6)$ hours $= \frac{1}{10}$ hour $= 6$ minutes.
    If α increases to $\frac{1}{2}$, then λ becomes 24 per hour and

$$\mu = \frac{60}{2 + 2(1 - \frac{1}{2})} = \frac{60}{3} = 20 \text{ per hour.}$$

Thus $\rho = \lambda/\mu = \frac{24}{20}$. This is greater than 1, so the queue explodes and tends to infinity (the arrival rate is faster than the service rate).
    Have *you* ever tried to buy petrol on budget day?

10.9 $M_n/M_n/1$ queue

Suppose that the arrival and service distributions depend on the number in the queue. It seems reasonable that long queues might discourage customers and so decrease the arrival rate and so make the server work faster. In fact, we can use those queues to model many different situations.
    Assume that the arrivals still form a Poisson process, but the rate of arrival is λ_n if there are n in the queue, where $n = 0, 1, 2$, etc. We also assume that the service distribution is still negative exponential but with parameter μ_n if there are n in the queue ($n = 1, 2, 3$, etc.). (Notice that if there are no customers, there is no service to perform.) In this case, the probability p_n that in the steady state there are n in the queue is

$$p_n = \frac{\lambda_{n-1}\lambda_{n-2} \cdots \lambda_1 \lambda_0}{\mu_n \mu_{n-1} \cdots \mu_2 \mu_1} p_0.$$

Notice that if $\lambda_{n-1} = \lambda_{n-2} = \cdots = \lambda_1 = \lambda_0 = \lambda$ and $\mu_n = \mu_{n-1} = \cdots = \mu_1$ $= \mu$, then we get the same result as the M/M/1 queue:

$$p_n = \frac{\lambda^n}{\mu^n} p_0.$$

The mechanic problem
A company has four machines, each of which fails after a time which is negative exponentially distributed with mean 120 hours. The machines are independent of

one another. It costs the company £6 per hour per machine when a machine is out of operation, unless all four machines are broken, in which case it costs £150 per hour. The company can hire one of the two mechanics to repair the machines. Both have exponential service times for repairing the machine, but one has an average service time of 30 hours and wants £3 per hour, while the other has mean service time of 20 hours and wants £6 per hour. Which should the company choose?

This is an $M_n/M/1$ queue, since the arrival rate—really the failure rate—of broken machines depends on the number of machines still operating. Each machine has a Poisson arrival rate, since its inter-arrival time is negative exponential. The combination of Poisson arrival rates is still Poisson, so the overall arrival process is also Poisson, but the rate varies depending on the number of machines operating. If all four have broken down, so that the number in the queue is 4, then the arrival rate is 0 per hour.

If three are broken down (3 in the queue), then the arrival rate is $\frac{1}{120}$ per hour. If two are broken down (2 in the queue), then the arrival rate is $2 \times \frac{1}{120}$ per hour. If one is broken down (1 in the queue), then the arrival rate is $3 \times \frac{1}{120}$ per hour. If none has broken down (none in the queue), then the arrival rate is $4 \times \frac{1}{120}$ per hour.

So

$$\lambda_0 = \tfrac{1}{30}, \quad \lambda_1 = \tfrac{1}{40}, \quad \lambda_2 = \tfrac{1}{60}, \quad \lambda_3 = \tfrac{1}{120}, \quad \lambda_4 = 0 = \lambda_i, \quad i > 4.$$

Consider the mechanic with average service time of 30 hours. In this case $\mu = \tfrac{1}{30}$, so

$$p_1 = \lambda_0 p_0 / \mu = \frac{\tfrac{1}{30}}{\tfrac{1}{30}} p_0 = p_0,$$

$$p_2 = \frac{\lambda_1 \lambda_0}{\mu^2} p_0 = \frac{\tfrac{1}{30} \times \tfrac{1}{40}}{\tfrac{1}{30} \times \tfrac{1}{30}} = \tfrac{3}{4} p_0,$$

$$p_3 = \frac{\lambda_0 \lambda_1 \lambda_2}{\mu^3} p_0 = \frac{\tfrac{1}{30} \times \tfrac{1}{40} \times \tfrac{1}{60}}{\tfrac{1}{30} \times \tfrac{1}{30} \times \tfrac{1}{30}} = \tfrac{3}{8} p_0,$$

$$p_4 = \frac{\lambda_0 \lambda_1 \lambda_2 \lambda_3}{\mu^4} p_0 = \frac{\tfrac{1}{30} \times \tfrac{1}{40} \times \tfrac{1}{60} \times \tfrac{1}{120}}{\tfrac{1}{30} \times \tfrac{1}{30} \times \tfrac{1}{30} \times \tfrac{1}{30}} = \tfrac{3}{32} p_0.$$

Since $\lambda_4 = 0$, $p_5 = 0 p_0$ and so are all p_i, $i \geqslant 5$. Now

$$p_0 + p_1 + p_2 + p_3 + p_4 = 1 = p_0 + p_0 + \tfrac{3}{4} p_0 + \tfrac{3}{8} p_0 + \tfrac{3}{32} p_0.$$

Thus $p_0 = \tfrac{32}{103}$.

Expected cost per hour with this employee is

$$£(0 p_0 + 6 p_1 + 12 p_2 + 18 p_3 + 150 p_4) + 3$$

$$= £(6 \times \tfrac{32}{103} + 12 \times \tfrac{24}{103} \times 18 \times \tfrac{12}{103} + 150 \times \tfrac{3}{103}) + 3$$

$$= £14.12.$$

For the second mechanic whose service rate is $\frac{1}{20}$ per hour we have

$$p_1 = \lambda_0 p_0 / \mu_0 = \tfrac{1}{30} p_0 / \tfrac{1}{20} = \tfrac{2}{3} p_0$$

$$p_2 = \frac{\tfrac{1}{30} \times \tfrac{1}{40}}{\tfrac{1}{20} \times \tfrac{1}{20}} p_0 = \tfrac{1}{3} p_0$$

$$p_3 = \frac{\tfrac{1}{30} \times \tfrac{1}{40} \times \tfrac{1}{60}}{\tfrac{1}{20} \times \tfrac{1}{20} \times \tfrac{1}{20}} p_0 = \tfrac{1}{9} p_0$$

$$p_4 = \frac{\tfrac{1}{30} \times \tfrac{1}{40} \times \tfrac{1}{60} \times \tfrac{1}{120}}{\tfrac{1}{20} \times \tfrac{1}{20} \times \tfrac{1}{20} \times \tfrac{1}{20}} p_0 = \tfrac{1}{54} p_0.$$

Now $p_0 + p_1 + p_2 + p_3 + p_4 = \frac{115}{54} p_0 = 1$. Thus $p_0 = \frac{54}{115}$. So expected cost per hour is $\pounds(0p_0 + 6p_1 + 12p_2 + 18p_3 + 150p_4) + 6 = \pounds 12.00$. So we should employ the faster and more expensive mechanic.

10.10   Limited capacity M/M/1 queue

There are many occasions when there is a limit to the number in the queue. This may be because there is only a finite number of possible customers or because there is room for only a few customers to queue and if this is occupied any new arrivals must be turned away. Suppose the limit is L, so that if there are less than L in the queue when a customer arrives, he joins the queue, but if L or more are in the queue, the customer leaves the system.

This can be thought of as a special case of the $M_n/M_n/1$ queue with $\lambda_n = \lambda$, $n < L$, $\lambda_n = 0$, $n \geqslant L$ and $\mu_n = \mu$ for all n. Thus if we define $\rho = \lambda/\mu$ to be the traffic intensity as in Section 10.8 we get from the formula in Section 10.9 that

$$p_n = \frac{\lambda \ldots \lambda \ldots \lambda}{\mu \ldots \mu \ldots \mu} = \rho^n p_0, \quad n < L; \qquad p_n = 0, \quad n \geqslant L.$$

Since $p_0 + p_1 + p_2 + \cdots + p_L = 1$, we get

$$p_0 + \rho p_0 + \rho^2 p_0 + \cdots + \rho^L p_0 = 1.$$

Multiplying both sides by $1 - \rho$ gives

$$p_0 (1 - \rho^{L+1}) = 1 - \rho$$

provided $\rho \neq 1$. So

$$p_n = \frac{\rho^n (1 - \rho)}{1 - \rho^{L+1}} \quad n \leqslant L, \quad \text{if } \rho \neq 1. \tag{10.2}$$

If $\rho = 1$, obviously

$$p_0 = p_1 = p_2 = \cdots = p_L = \frac{1}{L+1}.$$

Note that ρ can be greater than 1, since the queue cannot explode.

Petrol station II

A petrol station has enough space only for the vehicle that it is refuelling. If it is in use no other car will stop. Cars needing petrol pass in a Poisson process with rate 4 per hour. The service time is negative exponential with a mean time of $7\frac{1}{2}$ minutes. The average profit on the petrol sold to each car is £1.00. The garage can increase the size of its forecourt to take one more car and the interest charged on the money needed to do so corresponds to £50.00 per week. If the garage is open for 100 hours per week, should the owner extend his forecourt to accommodate another vehicle?

If he could keep extending his forecourt at a cost of £50.00 per vehicle, how much should he extend it by?

Since we have an M/M/1 system with initially a waiting limit of $L = 1$ and $\lambda = 4$ per hour, $\mu = 8$ per hour. Thus $\rho = \frac{1}{2}$ and (10.2) gives

$$p_0 = 1 - \rho/1 - \rho^2 = \tfrac{1}{2}/\tfrac{3}{4} = \tfrac{2}{3}$$

$$p_1 = \rho(1 - \rho)/(1 - \rho^2) = \tfrac{1}{2} \cdot \tfrac{1}{2}/\tfrac{3}{4} = \tfrac{1}{3}.$$

Expected number of vehicles which use petrol station per hour

= expected number of potential vehicles which could use petrol station × proportion of time the station is free

$$= 4 \times p_0 = \tfrac{8}{3}.$$

Therefore expected profit per hour is $£\tfrac{8}{3} \times 1 = £2.66$.

If we increase forecourt by one, so $L = 2$

$$p_0 = \frac{1 - \tfrac{1}{2}}{1 - (\tfrac{1}{2})^3} = \frac{\tfrac{1}{2}}{\tfrac{7}{8}} = \tfrac{4}{7}$$

$$p_1 = \rho p_0 = \tfrac{1}{2} \cdot \tfrac{4}{7} = \tfrac{2}{7}$$

$$p_2 = \rho p_1 = \tfrac{1}{2} \cdot \tfrac{2}{7} = \tfrac{1}{7}.$$

So average number of vehicles which use petrol station per hour

$$= 4 \times (1 - p_2) = 4 \times \tfrac{6}{7} = \tfrac{24}{7}.$$

So gross profit per hour is $£\tfrac{24}{7} \times 1.00 = £3.43$. While cost of extra forecourt per hour is $£\tfrac{50}{100} = £0.50$. So net profit is $£3.43 - 0.50 = £2.93$.

If forecourt is extended to N vehicles

$$p_0 = \frac{1 - (\tfrac{1}{2})}{1 - (\tfrac{1}{2})^{N+1}}, \qquad p_i = \frac{(\tfrac{1}{2})^i (1 - (\tfrac{1}{2}))}{1 - (\tfrac{1}{2})^{N+1}} \qquad p_N = \frac{(\tfrac{1}{2})^N \times \tfrac{1}{2}}{1 - (\tfrac{1}{2})^{N+1}}.$$

So average number of vehicles which use petrol station per hour

$$= 4 \times (1 - p_N) = 4 \left[1 - \frac{(\tfrac{1}{2})^{N+1}}{1 - (\tfrac{1}{2})^{N+1}} \right] = 4 \left[\frac{1 - (\tfrac{1}{2})^N}{1 - (\tfrac{1}{2})^{N+1}} \right].$$

So net profit per hour if we extend forecourt for N vehicles is

$$C(N) = £4\frac{1-(\frac{1}{2})^N}{1-(\frac{1}{2})^{N+1}} - £0.50(N-1)$$

which gives

N	1	2	3	4
$C(N)$	£2.66	£2.93	£2.73	£2.37

It is therefore best to extend to allow for 2 cars, which gives a profit of £2.93 per hour. For 4 or more cars it costs at least £1.50 per hour to rent the forecourt, so the maximum profit we could hope for is not more than £4.00 − £1.50, i.e. £2.50 per hour.

10.11   M/M/c queue

If, instead of having only one server, there are c servers available to deal with customers, what is the time now between the end of one customer's service and the next one to be finished? Suppose each server has a negative exponential service distribution with rate μ, then the lack of memory of this type of distribution, which we commented on in Section 10.6, means that the time between one customer's service completion and the next one's completion is the same as if all the servers just started their service when the last customer's service was completed. If it is longer than t between customers being served and there are k servers who are actually serving, then each of the k servers must take at least t to serve his customer. So if T_k is the time between the end of service with m servers serving and T is the service time for each individual server, then

$$\text{Prob}\,(T_k > t) = (\text{Prob}\,(T > t))^k.$$

Recall that for the negative exponential distribution with rate μ,

$$\text{Prob}\,(T > t) = e^{-\mu t}, \qquad \text{so} \qquad \text{Prob}\,(T_k > t) = e^{-k\mu t}.$$

Thus the service distribution with k servers actually serving is still negative exponential, but with rate μk.

We can use this fact and the formula for the $M_n/M_n/1$ queue to find the steady state probabilities when we have a queue with Poisson arrival rate parameter λ and c servers, each with exponential service distribution rate μ. Obviously the service rate of the servers considered as one group depends on the number in the queue, since if there are n in the queue and c servers ($n \leqslant c$), only n servers will operate. Hence if μ_n is the service rate with n in the queue,

$$\mu_n = \begin{cases} n\mu & n \leqslant c \\ c\mu & n > c. \end{cases}$$

Since the arrival rate λ is constant, substituting into the formula of Section 10.10 gives

$$\text{for } n \leq c \qquad p_n = \frac{\lambda \ldots \lambda \ldots \lambda}{\mu \cdot 2\mu \ldots n\mu} p_0 = \frac{\lambda^n}{n! \mu^n} p_0,$$

$$\text{for } n > c \qquad p_n = \frac{\lambda \ldots \lambda \ldots \lambda}{\mu \cdot 2\mu \ldots c\mu \cdot c\mu \ldots c\mu} p_0 = \frac{\lambda^n}{c! c^{n-c} \mu^n} p_0.$$

As the queue increases the service rate approaches $c\mu$, so the queue will explode to infinity if $\lambda \geq c\mu$. So, following the M/M/1 case, we denote the traffic intensity by $\rho = \lambda/c\mu$. Hence

$$p_n = \begin{cases} c^n \rho^n p_0/n! & n \leq c \\ c^c \rho^n p_0/c! & n > c. \end{cases} \tag{10.3}$$

We can find p_0 as usual by

$$\sum_{n=0}^{\infty} p_n = 1 = \sum_{n=0}^{c} \frac{c^n \rho^n}{n!} p_0 + \frac{c^c}{c!} \sum_{n=c+1}^{\infty} \rho^n p_0.$$

Let

$$A = \sum_{n=0}^{c} \frac{c^n \rho^n}{n!} + \frac{c^c}{c!} \frac{\rho^{c+1}}{1-\rho} \qquad \text{if } \rho < 1;$$

then

$$p_0 = A^{-1}.$$

Automatic bank teller example

A bank has to decide how many automatic teller machines to place outside a particular bank, where potential customers pass at a rate of 80 per hour. The time for a machine to service each customer is negative exponential with mean $1\frac{1}{2}$ minutes. Market research has shown that customers will not join the queue for these machines if there are three or more people waiting in addition to those actually being served. (Thus if there is only one machine, the queue will never be longer than four; if two machines, the queue will not be longer than five.) It costs £10 000 to install each machine and there is an estimated saving in staff cost of 10p for each customer that uses them. If the machines are in operation for 15 hours a day and the bank's criterion is to maximize the saving over the first year (365 days), how many machines should it install?

If it installs a machine, the queue will be M/M/c with waiting limit of $c + 3$ and $\lambda = 80$ per hour, $\mu = 40$ per hour. If $c = 1$, then in (10.3) we have

$$p_1 = 2p_0, \quad p_2 = 4p_0, \quad p_3 = 8p_0, \quad p_4 = 16p_0, \quad p_i = 0, i \geq 5.$$

Hence

$$p_0 + p_1 + p_2 + p_3 + p_4 = 31p_0 = 1.$$

The expected number of customers who will join the queue per hour is $80(1 - p_4) = 80 \times \frac{15}{31}$ because they will join the queue only if there are less than four customers in it. So the savings in the first year are

$$\pounds(80 \times \tfrac{15}{31} \times 0.1 \times 15 \times 365) - 10\,000 = \pounds11\,193.55.$$

If $c = 2$, (10.3) now gives

$$p_1 = p_2 = p_3 = p_4 = p_5 = 2p_0, \qquad p_i = 0, \quad i \geqslant 6.$$

So

$$p_0 + p_1 + p_2 + p_3 + p_4 + p_5 = 11p_0 = 1.$$

The expected number of customers who will join the queue in an hour is $80(1 - p_5) = 80 \times \frac{9}{11}$. So the savings in the first year will be

$$\pounds(80 \times \tfrac{9}{11} \times 0.1 \times 15 \times 365) - 20\,000 = \pounds15\,836.36.$$

If $c = 3$, (10.3) again gives

$$p_1 = 2p_0, \quad p_2 = 2p_0, \quad p_3 = \tfrac{4}{3}p_0, \quad p_4 = \tfrac{8}{9}p_0, \quad p_5 = \tfrac{16}{27}p_0,$$
$$p_6 = \tfrac{32}{81}p_0, \quad p_i = 0, i \geqslant 7.$$

Hence

$$p_0 + p_1 + p_2 + p_3 + p_4 + p_5 + p_6 = \tfrac{665}{81}p_0 = 1.$$

The expected number of customers who join the queue per hour is $80(1 - p_6)$ $= 80 \times \frac{633}{665}$. So the savings would be

$$\pounds(80 \times \frac{633}{665} \times 0.1 \times 15 \times 365) - 30\,000 = \pounds11\,692.33.$$

For any $c \geqslant 4$, since the most you can save in a year is $\pounds80 \times 0.1 \times 15 \times 365 = \pounds43\,800$, and the cost of tellers is $\pounds40\,000$ or more, we can see that the most saving will be made if two machines are installed.

Exercises

1 In a motorway service area you can eat either in the restaurant or in the self-service cafeteria. There is never any queue for tables in the restaurant, and it will take 25 minutes to eat your meal. In the self-service cafeteria the time for collecting your food, and paying for it, is exponentially distributed with mean 2 minutes, and it takes a further 10 minutes to eat your food. If people arrive at the cafeteria at the rate of 25 per hour, and each one cannot be served until the previous person has paid for his food, how many would you expect to find in the queue when you arrived? Hence decide which is the quicker way of getting a meal.

2 A market survey firm is paid $\pounds1$ by its clients for each person interviewed. It sends c researchers out into a market place where people pass in a Poisson

process at a rate of 60 per hour. It takes the researcher 6 minutes on average to interview someone, and the interview time has a negative exponential distribution. No-one queues up to be interviewed, but if the researcher is free when someone passes, they will be willing to be interviewed. The researchers are paid £7.50 per hour. Explain why this is an M/M/c queue with waiting capacity limited to c. Is it better to send 2, 3 or 4 researchers out?

3   A firm is designing a maintenance bay for its machine tools. Tools will arrive for repair at this bay in a Poisson process with rate 20 per week. The service times are exponentially distributed with rate μ. The value of μ is under the control of the firm. The complete cost of maintenance of such a facility is

$$£1000(\mu + 4\overline{W}) \text{ per week,}$$

where $\overline{W}$ is the mean time a broken tool has to wait until the completion of its repair. What is the optimal value of μ for the firm and how much does the firm expect to pay per week?

Suppose that the firm has the option to choose a different type of machine tool, which would lead to an arrival rate of broken tools of 5 per week. If the interest charges on this capital investment are £14 000 per week, should the firm take up this option?

4   A supermarket has customers arriving at the checkout at a rate of 2 per minute, and the service time for each is exponential with rate 2 per minute. If there are c servers, a customer will only wait to be served if there are less than $3c$ people in total already queueing or being served. Show that

$$\text{Exp (number of servers working at any one time)} = \begin{cases} \frac{3}{4} & \text{when } c = 1 \\ \frac{94}{95} & \text{when } c = 2 \end{cases}$$

and

$$\text{Prob (customer arriving will not join queue)} = \begin{cases} \frac{1}{4} & \text{when } c = 1 \\ \frac{1}{95} & \text{when } c = 2. \end{cases}$$

The supermarket is open for 38 hours in the week and the average profit on goods bought by a customer is 10 p. Given that it costs £40 to employ a server, find whether it is better to employ 1 or 2 servers by calculating:

(a) (average profit on goods bought per week) − (servers' wages). Check your results by calculating for each case:

(b) (profit lost by customers not joining queue) + (servers' wages). Why is the sum of (a) and (b) the same for any c?

5   The telephone switchboard of a firm is usually manned by one operator who handles incoming as well as outgoing calls. Incoming calls and outgoing calls both follow Poisson distributions with mean rates of 20 and 16 per hour respectively. The operator can handle, on the average, 60 calls per hour. The distribution of the time to service calls is approximately exponential.

   (a) Find the average number of units in the queue, the average waiting time of calls, and the average total waiting time of outgoing calls per hour.

   (b) The firm considers installing new equipment that would allow outgoing calls inside the local area to be made directly. This would reduce the arrival rate of outgoing calls to 8 per hour. The rental cost of this equipment is $240.00 per month ($= 200$ working hours). The average cost per hour for people requesting outgoing calls is estimated at $9. Should the firm install this equipment?

6 A salt company has four boilers which need descaling from time to time. The time until a descaling is necessary is a random variable which has an exponential distribution, with an average time of 120 hours. The length of time until descaling for each boiler is independent of the other boilers. The company loses £4 per hour for each boiler out of action being descaled, unless all four boilers are out of action, in which case the whole plant has to stop, at a cost of £100 per hour. The company can either employ one expert descaler whose time for descaling the boilers is a random variable with negative exponential distribution, mean 20 hours, or two apprentices. Only one person can descale a boiler at a time and either apprentice can descale a boiler in a time which is negative exponential with mean 30 hours. The company would have to pay the expert £4 per hour and each apprentice £2.50. By calculating the cost per hour to the company if the expert is hired, and then the cost if the two apprentices are hired, find which the company should employ.

   (*Hint*: in the one case the queue is $M_n/M/1$; in the other it is $M_n/M/2$. For an $M_n/M_n/1$ queue

$$p_n = \frac{\lambda_0 \lambda_1 \ldots \lambda_{n-1}}{\mu_1 \mu_2 \ldots \mu_n} p_0.)$$

7 A car service station has facilities for a maximum of 4 cars to be filled or waiting for service on its premises. Past experience indicates that no potential customers join the queue once these four places are filled. The arrival rate of customers is 24 per hour and the input process is approximately Poisson. The service times are exponential with a mean of 3 minutes.

   (a) Find the steady state probabilities for this system.

   (b) What is the average idle time of the attendant?

   (c) What is the fraction of customers lost? If the average profit per customer is £1.00, what is the lost profit per hour? What is the average waiting time of an arrival?

       The service station has two sets of pumps and considers using a second attendant at a cost of £6.25 per hour. His service time distribution would be the same as for the first attendant.

   (d) Find the steady-state probabilities for this system.

   (e) What is the average fraction of time both attendants are idle; only one is idle; both are busy?

   (f) What is the average fraction of customers lost now?

(g) If the average profit per customer is £1.00, is it more profitable to have one or two attendants?

[The steady-state probabilities for a general M_n/M_n 1 queue are

$$p_n = \frac{\lambda_{n-1}\lambda_{n-2} \cdots \lambda_0 p_0}{\mu_n \mu_{n-1} \cdots \mu_1}.]$$

11
Replacement, Maintenance and Inspection

11.1 Deteriorating and failing systems

Most things, whether they be machinery, electronic systems, components, vehicles (space or earth bound), buildings or even people, eventually wear out and fail. The time at which they fail however is not known in advance, and so it is quite possible that they will fail when in operation. These operating failures can be quite expensive not only in repairing or replacing the item, but also because of the disruption and delay involved to the operation of the system. Thus such items are often subject to a replacement, maintenance, or inspection policy.

The idea behind a replacement policy is to replace the item with a new one before it fails. Although this preventive replacement, as it is called, still involves the cost of a new item, it does avoid the costs due to an unexpected failure of the item and the resultant damage to the system. It is therefore cheaper than replacing the item after it has failed.

The object of a maintenance policy is very similar, except in this case the deteriorating item is given an overhaul rather than being replaced. This overhaul improves the state of the item, and so decreases its chance of a failure. Sometimes it is considered that the overhaul makes the item as good as new, in which case there is no difference as far as the model goes between a maintenance policy and a replacement policy. In some problems, as well as a cost of replacing on failure and the cost of preventive maintenance or replacement, the cost of actually running the machine is considered important. This running cost is assumed to increase as the machine deteriorates.

In the discussion on replacement and maintenance policy, it is assumed that the operator is immediately aware when the unit fails. Often however, this is not the case. A failure in a production system for example, may not lead to a halt in production, but rather to the production of unsatisfactory items. It is necessary to examine these items to realise the system has failed. An inspection policy may be introduced, decreeing how often a system should be inspected to check whether it has failed or not and so to determine whether a replacement or overhaul is necessary.

11.2 Lifetimes and failure rates of systems

Before finding these various policies, we must look at how long the equipment would last if we did nothing to it. This is called the lifetime, T, of the item we are interested in, and measures the time from when it started working until its failure. Since this lifetime, T, is unknown, we can only talk about the probability that T takes certain values. We call the probability that T is less than or equal to t the probability distribution function, $F(t)$, as in Chapter 10. So $F(t) = \text{Prob}\{T \leq t\}$ is the chance the item failed at or before time t.

The times at which the item can fail can be considered either to be continuous in time or to be divided into discrete time periods; thus, for example, it can either fail after 482.37 minutes or in the 9th hour. The discrete version, although less precise, is easier to work with and we will concentrate on that approach, although similar methods will work in the continuous case. Thus, we can now say p_k is the probability the item will fail in the kth time period and so the distribution function $P(k)$, where

$$P_k = F(k) = \text{Prob}\{T \leq k\} = \sum_{i=1}^{k} p_i$$

is the probability the item has failed by the end of the kth period. We define P_0 to be 0.

One way of getting a feel for the way an item fails is to define the failure rate $r(k)$, where

$$r(k) = p_k/(1 - P_{k-1}).$$

This is the probability the item will fail in the kth time period given that it has survived up to that time. For a typical item, $r(k)$ has three distinct regions, as indicated in Fig. 11.1.

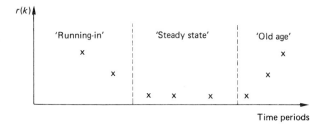

Fig. 11.1

There is a 'running-in' period where the failure rate is initially high but decreasing; then a 'steady state' period with a low and fairly constant failure rate; lastly in 'old age' the failure rate grows steadily. This is the case for humans, as mortality statistics also display this U-shaped trend, although for males there is a small extra peak at about eighteen years (why?)

11.3 Preventive replacement at a fixed age

Consider the following example. Coal is transferred from the coal face to the mine shaft by a conveyor belt, which can break. The cost of replacing it is £1000, but if the belt breaks during a shift, there will be a loss of output, which will on average cost an extra £1500, because work has to stop for that shift. The Coal Board decides to replace belts when they have been used for n shifts, and since they replace between shifts, this involves only the replacement cost. The probability of the belt breaking during its kth shift is p_k, where

$$p_1 = 0.2, \quad p_2 = 0.1, \quad p_3 = 0.1, \quad p_4 = 0.15, \quad p_5 = 0.2 \quad \text{and} \quad p_6 = 0.25.$$

What is the optimal time to replace in order to minimise the expected cost per shift?

This is an example of preventive replacement at a fixed age, because the item is replaced at a fixed age if it has not failed by then. The object is to find which policy of this type is best.

Let R_p be the cost of preventive replacement (£1000).

Let R_f be the cost of replacement at a failure (£1000 + £1500).

Let $\bar{P}_k = 1 - P_k = \sum\limits_{i=k+1}^{\infty} p_i$ be the probability the belt lasts at least k shifts.

Since every belt will cost either R_p or R_f to replace, the expected cost per belt, if we preventively replace after n shifts, is

$$R_p \text{ Prob (belt lasts at least } n \text{ shifts)} + R_f \text{ Prob (belt fails at } n\text{th}$$

$$\text{shift or earlier)} = R_p \bar{P}_n + R_f P_n. \tag{11.1}$$

The expected number of shifts between replacements of the belt if we preventively replace after n shifts is

$$1p_1 + 2p_2 + \cdots + (n-1)p_{n-1} + np_n + n\,\bar{P}_n. \tag{11.2}$$

Notice we can rewrite this expected number of shifts as

$$(p_1 + p_2 + p_3 + \cdots) + (p_2 + p_3 + \cdots) + (p_3 + p_4 + \cdots) + \cdots$$
$$+ (p_n + p_{n+1} + \cdots) = \bar{P}_0 + \bar{P}_1 + \bar{P}_2 + \cdots + \bar{P}_{n-1}.$$

Hence, since we have an expected cost given by (11.1) and the number of shifts between these costs is on average given by (11.2), the expected cost per shift if we replace preventively after n shifts is given by

$$C(n) = \frac{R_p \bar{P}_n + R_f(1 - \bar{P}_n)}{\bar{P}_0 + \bar{P}_1 + \cdots + \bar{P}_{n-1}}.$$

For the problem we are looking at

$$\bar{P}_0 = 1, \quad \bar{P}_1 = 0.8, \quad \bar{P}_2 = 0.7, \quad \bar{P}_3 = 0.6, \quad \bar{P}_4 = 0.45,$$
$$\bar{P}_5 = 0.25, \quad \bar{P}_k = 0, \; k \geqslant 6$$

and since $R_p = £1000$, $R_f = £2500$, we get

$$C(1) = £(1000 \times 0.8 + 2500 \times 0.2)/1 \qquad = £1300$$
$$C(2) = £(1000 \times 0.7 + 2500 \times 0.3)/1.8 \qquad = £855.56$$
$$C(3) = £(1000 \times 0.6 + 2500 \times 0.4)/2.5 \qquad = £640.00$$
$$C(4) = £(1000 \times 0.45 + 2500 \times 0.55)/3.1 \qquad = £588.44$$
$$C(5) = £(1000 \times 0.25 + 2500 \times 0.75)/3.55 \qquad = £598.58$$
$$C(6) = £(1000 \times 0 + 2500 \times 1)/3.8 \qquad = £657.90.$$

Similarly $C(n) = C(6)$ for all $n > 6$, since all these policies correspond to no preventive replacement. Thus we need never calculate $C(n)$ for n greater than the lifetime of the unit (just as in inventory problems, we never need consider maximum stock levels S greater than the maximum demand). So in this case it is best to replace after four shifts.

An even more general policy is to make preventive replacements at random ages rather than at a fixed age. Thus, for each new belt, there is a chance α_i that a preventive replacement will be made after i shifts $i = 1, 2, 3, \ldots$ provided the belt has not failed before then. Since the cost when the preventive replacement is made after i belts is $R_p \overline{P}_i + R_f P_i$, the expected cost under this random policy is

$$\sum_{i=1}^{n} \alpha_i (R_p \overline{P}_i + R_f P_i)$$

Similarly as the expected number of shifts between replacements when there is a preventive replacement after i shifts is $(\overline{P}_0 + \overline{P}_1 + \cdots + \overline{P}_{i-1})$, the expected number of shifts between replacements under the random policy is

$$\sum_{i=1}^{n} \alpha_i (\overline{P}_0 + \overline{P}_1 + \cdots + \overline{P}_{i-1}).$$

So the cost per shift for this policy is

$$\sum_{i=1}^{n} \alpha_i (R_p \overline{P}_i + R_f P_i) / \sum_{i=1}^{n} \alpha_i (\overline{P}_0 + \overline{P}_1 + \cdots + \overline{P}_{i-1}).$$

Since

$$\frac{(R_p \overline{P}_4 + R_f P_4)}{\overline{P}_0 + \overline{P}_1 + \overline{P}_2 + \overline{P}_3} \leqslant \frac{R_p \overline{P}_i + R_f P_i}{\overline{P}_0 + \overline{P}_1 + \cdots + \overline{P}_{i-1}} \qquad \text{for all } i = 1, 2, \ldots,$$

$$\alpha_i (\overline{P}_0 + \overline{P}_1 + \cdots + \overline{P}_{i-1})(R_p \overline{P}_4 + R_f P_4)$$
$$\leqslant \alpha_i (\overline{P}_0 + \overline{P}_1 + \cdots + \overline{P}_3)(R_p \overline{P}_i + R_f P_i).$$

So

$$\left(\sum_{i=1}^{n} \alpha_i \left(\overline{P}_0 + \overline{P}_1 + \cdots + \overline{P}_{i-1} \right) \right) \left(R_p \overline{P}_4 + R_f P_4 \right)$$

$$\leqslant \left(\sum_{i=1}^{n} \alpha_i \left(R_p \overline{P}_i + R_f P_i \right) \right) \left(\overline{P}_0 + \overline{P}_1 + \overline{P}_2 + \overline{P}_3 \right)$$

and hence

$$\frac{(R_p \overline{P}_4 + R_f P_4)}{(\overline{P}_0 + \overline{P}_1 + \overline{P}_2 + \overline{P}_3)} \leqslant \frac{\sum_{i=1}^{n} \alpha_i (R_p \overline{P}_i + R_f P_i)}{\sum_{i=1}^{n} \alpha_i (\overline{P}_0 + \overline{P}_1 + \ldots + \overline{P}_{i-1})} .$$

Thus replacement after four shifts is cheaper per shift than any possible randomized replacement policy. It is always true that some fixed age replacement policy will always be better than any randomized replacement policy. Thus the 'replacement at a fixed age' policy is the cheapest type of policy. However, it is difficult to implement because the preventive replacements do not follow a fixed pattern. They are all four shifts after the last replacement, be it preventive or due to failure. Since the failures could be at any shift, one cannot plan in advance when the preventive replacements will occur. In the next section we look at the system when preventive replacements are made at fixed predetermined times.

11.4   Preventive replacement at fixed times

Suppose that in the problem described above, the Coal Board decides to replace the belts after n shifts, irrespective of how many, if any, failures since the last preventive replacement, even if the belt has only just been replaced in the last shift. This ensures that the times of preventive replacements are always known.

In n shifts there will be one preventive replacement and a random number of failure replacements and the cost will be $R_p + R_f \operatorname{Exp} \{F_n\}$, where F_n is the number of failures in n shifts. Thus if we replace every n shifts, the cost per shift, $C(n)$, satisfies

$$C(n) = (R_p + R_f \operatorname{Exp} \{F_n\})/n.$$

To calculate $\operatorname{Exp} \{F_n\}$, we define f_i to be the probability that there is a failure, not necessarily the first such one, i periods after the last preventive replacement. Then

$$\operatorname{Exp} \{F_n\} = f_1 + f_2 + \cdots + f_n.$$

This follows, since if we call F^i the number of failures in the ith period since the last replacement, then $F_n = F^1 + F^2 + \cdots + F^n$, and so

$$\operatorname{Exp} \{F_n\} = \sum_{i=1}^{n} \operatorname{Exp} \{F^i\}.$$

Also

$$\operatorname{Exp} \{F^i\} = 1 f_i + 0(1 - f_i) = f_i.$$

To calculate the f_i we set our condition according to the length of time the belt that failed in period i has been in operation. If that belt had been working for k shifts, and so had probability p_k of failing, then there must also have been a failure in the $(i-k)$th shift. This leads to the following equations, which are called recurrence equations:

$$f_1 = p_1$$
$$f_2 = p_2 + p_1 f_1$$
$$f_3 = p_3 + p_2 f_1 + p_1 f_2$$
$$f_4 = p_4 + p_3 f_1 + p_2 f_2 + p_1 f_3$$
$$\vdots$$
$$f_n = p_n + \sum_{i=1}^{n-1} p_{n-i} f_i.$$

Using the same probabilities as in Section 11.3, namely

$$(p_1 = 0.2, \quad p_2 = p_3 = 0.1, \quad p_4 = 0.15, \quad p_5 = 0.2, \quad p_6 = 0.25),$$

we get

$$f_1 = 0.2$$
$$f_2 = 0.1 + 0.2 \times 0.2 = 0.14$$
$$f_3 = 0.1 + 0.1 \times 0.2 + 0.2 \times 0.14 = 0.148$$
$$f_4 = 0.15 + 0.1 \times 0.2 + 0.1 \times 0.14 + 0.2 \times 0.148 = 0.2136$$
$$f_5 = 0.2 + 0.15 \times 0.2 + 0.1 \times 0.14 + 0.1 \times 0.148 + 0.2 \times 0.2136 = 0.3015$$
$$f_6 = 0.25 + 0.2 \times 0.2 + 0.15 \times 0.14 + 0.1 \times 0.148 + 0.1 \times 0.2136 + 0.2 \times 0.3015$$
$$= 0.4075$$
$$f_7 = 0.25 \times 0.2 + 0.2 \times 0.14 + 0.15 \times 0.148 + 0.1 \times 0.2136 + 0.1 \times 0.3015 +$$
$$0.2 \times 0.4075 = 0.2332.$$

Similarly, we get $f_8 = 0.2142$, $f_9 = 0.2318$, $f_{10} = 0.2659$, etc.

We can now calculate $C(n)$ as follows:

$$
\begin{aligned}
C(1) &= (1000 + 2500 \times 0.2)/1 & &= \pounds 1500 \\
C(2) &= (1000 + 2500 \times 0.34)/2 & &= \pounds 925 \\
C(3) &= (1000 + 2500 \times 0.488)/3 & &= \pounds 740 \\
C(4) &= (1000 + 2500 \times 0.7016)/4 & &= \pounds 688.50 \\
C(5) &= (1000 + 2500 \times 1.0031)/5 & &= \pounds 701.54 \\
C(6) &= (1000 + 2500 \times 1.4106)/6 & &= \pounds 754.42 \\
C(7) &= (1000 + 2500 \times 1.6438)/7 & &= \pounds 729.92 \\
C(8) &= (1000 + 2500 \times 1.8580)/8 & &= \pounds 705.62 \\
C(9) &= (1000 + 2500 \times 2.00898)/9 & &= \pounds 691.61 \\
C(10) &= (1000 + 2500 \times 2.3557)/10 & &= \pounds 688.92
\end{aligned}
$$

The cost function is oscillating and it does not necessarily follow that the first relative minimum at $n = 4$ is the global minimum. As n tends to infinity, the cost tends to $R_f \operatorname{Exp}\{F_n\}/n$, since R_p/n tends to zero.

If μ is the expected lifetime of the belt, then one would expect $\lim_{n \to \infty} n/\operatorname{Exp}\{F_n\} = \mu$, and this is indeed the case, so as n tends to infinity the cost tends to R_f/μ. The result is called the ergodic theorem.

In this case $R_f/\mu = 2500/3.8 = £657.90$, so there are higher values of n which have costs less than $C(4)$. It seems best to take $n = \infty$, which means we never make preventive replacements.

A good rule of thumb in order to obtain reasonable solutions without too much work is to calculate R_f/μ and the first local minimum of $C(n)$, and choose the smaller of these. For most cases, this gives an answer very close to the optimal, and for several types of failure distribution it gives the actual minimum cost.

Although the costs of replacements at fixed time are higher than those of replacements at fixed age (this always holds), the ease of implementation makes it more widely used in practice than fixed-age replacements. This is the same position as for 'periodic review' and 'two-bin' order policies in probabilistic inventory control.

11.5   Group replacements at fixed times

Consider the problem where it is cheaper to replace items en masse. As an example, a group of 500 bulbs is replaced every n weeks, and if a bulb fails between replacements it is replaced individually. It costs £150 to replace all 500 bulbs and £1.00 to replace each bulb individually. The probability that a bulb fails in its kth week is p_k, where

$$p_1 = 0.2, \quad p_2 = 0.1, \quad p_3 = 0.1,$$
$$p_4 = 0.1, \quad p_5 = 0.1, \quad p_6 = 0.2, \quad p_7 = 0.2.$$

When should the group be replaced?

If we concentrate on one bulb, we realise it is replaced preventively at fixed times, i.e. every n weeks, and that $R_p = £150/500 = 30\text{p}$, while $R_f = 100\text{p}$. We can then follow the solution procedure of the previous section. We get

$$f_1 = 0.2, \quad f_2 = 0.14, \quad f_3 = 0.148, \quad f_4 = 0.1636, \quad f_5 = 0.1815,$$
$$f_6 = 0.3015, \quad f_7 = 0.3636, \quad f_8 = 0.2202, \quad f_9 = 0.2027, \quad f_{10} = 0.2096.$$

Substituting this into

$$C(n) = £\left(0.30 + 1.00 \sum_{i=1}^{n} f_i\right)\Big/ n$$

gives

$$C(1) = 50.00\text{p}, \quad C(2) = 32.00\text{p}, \quad C(3) = 26.26\text{p}, \quad C(4) = 23.79\text{p},$$
$$C(5) = 22.66\text{p}, \quad C(6) = 23.91\text{p}, \quad C(7) = 25.69\text{p}, \quad C(8) = 25.23\text{p},$$
$$C(9) = 24.68\text{p}, \quad C(10) = 24.30\text{p}.$$

As n tends to infinity $C(n)$ tends to $F_f/\mu = £100/4.2 = 23.81\text{p}$. Thus our approximate rule would say replace all the bulbs every five weeks.

11.6 Maintenance or replacement of a car fleet

Suppose we are running a car hire firm, and can buy cars at £7000 each. The cost of maintaining and repairing a car increases with the car's age, so that in its kth year the maintenance and repair cost is £1000k. There is also a chance each year that the car will be in a serious accident, or that it will break down irreparably and be replaced by a new one. This also depends on the age of the car, and if p_k is the probability it will have to be replaced in its kth year of service, then

$$p_1 = 0.1, \quad p_2 = 0.1, \quad p_3 = 0.2, \quad p_4 = 0.3, \quad p_5 = 0.3.$$

No car lasts longer than five years. Each year we have to decide whether to try and keep the car for another year or to replace it. As the repair and maintenance costs increase with age we eventually expect these costs to reach a limit at which point it is better to replace the car. This 'repair limit' policy corresponds to one where, say, we keep the car for n years if possible and then replace it. The problem is how big should n be to minimise the average annual costs.

Let c_k be the annual maintenance and repair cost for a car in its kth year, and let R be the cost of replacing with a new car.

As in Section 11.3, let $\overline{P}_k = 1 - P_k = \Sigma_{i=k+1}^{\infty} p_i$ be the probability that the car has not had a serious accident in the first k years. If $C(n)$ is the average cost per year when we decide to replace the cars after n years, we know that

$$C(n) = \frac{\text{Exp \{cost in buying and maintaining car\}}}{\text{Exp \{lifetime of car\}}}.$$

The buying cost is always R and the expected maintenance cost when we replace after n years is $c_1 + c_2\overline{P}_1 + c_3\overline{P}_2 + \cdots + c_n\overline{P}_{n-1}$, since we have the maintenance cost in the kth year only if the car has not had an accident in the first $k - 1$ years of its life. Just as in Section 11.3, we find that the lifetime of the car under this policy is

$$1p_1 + 2p_2 + 3p_3 + \cdots + (n-1)p_{n-1} + n\overline{P}_n$$
$$= (p_1 + p_2 + p_3 + \cdots) + (p_2 + p_3 + \cdots) + \cdots + (p_n + p_{n+1} + \cdots)$$
$$= \overline{P}_0 + \overline{P}_1 + \cdots + \overline{P}_{n-1}.$$

Thus

$$C(n) = \frac{R + c_1 + c_2 \overline{P}_1 + \cdots + c_n \overline{P}_{n-1}}{\overline{P}_0 + \overline{P}_1 + \cdots + \overline{P}_{n-1}}.$$

For this problem $R = 7000$, $c_i = 1000i$, and

$$\overline{P}_0 = 1, \quad \overline{P}_1 = 0.9, \quad \overline{P}_2 = 0.8, \quad \overline{P}_3 = 0.6, \quad \overline{P}_4 = 0.3, \quad \overline{P}_5 = 0.$$

Thus

$C(1) = \pounds(7000 + 1000 \times 1)/1 = \pounds8000$

$C(2) = \pounds(7000 + 1000 \times 1 + 2000 \times 0.9)/1.9 = \pounds5157.89$

$C(3) = \pounds(7000 + 1000 \times 1 + 2000 \times 0.9 + 3000 \times 0.8)/2.7 = \pounds4518.52$

$C(4) = \pounds(7000 + 1000 \times 1 + 2000 \times 0.9 + 3000 \times 0.8 + 4000 \times 0.6)/3.3$
$ = \pounds4424.24$

$C(5) = \pounds(7000 + 1000 \times 1 + 2000 \times 0.9 + 3000 \times 0.8 + 4000 \times 0.6 + 5000$
$ \times 0.3)/3 = \pounds4472.2.$

Thus it is best to replace after four years of service. In the chapter on dynamic programming we look at this problem again when we are interested in minimising the cost over a given time span rather than on average as here.

11.7   Inspection policy for a production process

A production process produces electronic chips, but the process can go wrong and start producing defective chips. These are not noticeable unless inspected. Once the process has gone wrong it will continue to produce defective chips until one is inspected, noticed to be defective and the machine repaired. Each defective chip costs the company $\pounds1$, while it costs $\pounds2$ to inspect a chip and $\pounds4$ to repair the process. Each time the process produces a chip, there is a 0.1 chance that it will go wrong, assuming it was working correctly until then. How often should the chips be inspected so as to minimise overall costs?

Let I be the cost of inspection, R the cost of repair and D the cost of each defective item. Let p be the chance that the process will work correctly on the next item given that it works correctly on the current one. $p = 0.9$ in our example. $C(n)$ is the cost per item when we inspect every n items. Under this policy the cost over n items consists of an inspection cost I, a possible repair cost and D times the expected number of defectives produced. The chance that the machine goes wrong on the kth chip produced is $p^{k-1}(1-p)$, since it must have worked correctly for the first $k-1$ and then failed on the kth chip. In that case the number of defective chips will be $(n-k)$ since the nth chip will be inspected and so will not be allowed to leave the production line. Thus the expected cost due to defective chips is

$$D((n-1)(1-p) + (n-2)(1-p)p + (n-3)(1-p)p^2 + \cdots + 1(1-p)p^{n-2})$$
$$= D(n-1-(n-1)p + (n-2)p - (n-2)p^2 + (n-3)p^2 - (n-3)p^3 + \cdots$$
$$+ p^{n-2} - p^{n-1})$$
$$= D((n-(1+p+p^2+\cdots+p^{n-1}) = D(n-(1-p^n)/(1-p)).$$

p^n is the probability that the process will still be working after producing n chips, and so $1 - p^n$ is the probability that it will not be working and so will need to be repaired on inspecting the nth chip. Hence the total cost over n chips is

$$I + R(1-p^n) + D(n - (1-p^n)/(1-p)),$$

so

$$C(n) = \frac{I + Dn + (R - D/(1-p))(1-p^n)}{n}.$$

For the example considered above $I = 2$, $R = 4$, $D = 1$, $p = 0.9$. Hence

$$C(n) = (2 + n - 6(1 - (0.9)^n))/n$$

$C(1) = 2.400,$ $\quad C(2) = 1.43,$ $\quad C(3) = 1.125,$ $\quad C(4) = 0.9841$
$C(5) = 0.9086,$ $\quad C(6) = 0.8647,$ $\quad C(7) = 0.8385,$ $\quad C(8) = 0.8228$
$C(9) = 0.8138,$ $\quad C(10) = 0.8092,$ $\quad C(11) = 0.8075,$ $\quad C(12) = 0.8078.$

As n gets very large $C(n)$ tends to 1, and so the lowest cost is when one inspects every 11 chips.

Exercises

1   Tyres which fail in service cause expensive accidents. It is estimated that a failure in service results in an average cost of £25, plus the cost of the new tyre. New tyres cost £10 each, and the probability of failure is as shown in Table 11.1.

Table 11.1

Age of tyre in miles	Probability of failure
0–5000	0.1
5000–10000	0.1
10000–15000	0.2
15000–20000	0.2
20000–25000	0.3
25000–30000	0.1

Given that tyres are replaced after a certain fixed mileage or on failure, determine optimal replacement policy. (Assume you can only replace at multiples of 5000 miles.)

2   A piece of drilling equipment has a failure distribution given by Table 11.2, where the time t is the number of shifts since installation. To replace the

Table 11.2

t	0	1	2	3	4	5	6
P (failure before t)	0	0.05	0.1	0.2	0.4	0.7	1.0

equipment costs £4000. It takes two shift periods to prepare the replacement and once prepared it must be installed immediately. Each period for which drilling is halted due to a failed machine costs £10 000 in lost profit. In order to minimise cost, how long after installing one machine should the mining company start preparing the next? Assume first that, if the machine fails before the preparation of the next has started, then the preparation is started immediately. There is only one preparation team, so only one drill can be in preparation at a time. Also assume that failures happen at the end of a shift (so no production is lost in that shift).

What would be the optimal policy if the machine were replaced every m periods, any failure before m resulting in loss of production until m? How much would be lost on average in following this policy instead of the former?

3   This is a similar problem to Section 11.3, but a continuous time version (check the definitions of probability distribution function and density function in Chapter 10).

A piece of equipment is subject to failure and its lifetime is given by a distribution function $F(t)$. Replacement after failure costs c_f, but if the equipment is replaced while still in operation the cost is only c_p ($c_p < c_f$). Show that if we decide to replace equipment at age T provided it has not yet failed, then the cost per unit time under this policy is

$$c(T) = \frac{c_p \bar{F}(T) + c_f F(T)}{T\bar{F}(T) + \int_0^T tf(t)\,dt},$$

where $\bar{F}(T) = 1 - F(T)$. Prove the denominator of this expression equals $\int_0^T \bar{F}(t)\,dt$.

Given that

$$c_p = 10, \quad c_f = 20, \quad F(t) = \{t/100,\ 0 \leqslant t \leqslant 100;\ 1, t > 100\},$$

find the optimal policy of this type.

Given that the failure rate of the equipment is constant, i.e. $r(t) = f(t)/\bar{F}(t) = \alpha$, show that whatever c_p and c_f, the cheapest replacement system of this type is to replace only on failure.

4   The failure rates shown in Table 11.3 have been observed for a certain type of light bulb. The cost of replacing an individual failed bulb is £1.25. The

Table 11.3

End of week	Probability of failure to date
1	0.1
2	0.2
3	0.3
4	0.6
5	1.0

decision is made to replace all bulbs simultaneously at fixed intervals, and also to replace individual bulbs as they fail in service. If the cost of group replacement is 30p per bulb, what is the best interval between group replacements? At what group replacement price per bulb would a policy of strict individual replacement become preferable to the adopted policy?

5 Prove that if $r(t) = \alpha$ for all time $t \geqslant 0$, where $r(t) = f(t)/(1 - F(t))$, then the distribution function of the life of the equipment is

$$F(t) = 1 - e^{-\alpha t}, \qquad t \geqslant 0.$$

Hence show that the expected lifetime of the equipment is $1/\alpha$.

A piece of equipment is subject to sudden failure and when it does fail a replacement is made at a cost c_2. To reduce the frequency of failure, the equipment is constantly replaced at intervals of time t, irrespective of the number of failures in the interval. The cost of this replacement is c_1. Find the cost per unit time of this replacement system as a function of c_1, c_2, t and $\mathrm{Exp}\,(n(t))$—the expected number of failures in time t.

Given that the failure rate of the equipment is $r(t) = \alpha$, for all $t \geqslant 0$, show that the cheapest replacement system of the above type is only to replace when the equipment fails. Explain why you would expect this result from consideration of $r(t)$.

6 The quality control department of a firm inspects items coming off a production line, where there is a $\frac{1}{6}$ chance that the production line will produce a substandard item. Once it does so it will continue to do so until repaired. The cost of each inspection is £10, that of loss of goodwill in each substandard item produced is £30, and that of repair is £100. Find when the department should inspect an item, assuming it will repair the machine as soon as it finds a defective item.

Assume the repair only has a $\frac{1}{2}$ chance of being successful, and if not successful, the process will continue to provide substandard items. Explain why a suitable inspection procedure now is to inspect m items after a repair or $n(n \geqslant m)$ items after the last inspection, provided that the item was then found to be satisfactory.

12
Dynamic Programming

12.1 Introduction

A jeweller has a small polishing machine which he uses to prepare semi-precious stones. Unfortunately it requires a lot of maintenance and so in three weeks' time he will take delivery of a modern, maintenance-free replacement. Thus in three weeks' time he will scrap his present machine, and because of this he has decided not to maintain it in the meantime. This, of course, means that it will become progressively more inefficient. The jeweller has two types of stone that he can polish. Both types require a week in the polisher. A complete charge of type A will earn the jeweller £30 when polished; a complete charge of type B earns the jeweller £50 when polished. However, polishing type B stones damages the machine more. After one week's polishing of type B stones the machine can only polish 40% as many stones in the following week, whereas after one week's polishing of type A stones its capacity is reduced only to 70%. How should he use the machine to make as much profit as possible in its last three weeks?

The jeweller has to make three interrelated decisions. Which stones should he polish this week; which should he polish next week; and which should he polish in the final week? If he tries to make as much money as possible this week, he reduces the capacity substantially for subsequent weeks. So clearly he should think ahead. Suppose that he thinks ahead to the final week. Suppose that when the final week begins the machine's capacity has been reduced to π_1, where $0 \leqslant \pi_1 \leqslant 1$ and π_1 is the fraction of full capacity that the machine can polish. In the final week it does not matter how much damage is done to the polisher. So he has a choice between making

$£(30\pi_1)$ if he polishes type A stones   and

$£(50\pi_1)$ if he polishes type B stones.

Clearly, whatever the value of π_1, he should choose to polish type B stones.

Consider now the situation at the beginning of the second week. Suppose that the machine's capacity has been reduced to π_2. Again he has the choice of polishing type A stones or type B stones. However, now he must bear in mind that polishing stones not only brings him money, but also reduces his capacity for the final week. If he polishes type A stones, he will earn $£(30\pi_2)$ and reduce his capacity in the final week to $\pi_1 = 0.7\pi_2$. If he polishes type B stones, he will earn $£(50\pi_2)$ and reduce his capacity in the final week to $\pi_1 = 0.4\pi_2$. However, he knows what he will do in the final week. Whatever the capacity π_1, he will polish type B stones and earn $£(50\pi_1)$. Thus, if at the beginning of the second week he chooses to grind type A stones, he will earn over the two weeks

$$£(30\pi_2 + 50 \times 0.7\pi_2) = £(65\pi_2),$$

the sum of his earnings in the second and third weeks. Similarly, if at the beginning of the second week he chooses to polish type B stones, he will earn over the second and third weeks

$$£(50\pi_2 + 50 \times 0.4\pi_2) = £(70\pi_2).$$

Since $£(70\pi_2) > £(65\pi_2)$, whatever π_2, he should choose to polish type B stones.

Finally consider the situation at the beginning of the first week. The capacity is 1.0. If he polishes type A stones in the first week he will earn $£30$ and reduce capacity at the beginning of the second week to $\pi_2 = 0.7$. If he polishes type B stones in the first week, he will earn $£50$ and reduce capacity at the beginning of the second week to $\pi_2 = 0.4$. But whatever the value of π_2 we know what the jeweller will do in the second and third weeks and in doing so he will earn $£(70\pi_2)$. So if the jeweller chooses to polish type A stones in the first week, he will earn in total over the three weeks:

$$£(30 + 70 \times 0.7) = £79.$$

Whereas if he chooses to polish type B stones he will earn in total

$$£(50 + 70 \times 0.4) = £78.$$

Since $£79 > £78$ he should polish type A stones in the first week.

Gathering the above together we see that the jeweller's optimal policy is:

polish type A stones in the first week;
polish type B stones in the second week;
polish type B stones in the final week.

If he follows this policy he will earn $£79$.

The method that we have used to solve the above problem is known as **dynamic programming**. It is a method that is much easier to understand in the context of particular examples than it is when stated in full generality. So in this chapter we will concentrate on solving particular problems, relying on our intuition to justify the good sense of the dynamic programming approach in each case. Only in the final section do we make any remarks on the general underlying principle upon which the method is based.

Before turning to other examples it will be helpful to run through the above example again in order to introduce some notational ideas.

Define $v_n(\pi_n)$ to be the earnings from an *optimal* polishing policy over the *last n* weeks, if there are n weeks left before the machine is scrapped, and at the beginning of the last n weeks the capacity of the machine is π_n. Now that definition is long, involved and, to say the least, difficult to understand at first encounter. So don't panic: read it again and then read the following. All will become clear with practice.

Consider the case $n = 1$; that is 1 week left before the machine is scrapped, the last week. Then $v_1(\pi_1)$ is the optimal earnings from the last week when the capacity has been reduced to π_1 at the beginning of the week. From the above we can see that

$$v_1(\pi_1) = \max\{30\pi_1, 50\pi_1\} = 50\pi_1. \tag{12.1}$$

The first term in the maximum arises when type A stones are polished in the last week, the second term when type B are polished. Since the maximum is the second term, (12.1) also implicitly tells us that the jeweller should polish type B in the last week.

Consider the case $n = 2$; that is 2 weeks left before the machine is scrapped. $v_2(\pi_2)$ is the optimal earnings from the last two weeks when the capacity has been reduced to π_2 at the beginning of the second to last week. From our working above, we see that

$$v_2(\pi_2) = \max\{65\pi_2, 70\pi_2\} = 70\pi_2. \tag{12.2}$$

The first term in the maximum corresponds to polishing type A stones; the second to type B. Since the maximum is the second term, (12.2) tells us that type B stones should be polished in the second to last week.

It is instructive to investigate (12.2) further.

$$v_2(\pi_2) = \max\{65\pi_2, 70\pi_2\}$$
$$= \max\{30\pi_2 + 50 \times 0.7\pi_2, 50\pi_2 + 50 \times 0.4\pi_2\},$$

where we have substituted for $65\pi_2$ and $70\pi_2$ the expressions that gave them. Now noting that $v_1(\pi_1) = 50\pi_1$, we see that

$$v_2(\pi_2) = \max\{30\pi_2 + v_1(0.7\pi_2), 50\pi_2 + v_1(0.4\pi_2)\}. \tag{12.3}$$

We have arrived at (12.3) by a somewhat tortuous route, but a little thought shows that we could have written it down directly. Think about what it is saying. Read it term by term. The optimal return from the last two weeks is the larger of two quantities:

either	$30\pi_2$	arising from polishing type A stones for the first of the two weeks,
	$+ v_1(0.7\pi_2),$	the optimal earnings from the last week given that polishing type A stones will have reduced the capacity to $0.7\pi_2$;
or	$50\pi_2$	arising from polishing type B stones for the first of the two weeks,
	$+ v_1(0.4\pi_2)$	the optimal earnings from the last week given that polishing type B stones will have reduced the capacity to $0.4\pi_2$.

Given this interpretation (12.3) is obvious. Let us confirm it by writing down the appropriate equation for $v_3(\pi_3)$, the optimal earnings when there are three weeks left before the machine is scrapped. Of course, $\pi_3 = 1$, but we ignore this for generality.

$$v_3(\pi_3) = \max\{30\pi_3 + v_2(0.7\pi_3),\ 50\pi_3 + v_2(0.4\pi_3)\}, \tag{12.4}$$

since the jeweller can either polish type A stones for the first week and then continue optimally for the remaining two weeks with capacity reduced to $0.7\pi_3$, or polish type B stones and then continue optimally with capacity reduced to $0.4\pi_3$. We may check (12.4) by setting $\pi_3 = 1$ and remembering that equation (12.2) gives $v_2(\pi_2) = 70\pi_2$.

$$v_3(1) = \max\{30 \times 1 + 70 \times 0.7 \times 1,\ 50 \times 1 + 70 \times 0.4 \times 1\}$$
$$= \max\{79, 78\},$$

as expected.

Suppose that we set $v_0(\pi_0) = 0$ for all π_0. This has the obvious and reasonable interpretation that when the machine is to be scrapped immediately, the optimal earnings are zero whatever its capacity. Having so defined $v_0(\pi_0)$, (12.1), (12.3) and (12.4) may be written in a common form:

$$v_n(\pi_n) = \max\{30\pi_n + v_{n-1}(0.7\pi_n),\ 50\pi_n + v_{n-1}(0.4\pi_n)\} \tag{12.5}$$

for $1 \leqslant n \leqslant 3$. Equation (12.5) says simply that the optimal earnings when n weeks remain before the polisher is scrapped is achieved *either* by polishing type A stones for the first week and then continuing optimally for the remaining $(n-1)$ weeks with capacity reduced to $0.7\pi_n$ *or* by polishing type B stones for the first week and then continuing optimally for the remaining $(n-1)$ weeks with capacity reduced to $0.4\pi_n$. Moreover, we can see how to solve the system of equations given by (12.5). We know $v_0(\pi_0) = 0$, so setting $n = 1$, we can calculate $v_1(\pi_1)$ directly. Next, knowing $v_1(\pi_1)$, we can set $n = 2$ and calculate $v_2(\pi_2)$ directly. Finally, knowing $v_3(\pi_3)$, we can set $n = 3$ and calculate $v_3(\pi_3)$ directly. Indeed, way back at the beginning of the example, before we introduced this notation, that is precisely what we did.

To say the least, we have belaboured this example far more than it is worth. We shall not be so exhaustive in the subsequent examples. Instead we shall construct directly an equation analogous to (12.5) and, starting from $n = 0$, recursively calculate $v_n(.)$ for $n = 1, 2, 3, \ldots$.

Finally, if you solved this example in your head without using dynamic programming, well done: so did we. However, we shall soon encounter problems too difficult for mental arithmetic and trial and error.

12.2 Equipment replacement

Our next example in a sense generalises the previous one. A machine deteriorates with use and hence with age. Eventually the cost of operation will become so great that the machine should be traded in for a new one. A firm has one of these machines, which is currently two years old. It uses the machine to manufacture a domestic appliance, for which there will be no market in four years time since the firm will launch a new model then. Moreover, advanced planning of the new model indicates that this type of machine will not be needed in its production. Thus the firm is interested in an optimal replacement policy for the machine over the next four years. How should it determine this?

Let us introduce some notation:

c_i = cost of operating the machine for one year when at the beginning of that year the machine is i years old

a = price of a new machine

t_i = trade-in value of a machine of age i

s_i = scrap value of a machine of age i

As we have indicated, c_i increases with i; the older the machine the more it costs to run. Typically we might expect $t_i > s_i$, since one can always get a better price for an old machine if one is also buying a new one. Now let us define a quality $v_n(i)$ in a parallel fashion to that in the previous section. Let

$v_n(i)$ = cost of the optimal replacement policy for the machine tool when it is currently i years old and in n year's time it will no longer be needed.

Since the firm requires to use a machine in its production line for the next four years and since it is currently two years old, we are required to calculate $v_4(2)$ and to determine the policy which achieves this cost. As previously, we do this by calculating $v_0(i)$, then $v_1(i)$, then $v_2(i)$, and so on.

When $n = 0$, i.e. when this type of machine is no longer needed, it will be sold for scrap. Thus $v_0(i) = -s_i$ for all i, i.e. whatever the current age of the machine. Note that $v_0(i)$ has been defined as a *cost*, hence it is equal to *minus* the scrap value.

When $n = 1$, the firm can

either   operate the current machine age i for a further year and then scrap it at a total cost $(c_i - s_{i+1})$ (obviously it will be one year older than its current age when scrapped),

or   trade in the current machine for a new one at a cost $(a - t_i)$, operate that for a year at a cost c_0, and then scrap that earning s_1 giving a total cost $(a - t_i + c_0 - s_1)$.

Clearly the optimal policy is the cheaper of these.

Thus

$$v_1(i) = \min\{c_i - s_{i+1}, a - t_i + c_0 - s_1\}.$$

Since $v_0(i) = -s_i$, we may write

$$v_1(i) = \min\{c_i + v_0(i+1), a - t_i + c_0 + v_0(1)\}. \tag{12.6}$$

Next consider the case for the arbitrary $n \geqslant 1$. At the beginning of the year the firm needs to operate a machine tool, the current one being age i, for a further n years. It can

either	operate the current machine for a further year at a cost c_i and then continue optimally for the remaining $(n-1)$ years with a machine age $(i+1)$ at a cost $v_{n-1}(i+1)$,
or	trade in the current machine for a new one at a cost $(a-t_i)$, operate that for a year at a cost c_0, and then continue optimally for the remaining $(n-1)$ years with a one-year-old machine at a cost $v_{n-1}(1)$.

The optimal policy must select the cheaper of these.
Thus

$$v_n(i) = \min\{c_i + v_{n-1}(i+1), a - t_i + c_0 + v_{n-1}(1)\}. \qquad (12.7)$$

Notice that (12.6) has a similar form.

To identify the optimal policy, it is useful to introduce one further piece of notation. Let

$$d_n(i) = \begin{cases} K & \text{(for Keep) if the optimal policy operates a machine aged } i \\ & \text{for at least one further year when there are } n \text{ years of the} \\ & \text{policy remaining,} \\ R & \text{(for Replace) if the optimal policy immediately replaces a} \\ & \text{machine aged } i \text{ when there are } n \text{ years of the policy} \\ & \text{remaining.} \end{cases}$$

Thus $d_n(i) = K$ or R as the minimum in (12.7) occurs on the first or second term respectively.

Now let us see how (12.7) allows us to solve the problem. We wish to find $v_4(2)$. Let us assume that the numerical values of a, c_i, t_i and s_i are those given in Table 12.1.

Table 12.1 The data for the equipment replacement problem. The costs are in £1000s.

i	0	1	2	3	4	5	6
c_i	10	13	20	60	100	180	300
t_i		35	22	15	5	0	0
s_i		25	15	9	2	0	0
				$a = 50$			

$n = 0 \quad v_0(i) = -s_i \text{ for } i = 1, 2, 3, 4, 5, 6.$

$n = 1 \quad v_1(i) = \min\{c_i + v_0(i+1), a - t_i + c_0 + v_0(1)\}$

$$v_1(1) = \min\{13 \ -15, \ 50 - 35 + 10 - 25\} = -2 \qquad d_1(1) = K$$
$$v_1(2) = \min\{20 \ - \ 9, \ 50 - 22 + 10 - 25\} = \ 11 \qquad d_1(2) = K$$
$$v_1(3) = \min\{60 \ - \ 2, \ 50 - 15 + 10 - 25\} = \ 20 \qquad d_1(3) = R$$
$$v_1(4) = \min\{100 - \ 0, \ 50 - \ 5 + 10 - 25\} = \ 30 \qquad d_1(4) = R$$
$$v_1(5) = \min\{180 - \ 0, \ 50 - \ 0 + 10 - 25\} = \ 35 \qquad d_1(5) = R$$

Note.

As the machine tool is currently two years old and the policy has four years to run, the machine tool can be at most five years old when there is one year left to run. Hence there is no need to calculate $v_1(1)$ for $i > 5$.

$$n = 2 \quad v_2(i) = \min\{c_i + v_1(i+1), \ a - t_i + c_0 + v_1(1)\}$$

$$v_2(1) = \min\{13 \ +11, \ 50 - 35 + 10 - 2\} = 23 \qquad d_2(1) = R$$
$$v_2(2) = \min\{20 \ +20, \ 50 - 22 + 10 - 2\} = 36 \qquad d_2(2) = R$$
$$v_2(3) = \min\{60 \ +30, \ 50 - 15 + 10 - 2\} = 43 \qquad d_2(3) = R$$
$$v_2(4) = \min\{100 + 35, \ 50 - \ 5 + 10 - 2\} = 53 \qquad d_2(4) = R$$

$$n = 3 \quad v_3(i) = \min\{c_i + v_2(i+1), \ a - t_i + c_0 + v_2(1)\}$$

$$v_3(1) = \min\{13 + 36, \ 50 - 35 + 10 + 23\} = 48 \qquad d_3(1) = R$$
$$v_3(2) = \min\{20 + 43, \ 50 - 22 + 10 + 23\} = 61 \qquad d_3(2) = R$$
$$v_3(3) = \min\{60 + 53, \ 50 - 15 + 10 + 23\} = 68 \qquad d_3(3) = R$$

$$n = 4 \quad v_4(i) = \min\{c_i + v_3(i+1), \ a - t_i + c_0 + v_3(1)\}$$

$$v_4(2) = \min\{20 + 68, \ 50 - 22 + 10 + 48\} = 86 \qquad d_4(2) = R.$$

Thus we have determined that the cost of the optimal policy for replacing the machine tool, currently two years, old, for the next four years is £86 000, since $v_4(2) = 86$. Moreover we can use the $d_n(i)$ to determine the optimal policy easily.

$d_4(2) = R \Rightarrow$ the machine should be replaced immediately
  $\Rightarrow$ in one year's time the machine will be one year old.

$d_3(1) = R \Rightarrow$ the machine should be replaced again in one year's time
  $\Rightarrow$ in another year's time the machine will again be one year old.

$d_2(1) = R \Rightarrow$ the machine should be replaced again in a further year's time
  $\Rightarrow$ the machine will again be one year old.

$d_1(1) = K \Rightarrow$ the machine should be kept for the final year.

Two points should be noted about this example. First, a general point: $v_n(i)$ need only be calculated for those values of i that are possible given the initial conditions in the problem. When $n = 4$, we know the machine is two years old. So for $n = 3$, the machine can be at most three years old, for $n = 2$, at most four years old, etc. Second, a point particular to this problem: if you calculate $v_5(1)$ (you'll also need $v_4(1)$) you will find $d_5(1) = R$. So, since the machine tool is two years old when $n = 4$ we see that the firm has not been using the optimal replacement policy in the past. But that does not affect what it should do in the future. The firm should forget its past mistakes and adopt the optimal policy from now on.

12.3 Maintenance or replacement of a car fleet

The two problems that we have discussed involve the operation of a piece of equipment in the future. The future is always uncertain: machines may break down irreparably, etc. So to be realistic, our models should be probabilistic, not deterministic. In fact introducing probabilistic aspects into dynamic programming is very straightforward. We illustrate this by considering again the problem discussed in Section 10.6.

There we considered a car hire firm which sought the replacement policy that minimised its *average yearly cost*. By implication, in taking average yearly cost as the objective, we are assuming that the firm intends to remain in business indefinitely. Suppose, however, the firm's owner is retiring in three year's time and that the age of the car fleet will then have no effect on the value of the business when he comes to sell it. In this case it would be better to minimise the total operating costs over the next three years.

The data for the problem were as follows. The firm can buy new cars at £7000 each. The cost of maintaining a car for a year given that it is i years old at the beginning of the year is £$1000 \times (i + 1)$. (*Note*. There is a slight change of notation here: a car i years old begins its $(i + 1)$st year of maintenance.) p_i is the chance that a car will be written off following either an accident or a breakdown when it is i years old, where

$$p_0 = 0.1, \quad p_1 = 0.1, \quad p_2 = 0.2, \quad p_3 = 0.3, \quad p_4 = 0.3.$$

Let $v_n(i)$ = expected cost of the optimal replacement and maintenance policy for a car i years old when n years remain before the business closes.

Rather than beginning slowly by developing expressions for $v_0(i)$ and $v_1(i)$ as we have done in the previous example, let us plunge in and develop an expression for $v_n(i)$ in terms of $v_{n-1}(i)$. At the beginning of the year with n years remaining the firm may either run the car for a further year or replace it immediately. In either case, the car may be written off during the year or it may operate satisfactorily for the year. Now the probability that a car of age i is written off in the next year is

$$r_i = p_i \bigg/ \sum_{k=i}^{\infty} p_k$$

(see Section 10.2). So we may calculate the expected costs of the two options as follows.

If a car of age i is operated for a further year, maintenance costs of £$1000(i + 1)$ are incurred. There is a probability r_i that the car will be written off during the year, incurring a replacement cost £7000 and leading to a car of age 0 at the beginning of the remaining $(n - 1)$ years. The expected cost for the remaining

$(n-1)$ years in this case is $v_{n-1}(0)$. There is also a chance $(1-r_i)$ that the present car will not be written off. In this case the firm will have a car of age $(i+1)$ at the beginning of the remaining $(n-1)$ years, so incurring an expected cost $v_{n-1}(i-1)$. In total the expected cost is

$$1000(i+1) + r_i(7000 + v_{n-1}(0)) + (1-r_i)v_{n-1}(i+1).$$

Similarly, if the car is replaced immediately the expected cost is

$$7000 + 1000 + r_0(7000 + v_{n-1}(0)) + (1-r_0)v_{n-1}(1),$$

the sum of the replacement cost, maintenance cost, and the expected cost of subsequent years, account being taken of the fact that it may or may not be written off. The optimal policy clearly chooses the cheaper of these two expected costs. Hence

$$v_n(i) = \min\{1000(i+1) + r_i(7000 + v_{n-1}(0)) + (1-r_i)v_{n-1}(i+1),$$
$$7000 + 1000 + r_0(7000 + v_{n-1}(0)) + (1-r_0)v_{n-1}(1)\}. \quad (12.8)$$

Again it will help determine the optimal policy if we introduce the notation

$$d_n(i) = \begin{cases} K & \text{if the optimal policy keeps a car of age } i \text{ when } n \text{ years of operation remain} \\ R & \text{if the optimal policy replaces a car of age } i \text{ when } n \text{ years of operation remain.} \end{cases}$$

The failure rates r_i are

$$r_0 = 0.10, \quad r_1 = 0.11, \quad r_2 = 0.25, \quad r_3 = 0.50, \quad r_4 = 1.00.$$

Moreover, it is clear that $v_0(i) = 0$ for any i, since the firm will incur no further costs if it has closed.

Let us suppose that a firm begins its last three years with cars aged one, two and three years old. Thus we need to calculate

$$v_3(1), \ v_3(2) \text{ and } v_3(3)$$

$n = 0 \quad v_0(i) = 0 \text{ for } i = 0, 1, 2, 3, 4$

$n = 1 \quad v_1(i) = \min\{1000(i+1) + r_i(7000 + v_0(0)) + (1-r_i)v_0(i+1),$
$$8000 + r_0(7000 + v_0(0)) + (1-r_0)v_0(1)\}$$

$$
\begin{aligned}
v_1(0) &= \min\{1700, \quad 8700\} = 1700 & d_1(0) &= K \\
v_1(1) &= \min\{2770, \quad 8700\} = 2770 & d_1(1) &= K \\
v_1(2) &= \min\{4750, \quad 8700\} = 4750 & d_1(2) &= K \\
v_1(3) &= \min\{7500, \quad 8700\} = 7500 & d_1(3) &= K \\
v_1(4) &= \min\{12\,000, \ 8700\} = 8700 & d_1(4) &= R
\end{aligned}
$$

$n = 2 \quad v_2(i) = \min\{1000(i+1) + r_i(7000 + v_1(0)) + (1-r_i)v_1(i+1),$
$$8000 + r_0(7000 + v_1(0)) + (1-r_0)v_1(1)\}$$

$$v_2(0) = \min\{\ 4363,\ 11\,363\} = 4363 \qquad d_2(0) = K$$
$$v_2(1) = \min\{\ 7185,\ 11\,363\} = 7185 \qquad d_2(1) = K$$
$$v_2(2) = \min\{10\,800,\ 11\,363\} = 10\,800 \qquad d_2(2) = K$$
$$v_2(3) = \min\{12\,700,\ 11\,363\} = 11\,363 \qquad d_2(3) = R$$
$$v_2(4) = \min\{13\,700,\ 11\,363\} = 11\,363 \qquad d_2(4) = R$$

$$n = 3 \quad v_3(i) = \min\{1000(i+1) + r_i(7000 + v_2(0)) + (1 - r_i)v_2(i+1),$$
$$8000 + r_0(7000 + v_2(0)) + (1 - r_0)v_2(1)\}$$

$$v_3(1) = \min\{12\,862,\ 15\,603\} = 12\,862 \qquad d_3(1) = K$$
$$v_3(2) = \min\{14\,363,\ 15\,603\} = 14\,363 \qquad d_3(2) = K$$
$$v_3(3) = \min\{15\,363,\ 15\,603\} = 15\,363 \qquad d_3(3) = K$$

Thus for the remaining three years the expected operating costs are £12 862 for each one-year-old car, £14 363 for each two-year-old car and £15 363 for each three-year-old car. The optimal policy is to keep all the cars for the first year $(d_3(1) = d_3(2) = d_3(3) = K)$; replace those three or more years old at the beginning of the second year, keeping the rest $(d_2(3) = d_2(4) = R; d_2(0) = d_2(1) = d_2(2) = K)$; and replace those four years old at the beginning of the final year, keeping the rest $(d_1(4) = R; d_1(0) = d_1(1) = d_1(2) = d_1(3) = K)$. Notice that the optimal policy treats three-year-old cars differently depending on the number of years before the firm closes.

It is worth pausing to consider our calculations of $v_1(i)$.

Remembering $v_0(i) = 0$,

$$v_1(i) = \min\{1000(i+1) + 7000r_i,\ 8000 + 7000r_0\}.$$

The two terms $7000r_i$ and $7000r_0$ arise because our model implicitly assumes that, if any car is written off during the final year, it is replaced. This may be the case if the owner feels that to sell the firm as a going concern there must be a full fleet of cars. But, if this is not the case, the two terms should be omitted—which, of course, may lead to a different solution to the problem.

12.4 An allocation problem

The problems discussed so far have much in common. All are concerned with the operation of machinery whose efficiency decreases with use. Moreover, the decisions required are to be made at a sequence of times. The problems differed essentially only in increasing complexity of the cost structure and in the introduction of uncertainty. However, dynamic programming has a range of application far wider than problems of equipment replacement and, moreover, may be applied in circumstances when the dimension of time is entirely absent. We have concentrated on equipment replacement so that the techniques of dynamic programming might be introduced without confusing the issue with differing contexts. Now that we are familiar with its methods, the time has come to explore the range of its applications.

A firm is about to launch a new type of potato crisp. It has budgeted £100 000 for advertising and may spend this on a mixture of television advertising, radio advertising and newspaper advertising. Table 12.2 gives the estimated increase in revenue brought about by spending different amounts on each of these. Note that money can only be spent on advertising in units of £20 000.

Table 12.2 Increases in revenue brought about by different advertising methods

Methods	Increase in revenue arising from sum spent					
	0	20 000	40 000	60 000	80 000	100 000
Television	0	30 000	60 000	90 000	120 000	150 000
Radio	0	35 000	50 000	65 000	80 000	95 000
Newspapers	0	35 000	65 000	75 000	85 000	100 000

These increases in revenue are additive. Thus, if the £100 000 budget is split into £20 000 on television, £20 000 on radio and £60 000 on newspapers, the total estimated increase in revenue will be

$$£(30\,000 + 35\,000 + 75\,000) = £140\,000.$$

The question is, of course, what is the optimal allocation of the budget.

At first glance this problem looks nothing like the problems that we have been studying. However, we shall soon change that. Let

$v_1(a)$ be the estimated increase in revenue obtained by spending £a optimally on television advertising alone;

$v_2(a)$ be the estimated increase in revenue obtained by spending £a in total optimally between television and radio advertising;

$v_3(a)$ be the estimated increase in revenue obtained by spending £a in total optimally between television, radio and newspaper advertising.

We wish to calculate $v_3(100\,000)$ and to identify the allocation which achieves this. Now to calculate $v_1(a)$ we need only look at Table 12.2: there is no decision to be made if all £a is spent on television advertising. Thus

$$
\begin{aligned}
v_1(0) &= 0, \\
v_1(20\,000) &= 30\,000, \\
v_1(40\,000) &= 60\,000, \\
v_1(60\,000) &= 90\,000, \\
v_1(80\,000) &= 120\,000, \\
v_1(100\,000) &= 150\,000.
\end{aligned}
$$

To calculate $v_2(a)$, note that, if $£x$ is spent on radio advertising, the remaining $£(a-x)$ is spent on television advertising, and this remaining $£(a-x)$ increases the revenue by $v_1(a-x)$. Thus to calculate $v_2(40\,000)$, say, we consider three cases:

(1) spend $£0$ on radio, hence $£40\,000$ on television

$$\Rightarrow \text{revenue increase} = £0 + 60\,000 = £60\,000;$$

(2) spend $£20\,000$ on radio, hence $£20\,000$ on television

$$\Rightarrow \text{revenue increase} = £35\,000 + 30\,000 = £65\,000;$$

(3) spend $£40\,000$ on radio, hence $£0$ on television

$$\Rightarrow \text{revenue increase} = £50\,000 + 0 = £50\,000.$$

The largest of these is $£65\,000$ and is achieved by spending $£20\,000$ on radio and $£20\,000$ on television. So $v_2(40\,000) = 65\,000$.

Table 12.3 Increase in revenue brought by spending $£x$ on radio and $£(a-x)$ on television advertising

| a | Amount, x, spent on radio hence $(a-x)$ is spent on television | | | | | |
	0	20 000	40 000	60 000	80 000	100 000
0	0†					
20 000	30 000	35 000†				
40 000	60 000	65 000†	50 000			
60 000	90 000	95 000†	80 000	65 000		
80 000	120 000	125 000†	110 000	95 000	80 000	
100 000	150 000	155 000†	140 000	125 000	110 000	95 000

The calculation of $v_2(a)$ for other values of a is given in Table 12.3. $v_2(a)$ is the largest quantity in row a of Table 12.3. This quantity has been marked by a 'dagger'. Hence

$$v_2(0) \quad = \quad 0$$
$$v_2(20\,000) \quad = \quad 35\,000$$
$$v_2(40\,000) \quad = \quad 65\,000$$
$$v_2(60\,000) \quad = \quad 95\,000$$
$$v_2(80\,000) \quad = \quad 125\,000$$
$$v_2(100\,000) = 155\,000.$$

We are now in a position to calculate $v_3(a)$. Although we only need $v_3(100\,000)$, we shall calculate $v_3(a)$ for all values of a to illustrate the method. To calculate $v_3(a)$, note that, if $£x$ is spent on newspaper advertising, then $£(a-x)$ is to be spent in total between television and radio advertising. This $£(a-x)$, if allocated optimally, will increase revenue by $v_2(a-x)$. Thus to calculate $v_3(60\,000)$ we consider four cases:

(1) spend £0 on newspapers, hence £60 000 between television and radio revenue ⇒ revenue increase = £0 + 95 000 = £95 000;
(2) spend £20 000 on newspapers, hence £40 000 between television and radio ⇒ revenue increase = £35 000 + £65 000 = £100 000;
(3) spend £40 000 on newspapers, hence £20 000 between television and radio ⇒ revenue increase £65 000 + 35 000 = £100 000;
(4) spend £60 000 on newspapers, hence £0 between television and radio ⇒ revenue increase = £75 000 + 0 = £75 000.

The largest is £100 000, so $v_3(60\,000) = 1\,000\,000$. $v_3(a)$ is calculated for other values of a by means of Table 12.4. $v_3(a)$ is the largest quantity in row a, and this has been marked with a 'dagger'.

Table 12.4 Calculation of $v_3(a)$

a	Amount, x, spent on newspapers: hence $(a-x)$ spent optimally on television and radio						
	0	20 000	40 000	60 000	80 000	100 000	$v_3(a)$
0	0†						0
20 000	35 000†	35 000†					35 000
40 000	65 000	70 000†	65 000				70 000
60 000	95 000	100 000†	100 000†	75 000			100 000
80 000	125 000	130 000	135 000†	120 000	85 000		135 000
100 000	155 000	160 000†	160 000†	150 000	120 000	100 000	160 000

We are now in a position to solve our problem.

From Table 12.4 $v_3(100\,000) = 160\,000$. So the optimal allocation of the advertising budget will increase revenue by an estimated £160 000. Moreover, it is easy to discover an optimal allocation of the budget. There are two daggers in the $a = 100\,000$ row of Table 12.4; hence there is more than one way of achieving an increase in revenue of £160 000. Either £20 000 or £40 000 can be spent on newspaper advertising. Let us consider the former; thus £80 000 in total is to be spent between television and radio. The $a = 80\,000$ row of Table 12.3 has a dagger in the $x = 20\,000$ column. So £20 000 should be spent on radio and the remaining £60 000 on television advertising. Had we looked for an optimal allocation with £40 000 spent on newspaper advertising, the $a = 60\,000$ row of Table 12.3 would have shown that £20 000 should be spent on radio and £40 000 on television advertising. In solving this problem we have avoided too much notation, in order to concentrate on the underlying ideas. Let us now introduce suitable notation in the context of a general allocation problem.

Suppose that we have a sum of money, £A, to allocate between N processes, each of which makes a profit depending on the sum allocated to it. Let $g_i(a)$ be the profit made by the ith process if £a is allocated to it. Then our aim is to determine $a_1, a_2, \ldots, a_N$, the individual sums allocated to the n processes, so that

$$g_1(a_1) + g_2(a_2) + \cdots + g_N(a_N)$$

is maximised subject to

$$a_1 + a_2 + \cdots + a_N = A.$$

We assume that the a_i can take only a restricted set of values: in the example they had to be multiples of £20 000. In the above problem $A = 100\,000$, $N = 3$ and the functions $g_i(a)$ are given by the rows of Table 12.2. Now let $v_n(a)$ be the profit made by allocating optimally £a between processes $1, 2, \ldots, n$ only. The aim is to calculate $v_N(A)$ and the allocation by which to achieve this profit.

Clearly $v_1(a) = \max_{0 \leqslant x \leqslant a}\{g_1(a)\}$. Two points should be noted. First, by the notation $\max_{0 \leqslant x \leqslant a}\{.\}$ we mean that the maximum is taken over all *feasible* values of x between 0 and a; remember that we are assuming that x can only be a restricted set of values. Second, it is likely, but not necessary, that $g_1(x)$ is an increasing function of x, in which case the maximising x in $\max_{0 \leqslant x \leqslant a}\{g_i(x)\}$ is the largest feasible value of x less than or equal to a. If £a is to be allocated to the processes $1, 2, \ldots, (n+1)$, and if £x is allocated to process $(n+1)$, then £$(a-x)$ must be allocated to processes $1, 2, \ldots, n$. Now it is clear that the £$(a-x)$ should be allocated *optimally* to processes $1, 2, \ldots, n$; hence it will earn $v_n(a-x)$. Thus the total profit from this allocation is $(g_{n+1}(x) + v_n(a-x))$. It follows that $v_{n+1}(a)$ is achieved by choosing x to maximise this:

$$v_{n+1}(a) = \max_{0 \leqslant x \leqslant a}\{g_{n+1}(x) + v_n(a-x)\}. \tag{12.9}$$

Given that $v_1(a)$ is known it is possible to use (12.9) to find $v_2(a)$. Given $v_2(a)$, (12.9) allows $v_3(a)$ to be found, and so on, until $v_N(a)$ is found. Setting $a = A$ gives $v_N(A)$, the profit from the optimal allocation in the underlying problem. An optimal allocation may be found by considering first $v_N(A)$: from (12.9),

$$v_N(A) = \max_{0 \leqslant x \leqslant A}\{g_N(x) + v_{N-1}(A-x)\}. \tag{12.10}$$

Let x_N be an optimising x in (12.10). Then x_N should be allocated to process N. Next look at

$$v_{N-1}(a) = \max_{0 \leqslant x \leqslant a}\{g_{N-1}(x) + v_{N-2}(a-x)\} \tag{12.11}$$

with $a = A - x_N$. Let x_{N-1} be an optimising x in (12.11). Then x_{N-1} should be allocated to process $(N-1)$ and so on. Of course, to find x_N, x_{N-1}, etc. one does not maximise expressions (12.10), (12.11), etc. again. They have already been maximised in calculating $v_N(A)$, $v_{N-1}(A - x_N)$, etc. One simply looks back to those calculations to identify the maximising values of x, and that is why they were marked for easy identification in Tables 12.3 and 12.4.

It should be noted that throughout this section we have restricted x to be a multiple of £20 000. If x may take any value then the problem may be solved much more efficiently by mathematical programming approaches (see Exercise 2).

12.5   Production overage problems: economic production quantities

The Easismash Glass Co. produces a particularly beautiful vase, which is often used as a prize in various competitions. In consequence, the company offers the option of etching crests into the glass. To set up the etching process costs £30 and to process each vase costs £12. Unfortunately the processing is not necessarily perfect and some of the etched vases may have to be scrapped. Even more unfortunately it is not possible to tell whether a vase is perfect until some 24 hours after it is processed. Obviously the production line cannot be kept idle till the check is made. So if many vases are imperfect it may be necessary to have a second production run some days later incurring extra set-up costs. The obvious answer is to overproduce vases, knowing that by this the company is almost certain to satisfy demand. But, in doing so, the company will almost certainly produce an excess of perfect vases, which will have to be scrapped (since a particular crest is appropriate for only one competition). The problem is to balance these conflicting risks and determine an optimal production policy.

Suppose that the company has an order for N vases. Suppose too, for generality, that

$a =$ set-up cost,

$c =$ cost of producing one vase.

Let $p_q(m)$ be the probability that if q vases are put into production, then in a single production run m perfect vases will be produced ($0 \leqslant m \leqslant q$). We begin with the simplest case, $N = 1$: the company has an order for 1 vase.

Let $v_1(q)$ be the expected cost of the policy which puts q vases into production *each* run and continues to do so until at least one perfect vase is made, i.e. until the order has been satisfied:

$$v_1(q) = a + cq + p_q(0)v_1(q) + (1 - p_q(0)) \times 0. \tag{12.12}$$

The terms $a + cq$ arise because this policy will certainly incur the production costs of one run. There is then a probability $p_q(0)$ that no perfect vases will have been made and thus that the company is back where it started, facing an expected cost of $v_1(q)$ for producing the required vase. There is also probability $(1 - p_q(0))$ that at least one perfect vase has been produced and so the company will incur no further cost, being able to satisfy the order.

Simplifying (12.12) gives

$$v_1(q) = (a + cq)/(1 - p_q(0)).$$

So the policy which minimises the expected cost chooses $q = q_1$ such that

$$v_1 = \min_{q=1}^{\infty} \{a + cq)/(1 - p_q(0)\} = v_1(q_1). \tag{12.13}$$

Here v_1 is the expected cost of an optimal policy to produce 1 vase.

Suppose now that there is an order for $N = 2$ vases. What sort of production policy would the company use? Well an obvious decision is to put q vases into production. If all turn out to be imperfect, then the company is back where it started and should put q vases into production again. If exactly one perfect vase has been made, then one more remains to be made. But the optimal policy for making one vase is known: put q_1 into production repeatedly until one perfect vase is made. Finally, if 2 or more vases have been made during the first production run, then the company can satisfy the customer's order and no further cost is incurred. Hence if $v_2(q)$ is the expected cost of this policy to satisfy an order for two vases,

$$v_2(q) = a + cq + p_q(0)v_2(q) + p_q(1)v_1 + (1 - p_q(0) - p_q(1)) \times 0$$

$$\Rightarrow v_2(q) = (a + cq + p_q(1)v_1)/(1 - p_q(0)). \tag{12.14}$$

So the policy which minimises the expected cost chooses $q = q_2$ such that

$$v_2 = \min_{q=1}^{\infty} \{(a + cq + p_q(1)v_1)/(1 - p_q(0))\} \tag{12.15}$$

$$= v_2(q_2).$$

Here v_2 is clearly the expected cost of the optimal policy to produce two vases.

Now suppose that the company has determined the optimal policies for making $1, 2, \ldots, n$ vases. Specifically to make r vases ($1 \leqslant r \leqslant n$) put q_r into production repeatedly until at least one perfect vase is made. If s remain to be made put q_s into production. Continue in this way until all r vases are made. The cost to make r vases is v_r. Suppose that the company wishes to make $(n + 1)$ vases. By parallel arguments to those above, it should put q items into production repeatedly until at least one is made. Then if r vases remain to be made, the company should make them according to the optimal policy above at an expected cost v_r. Let $v_{n+1}(q)$ be the expected cost of this. Then

$$v_{n+1}(q) = a + cq + p_q(0)v_{n+1}(q) + p_q(1)v_n + p_q(2)v_{n-1} + \cdots$$

$$+ p_q(n)v_1 + (p_q(n+1) + p_q(n+2) + \cdots) \times 0$$

$$\Rightarrow v_{n+1}(q) = (a + cq + \sum_{r=1}^{n} p_q(n+1-r)v_r)/(1 - p_q(0)).$$

Hence the policy which minimises $v_{n+1}(q)$ chooses $q = q_{n+1}$ such that

$$v_{n+1} = \min_{q=1}^{\infty} \{(a + cq + \sum_{r=1}^{n} p_q(n+1-r)v_r)/(1 - p_q(0))\} = v_{n+1}(q_{n+1}). \tag{12.16}$$

So knowing the optimal policies to make n or less perfect vases means that the company can find the optimal policy to make $(n + 1)$ perfect vases. In other words, it can find the optimal policy for making any number of vases.

Let us solve a particular problem for Easismash. Remember that $a = 30$ and $c = 12$. Suppose that $N = 3$ vases are required. Also take $p_q(m)$ to be given by Table 12.5.

Table 12.5 The probabilities $p_q(m)$

$p_q(m)$		q		
	1	2	3	4
0	0.4	0.2	0.1	0.1
1	0.6	0.4	0.2	0.1
m 2	0	0.4	0.3	0.2
3	0	0	0.4	0.3
4	0	0	0	0.3

Note that $p_q(m) = 0$ for $m \geqslant 1, q > 4$. This implies that the etching process can cope with at most 4 vases at a time. A little thought shows that *none* of the above theory is affected by this.

From the above

$$v_1(q) = (30 + 12q)/(1 - p_q(0)) \qquad \text{for } q = 1, 2, 3, 4.$$

Thus

$$v_1(1) = 42/0.6 = 70.0$$
$$v_1(2) = 54/0.8 = 67.5$$
$$v_1(3) = 66/0.9 = 73.3$$
$$v_1(4) = 78/0.9 = 86.7.$$

Hence $v_1 = \min_{q=1}^{4} \{v_1(q)\} = 67.5$ and $q_1 = 2$.

Similarly

$$v_2(q) = (30 + 12q + p_q(1)v_1)/(1 - p_q(0)) \qquad \text{for } q = 1, 2, 3, 4.$$

Hence

$$v_2(1) = (42 + 0.6 \times 67.5)/0.6 = 137.5$$
$$v_2(2) = (54 + 0.4 \times 67.5)/0.8 = 101.3$$
$$v_2(3) = (66 + 0.2 \times 67.5)/0.9 = 88.3$$
$$v_2(4) = (78 + 0.1 \times 67.5)/0.9 = 94.2.$$

Hence

$$v_2 = \min_{q=1}^{4} \{v_2(q)\} = 88.3 \text{ and } q_2 = 3.$$

Lastly

$$v_3(q) = (30 + 12q + p_q(1)v_2 + p_q(2)v_1)/(1 - p_q(0)) \qquad \text{for } q = 1, 2, 3, 4.$$

Hence

$$v_3(1) = (42 + 0.6 \times 88.3 + 0.0 \times 67.5) = 158.3$$
$$v_3(2) = (54 + 0.4 \times 88.3 + 0.4 \times 67.5) = 145.4$$
$$v_3(3) = (66 + 0.2 \times 88.3 + 0.3 \times 67.5) = 115.5$$
$$v_3(4) = (78 + 0.1 \times 88.3 + 0.2 \times 67.5) = 111.5.$$

Hence $v_3 = \min_{q=1}^{4} \{v_3(q)\} = 111.5$ and $q_3 = 4$.

So the optimal expected cost of making 3 vases is £111.5 and the optimal policy is:

(1) repeatedly put 4 into production *until* at least 1 perfect vase is made;
(2) *then* if 2 remain to be made, repeatedly put 3 into production *until* at least 1 more perfect vase is made. If 1 remains to be made, repeatedly put 2 into production until at least 1 more perfect vase is made. If 0 remain to be made, stop.

12.6 General remarks and further examples

The underlying idea of dynamic programming should by now be becoming clear. Roughly, the method applies to any problem which can be broken down into a sequence of nested sub-problems, the solution of one being derived in a straightforward fashion from the solution of the preceding sub-problem. For instance, in the jeweller's problem of Section 12.1, the overall problem was to maximise the total income from the polishing machine over a period of three weeks. This was decomposed into a sequence of three sub-problems:

(1) what should be done if the period were only one week;
(2) what should be done if the period were only two weeks; and, finally the actual problem,
(3) what should be done if the period were three weeks?

Solving the first sub-problem was easy; solving the second was easy *once the first sub-problem had been solved*; and solving the third was easy *once the second sub-problem had been solved*.

Very often the decomposition of a problem into a sequence of nested sub-problems is a natural consequence of a time dimension. The overall problem is actually to choose a sequence of decisions over some finite time horizon. This was the case in the examples discussed in Sections 12.1–3. But time need not enter into a problem in order for it to be solvable by dynamic programming. In the allocation problem of Section 12.4 there was no time dimension; there the overall problem was decomposed into a sequence of sub-problems in a different fashion.

(1)   What to do if advertising were limited to television;
 (2)   what to do if it were limited to television and radio;
(3)   what to do if it were limited between television, radio and newspapers?

Again in Section 12.5 there was no time dimension; the nesting of sub-problems was achieved by considering how to make 1 vase, 2 vases, 3 vases, etc.

Dynamic programming involves more than the decomposition of a problem into a sequence of sub-problems. It requires that the solution of one sub-problem is derived from the solution of the preceding one. Specifically it demands that the *optimal* solution of one sub-problem involves the *optimal* solution of the preceding problem. This requirement has been stated precisely by Bellman as the *principle of optimality*:

> An optimal sequence of decisions has the property that whatever the initial circumstances and whatever the initial decision, the remaining decisions must be optimal with respect to the circumstances that arise as a result of the initial decision.

This principle may seem confusing at first reading, but it is really very simple. We have used it intuitively in solving each of the five examples above.

Consider equation (12.7) of the equipment replacement example of Section 12.2

$$v_n(i) = \min \{c_i + v_{n-1}(i+1), \, a - t_i + c_0 + v_{n-1}(1)\}. \tag{12.7}$$

This equation is justified entirely by the principle of optimality. $v_n(i)$ is the cost of the optimal policy of equipment replacement over the next n periods given that the current machine is i years old. Thus $v_n(i)$ is determined by the optimal sequence of decisions over the next n periods. The first of these decisions is to choose whether to operate the current machine for a further year or to trade it in for a new machine. Now the principle of optimality states that whichever of these we choose the remaining decisions must form an optimal sequence for the remaining $(n-1)$ periods given that the machine's age at the beginning of these $(n-1)$ periods will be determined by the first decision. Thus the cost of the remaining $(n-1)$ periods will be either $v_{n-1}(i+1)$ or $v_{n-1}(1)$, depending on whether the current machine is operated for a further year.

In each of the other four examples we have based the solution on a recursion which, like (12.5), is justified entirely through the principle of optimality: see (12.5), (12.8), (12.9) and (12.16).

Experts on dynamic programming will have been bemoaning our slipshod approach in this chapter, because we have ignored a very important property of the method. Dynamic programming finds an optimal *policy*, where by 'policy' we have in mind a technical meaning that we have yet to make clear. To date we have used the term 'policy' in its everyday sense.

It is, perhaps, easiest to introduce the concept of a policy in the context of a problem with a time dimension, say the car fleet example of Section 12.3. For each year the method determines the optimal replacement/keep running decision for each age of car, i.e. it determines $d_n(i)$. Consider $d_n(i)$ for n fixed and i varying, i.e. consider cars of different ages for a fixed year. Then $d_n(i)$ gives a *decision rule* which tells the car fleet owner exactly what to do with each car in his fleet depending on its age. As n varies, i.e. as we consider different years, the sequence of decision rules $d_1(i)$, $d_2(i)$, ... define a *policy*, which tells the car fleet owner exactly what he should do in each of the years before him whatever happens to the car fleet before then (see Table 12.6). A policy is a complete contingency plan.

Table 12.6 The optimal policy for the example of Section 12.3

		Years n to sale of car hire firm		
	$d_n(i)$	3	2	1
	0		K	K
Age of	1	K	K	K
car	2	K	K	K
i	3	K	R	K
	4		R	R
		decision rule when 3 years left	decision rule when 2 years left	decision rule when 1 year left

Similarly, if you look at the production overage example of Section 12.5, you will discover again that the optimal policy was a complete contingency plan. It determined not only what the company should do initially in order to fulfil a contract for a given number of vases, but also what it should do in any circumstance that might arise in the production process.

In the other three examples that we have discussed the same point may be made, although perhaps not so clearly because of their simplicity. Dynamic programming finds an optimal policy, a complete contingency plan.

Two further points should be made about dynamic programming. First, we have only considered problems which can be decomposed into a *finite* number of nested sub-problems. This is not a restriction of dynamic programming; the technique may be applied to determine optimal policies for infinite sequences of decisions. However, such applications require considerable mathematical sophistication—far greater than we are assuming in this book. Second, in our examples we have chosen in all but one case problems that can be decomposed into *three* sub-problems. There is nothing magical about the number *three*; it was chosen simply to make the examples an appropriate length.

Dynamic programming is a technique that has a wide range of application. We have discussed five examples above. As a cursory glance will show, the calculation of early and late dates in critical path analysis (Section 6.4) provide two further, closely related applications of dynamic programming. We close this chapter by indicating several other areas of application—some of which are explored in more detail by the problems at the end of the chapter.

Shortest path problems

In Chapter 7 we solved shortest path problems by Dijkstra's algorithm. It is also possible and instructive, but less computationally efficient, to solve these problems by dynamic programming. Suppose we have a network on N vertices and that we wish to find the shortest path between vertex 1 and vertex N. Let $l(i,j)$ be the length of the arc from vertex i to vertex j. If there is no arc between i and j, $l(i,j) = \infty$ and, of course, $l(i,i) = 0$. Define $v_n(j)$ to be the length of the shortest path from vertex 1 to vertex j which involves no more than n arcs. Then

$$v_1(j) = l(1,j) \qquad \text{for } j = 2, \ldots, N$$

and for $n \geqslant 2$ and $j \geqslant 2$

$$v_n(j) = \min_{k=2}^{N} \{v_{n-1}(k) + l(k,j)\}. \tag{12.17}$$

The minimisation in (12.17) considers in turn the path length achieved by going from vertex 1 to vertex k along the shortest path involving no more than $(n-1)$ arcs and then going directly from vertex k to j along 1 arc. It may be shown that if $l(i,j) \geqslant 0$ for all i,j, then $v_{N-1}(j)$ is the shortest path length from vertex 1 to vertex j, no matter how many arcs are allowed. Indeed, a little thought shows that this result is very intuitive. It follows that $v_{N-1}(N)$ is the length of the shortest path from vertex 1 to vertex N.

We might have solved this problem another way. Let $w_n(j)$ be the length of a shortest path from vertex j to vertex N in no more than n arcs. Then

$$w_1(j) = l(j,N) \qquad \text{for } j = 1, 2, \ldots, N-1$$

and for $n \geqslant 2, j \leqslant N-1$

$$w_n(j) = \min_{k=1}^{N-1} \{l(j,k) + w_{n-1}(k)\}. \tag{12.18}$$

It may be shown that $w_{N-1}(N)$ gives the length of the shortest path from vertex 1 to vertex N without any restriction on the number of arcs in the path.

Note that here we have two distinct dynamic programming solutions of the same problem. This is often the case: when a problem can be solved by dynamic programming, there may be more than one way of doing it.

Inventory problems

In Chapters 8 and 9 we considered inventory problems in which the aim was to find an optimal ordering policy when it was assumed that the system would continue indefinitely. What would happen if the inventory system were only to run for n periods? Consider, for instance, the problem of an ice cream salesman who orders fresh stocks of ice cream once a week for a 10-week summer season and then closes down until next year. Since stock left at the end of the final period may well be wasted, an optimal policy might be quite different from those discussed in the earlier chapters.

We briefly sketch the formulation of an inventory problem as a dynamic program. Let $v_n(I)$ be the expected profit from the optimal ordering policy given that n periods remain until the system is closed and that the inventory at the beginning of the n periods is I. Suppose q items are ordered initially and delivered immediately. Let the random demand in a period be X with probabilities p_X, $X = 0, 1, 2, \ldots$. Let J_X be the inventory at the end of the first period with $(n-1)$ periods remaining:

$$J_X = \begin{cases} I+q-X & \text{if } X \leqslant I+q \\ 0 & \text{if } X > I+q. \end{cases}$$

Now in this sketch we wish to avoid writing out complicated sums for expected holding costs, etc. So let

$$S(I+q) = \text{expected income from sales in the first} \\ \text{of the remaining periods}$$

$$H(I+q) = \text{expected holding cost in the first of} \\ \text{the remaining periods.}$$

Both these quantities can be given explicit formulae, as they were in Chapter 9. Let $c(q)$ be the cost of ordering q items:

$$c(q) = \begin{cases} 0 & \text{if } q = 0 \\ a+cq & \text{if } q > 0. \end{cases}$$

Then assuming backlogging is now allowed, $v_n(I)$ must satisfy

$$v_n(I) = \min_{q=1}^{\infty} \left\{ S(I+q) - H(I+q) - c(q) + \sum_{X=0}^{\infty} v_{n-1}(J_X)p_X \right\}. \tag{12.19}$$

The term $\sum_{x=0}^{\infty} v_{n-1}(J_X)p_X$ is the expected profit from operating the system optimally for the remaining $(n-1)$ periods. If all stock remaining at the end of the final period is to be scrapped, then

$$v_0(I) = 0 \qquad \text{for all } I.$$

Thus we may begin a recursion based upon (12.19) to find

$$v_1(I), v_2(I), \text{ etc.}$$

Optimal capacity expansion

In installing capacity to meet a growing demand for service a firm has to decide by how much and when to increase capacity. Should it make one large investment, dramatically increasing its capacity above current demand, and then wait for demand to catch up; or should it make several smaller investments, staggered over time, so that its capacity keeps pace with demand but does not greatly overshoot. Such problems have a natural formulation in dynamic programming. See Exercise 6.

Exercises

1   A piece of equipment is to be operated over 5 years. At the beginning of each year it may be overhauled. Overhauls take negligible time, but cost £1200. The cost of operating the machine for a year depends on the number of years since the machine was last overhauled (see Table 12.7). Initially the machine is 2 years from its last overhaul. What is the optimal overhaul policy for the 5 year period?

Table 12.7

Number of years since last overhaul	0	1	2	3	4	5	6	7
Operating cost in next year	£1000	£1500	£2000	£2500	£2500	£2500	£2500	£2500

2   A company has £200 000 to allocate to 3 revenue-producing activities. It can allocate money to these activities only in units of £25 000. The net revenue generated by each activity for differing investments is given in Table 12.8. The company wishes to maximise its net revenue. What is its optimal allocation?

Table 12.8

	Amount allocated to activity in £1000s								
	0	25	50	75	100	125	150	175	200
Activity 1	0	10	20	30	40	55	65	75	80
Activity 2	0	15	25	35	60	65	65	65	65
Activity 3	0	5	10	20	30	50	70	75	80

Suppose that the problem is altered in the following way. Firstly, assume that money need no longer be allocated in units of £25 000—any sum may be allocated. Secondly, assume that the net revenues for an investment of £x in the three activities are given respectively by £$(0.5x - 20\,000)$, £$(0.6x - 30\,000)$, and £$(0.7x - 25\,000)$.
Ignoring the triviality of the problem, formulate it as a linear program.

3 Consider the example of Section 12.5. Using the probabilities given there, but a set-up cost of £45 and a cost per vase of £20, find the optimal policy to make 4 vases.

Suppose now that it is possible to sell excess perfect vases at a scrap value of £10. Modify the dynamic programming formulation to find the optimal policy for fulfilling an order for 4 vases. Assume still that the set-up cost is £45 and the cost per vase is £20.

4 Formulate the problem of Exercise 3, Chapter 3 as a dynamic program. Solve the problem by dynamic programming and compare the effort required with the solution based upon the transportation algorithm.

5 Consider the network of Exercise 1, Chapter 7. Use the dynamic programming formulation (12.17) to calculate the shortest distances from vertex 1 to all other vertices. For a large network with arcs joining all distinct pairs of vertices, would you expect this method to be faster or slower than Dijkstra's algorithm?

6 A company is expanding to meet the demand for service over N time periods. Decisions are made at the beginning of each time period as to how much extra service capacity to install. All demand must be met. The demand for service in time period n is known to be exactly D_n. The cost of putting in extra capacity to meet an increase in demand of k is

$$1 + k \qquad \text{if } k > 0$$
$$0 \qquad \text{if } k = 0.$$

Thus it costs $1 + k$ to increase capacity from C to $(C + k)$. There is a discount factor $\alpha\,(0 \leqslant \alpha \leqslant 1)$ so that £1 cost incurred in period n is worth £α^n at time 0 and £$\alpha^{(n-t)}$ at time t. Extra capacity can be installed almost instantaneously and no loss is incurred if some capacity is unused in a particular year. How would you determine by dynamic programming when, and how much, extra capacity should be installed to meet all demand over the next N time periods at minimum discounted cost. Assume that initially capacity equals demand.

7 A weather satellite manufacturer has the capability to produce at most two satellites a year. The national meteorological office places orders in July for delivery in December: but since the satellites take a year to make, the manufacturer must begin production before the orders are known. The order will be for either one or two satellites, with probabilities 0.7 and 0.3 respectively. The orders in different years are independent. It costs £10 million to manufacture one satellite in a year and £18 million to manufacture two. Unsold satellites can be stored at a cost of £2.5 million per year, but at most one can be stored. Unfulfilled orders incur a penalty cost of £3 million and *must* be fulfilled the next year. What production policy should the manufacturer follow to minimise total cost over the next 3 years if it has one satellite in store at present? If any unfulfilled order remains at the end of a 3-year period, a further penalty cost of £10 million is incurred.

13
Simulation

13.1 Introduction

In the earlier chapters special classes of problems involving chance events were studied, such as inventory control, queueing, defective products. These examples were very simply structured so that analytic or numerical solutions could be obtained easily. Real life problems are far larger and more complex in structure, and although it is possible in principle to use similar approaches, in many cases the existing solution procedures can be very time consuming. In such cases the standard technique for dealing with these problems is simulation.

Simulation is a procedure by which an actual sequence of realisations of chance events, decisions and outcomes may be traced out as if we were actually observing the particular system in operation. It is an alternative form of modelling to **mathematical modelling**, or **symbolic modelling** as it is often called, which is the type of modelling so far presented in this text. Simulation is often referred to as a form of **look-alike modelling**, or, to give it its correct name, **iconic modelling**.

One clear advantage of simulation is that it is easy for the decision maker to understand, and hence more likely for him to accept as a way of handling his problem.

In this chapter we will merely introduce the element of simulation using some of the simple examples of previous chapters, even though it is more appropriate to use the techniques already developed for such problems. To use more complicated examples, where simulation would normally be necessary, would obscure the basic ideas. In addition it should be pointed out that there are many other facets of simulation which are important in practice and which we do not have the space to discuss in this text.

We will first of all proceed by showing how simulation might be applied to some of the simple problems discussed earlier in the text, and then look briefly at the general principles.

13.2 Some simple illustrations of simulation

An inventory problem

Let us consider the first inventory example of Chapter 9. For this example the problem is to determine the level, S, to which we should restore the stock level at the beginning of each week, allowing for backlogging. We will take $T = 1$ week. The demand X in each week has a probability distribution given in Table 13.1.

Table 13.1

X	0	1	2	3	4	5	6
p_X	0.05	0.1	0.2	0.3	0.2	0.1	0.05

The first step in a simulation is to set up a mechanism for generating a demand according to the above probability distribution. This is achieved by generating a *random number*, Y, in such a way that Y will be associated with a particular demand level, or *random event*, and so that the probabilities associated with Y will lead to the appropriate probabilities for X. We may proceed as follows.

Select a set of numbers, for example 0–99, i.e. 100 numbers in total. This is not the only set which may be chosen, and the set chosen depends upon the problem and the precision required. We then associate each X value with *every* Y value in a specified subset of these numbers. For the data given in Table 13.1 we will use the equivalence between random numbers Y and random events X shown in Table 13.2. Then X is a random variable on the *sample space* $\{0, 1, \ldots, 99\}$. It will be seen that the random event X (demand) has the same probability as its random number Y range.

Table 13.2

Y	X	Probability
0–4	0	0.05
5–14	1	0.10
15–34	2	0.20
35–64	3	0.30
65–84	4	0.20
85–94	5	0.10
95–99	6	0.05

The generation of members of Y can be accomplished by one of several mechanisms. We will use a readily available table of random numbers generated by a mechanism which produces numbers which, for large strings of such, satisfy reasonable properties of randomness, although, of course, this will not be so for small strings. Table 13.3 is an extraction from such a table. One reasonable property is that each number appears with the same frequency, and, although this is true for large strings, a glance at Table 13.3 will show that this is not so for small strings. In order to ensure that the actual simulation is representative of the problem simulation run lengths must be large.

Table 13.3

21	47	75	48	59	01	83	72	59	93	76	24	97	08	86	95	23	03	67	44
82	32	55	50	43	10	53	74	35	08	90	61	18	37	44	10	96	22	13	43
94	66	16	03	50	32	40	43	62	23	50	05	10	03	22	11	54	38	08	34
17	58	67	49	51	94	05	17	58	53	78	80	59	01	94	32	42	87	16	95
38	87	26	17	18	99	75	53	08	70	94	25	12	58	41	54	88	21	05	13
11	74	26	93	81	44	33	93	08	72	32	79	73	31	18	22	64	70	68	50
43	36	12	88	59	11	01	64	56	23	93	00	90	04	99	43	64	07	40	36
93	80	62	04	78	38	26	80	44	91	55	75	11	89	32	58	47	55	25	71
49	54	01	31	81	08	42	98	41	87	69	53	82	96	61	77	73	80	95	27
36	76	87	26	33	37	94	82	15	69	41	95	96	86	70	45	27	48	38	80
07	09	25	23	92	24	62	71	26	07	06	55	84	53	44	67	33	84	53	20
43	31	00	10	81	44	86	38	03	07	52	55	51	61	48	89	74	29	46	47
61	57	00	63	60	06	17	36	37	75	63	14	89	51	23	25	01	74	69	93
31	35	28	37	99	10	77	91	89	41	31	57	97	64	48	62	58	48	69	19
57	04	88	65	26	27	79	59	36	82	90	52	95	65	46	35	06	53	22	54
09	24	34	42	00	68	72	10	71	37	30	72	97	57	59	09	29	82	76	50
97	95	53	50	18	40	89	48	83	29	52	23	08	25	21	22	53	26	15	87
93	73	25	95	70	43	78	19	88	85	56	67	16	68	26	95	99	64	45	69
72	62	11	12	25	00	92	26	82	64	35	66	65	94	34	71	68	75	18	67
61	02	07	44	18	45	37	12	07	94	95	91	73	78	66	99	53	21	93	78
97	83	98	54	74	33	05	59	17	18	45	47	35	41	44	22	03	42	30	00
89	16	09	71	92	22	23	29	06	37	35	05	54	54	89	88	43	81	63	61
25	96	68	82	20	62	87	17	92	65	02	82	35	28	62	84	91	95	48	83
81	44	33	17	19	05	04	95	48	06	74	69	00	75	67	65	01	71	65	45
11	32	25	49	31	42	36	23	43	86	08	62	49	76	67	42	24	52	32	45

Let us now simulate the sequence of decisions, demands, and so on for $S = 2$, using the random numbers as given in the Table 13.4. We will also tabulate the inventory levels at the beginning of each period immediately after an order has been placed and received, the inventory levels at the end of each period, and

Table 13.4

Period	Y	X	Initial inventory	Order quantity	Final inventory	Shortage	Cost
1	74	4	2	2	0	2	$42\frac{1}{2}$
2	92	5	2	4	0	3	77
3	20	2	2	5	0	0	5
4	19	2	2	2	0	0	5
5	31	2	2	2	0	0	5
6	33	2	2	2	0	0	5
7	22	2	2	2	0	0	5
8	62	3	2	2	0	1	$18\frac{1}{3}$
9	05	1	2	3	1	0	$7\frac{1}{2}$

Table 13.4 (continued)

Period	Y	X	Initial inventory	Order quantity	Final inventory	Shortage	Cost
10	42	3	2	1	0	1	$18\frac{1}{3}$
11	05	1	2	3	1	0	$7\frac{1}{2}$
12	23	2	2	1	0	0	5
13	87	5	2	2	0	3	77
14	04	0	2	5	2	0	10
15	36	3	2	0	0	1	$18\frac{1}{3}$
16	59	3	2	3	0	1	$18\frac{1}{3}$
17	29	2	2	3	0	0	5
18	17	2	2	2	0	0	5
19	95	6	2	2	0	4	$121\frac{2}{3}$
20	23	2	2	6	0	0	5
21	17	2	2	2	0	0	5
22	06	1	2	2	1	0	$7\frac{1}{2}$
23	92	5	2	1	0	3	77
24	48	3	2	5	0	1	$18\frac{1}{3}$
25	43	3	2	3	0	1	$18\frac{1}{3}$
26	18	2	2	3	0	0	5
27	37	3	2	2	0	1	$18\frac{1}{3}$
28	65	4	2	3	0	2	$42\frac{1}{2}$
29	06	1	2	4	1	0	$7\frac{1}{2}$
30	86	5	2	1	0	3	77
31	45	3	2	5	0	1	$18\frac{1}{3}$
32	35	3	2	3	0	1	$18\frac{1}{3}$
33	02	0	2	3	2	0	10
34	74	4	2	0	0	2	$42\frac{1}{2}$
35	08	1	2	4	1	0	$7\frac{1}{2}$
36	47	3	2	1	0	1	$18\frac{1}{3}$
37	05	1	2	3	1	0	$7\frac{1}{2}$
38	82	4	2	1	0	2	$42\frac{1}{2}$
39	69	4	2	4	0	2	$42\frac{1}{2}$
40	62	3	2	4	0	1	$18\frac{1}{3}$
41	35	3	2	3	0	1	$18\frac{1}{3}$
42	54	3	2	3	0	1	$18\frac{1}{3}$
43	35	3	2	3	0	1	$18\frac{1}{3}$
44	00	0	2	3	2	0	10
45	49	3	2	0	0	1	$18\frac{1}{3}$
46	41	3	2	3	0	1	$18\frac{1}{3}$
47	54	3	2	3	0	1	$18\frac{1}{3}$
48	28	2	2	3	0	0	$7\frac{1}{3}$
49	75	4	2	2	0	2	$42\frac{1}{2}$
50	76	4	2	4	0	2	$42\frac{1}{2}$

Average cost per week (excluding fixed and order costs)	23.2

shortage in each period, as well as the actual quantities ordered. We begin with zero inventory.

Table 13.4 is the result of 50 weeks' simulation with our decision $S = 2$. The table is obtained as follows. We first of all select the random numbers to be used for generating the demand in each week. For this problem we may select the 50 numbers in advance. The numbers we use are as follows:

> 74, 92, 20, 19, 31, 33, 22, 62, 05, 42
> 05, 23, 87, 04, 36, 59, 29, 17, 95, 23
> 17, 06, 92, 48, 43, 18, 37, 65, 06, 86
> 45, 35, 02, 74, 08, 47, 05, 82, 69, 62
> 35, 54, 35, 00, 49, 41, 54, 28, 75, 76

These are taken from the central bottom blocks of Table 13.3.

We begin with $Y = 74$. From Table 13.2 we see that the demand X is 4. Our decision rule requires that we increase our inventory level to 2 by ordering a quantity 2. The final inventory drops to 0. There is a shortage of 2. We will record only that part of the cost which matters to our decision since the expected costs per week from fixed costs and order costs are independent of the decision S. Thus only shortage plus stock-holding costs will be recorded. With $k = b = 10, h = 5$, the cost for the first week is then

$$10(4 - 2) + \tfrac{1}{2}(10)(4 - 2)^2 + (\tfrac{1}{2})(5)(2^2/4) = 42.5,$$

noting that $X > S$. We then continue with the second period, with the initial inventory increased from 0 to 2 by an order quantity 4 to make up for the deficit of 2 in the first week, with random number $Y = 92$, corresponding to a demand of $X = 5$ in Table 13.2, and the whole procedure is repeated for 50 weeks.

The purpose of this simulation is to obtain a good estimate of the expected weekly variable cost for each value of S which we may wish to examine. We have chosen a 50-week simulation.

The average weekly cost (excluding fixed and order costs) for this simulation is 23.2. The actual expected cost, calculated from the formula in Chapter 9, is 19.1. The simulation would need to be run for much more than 50 weeks to approximate this.

Now suppose we wish to determine the effect of changing S from 2 to 3. We can run the simulation again for $S = 3$ and a different set of random numbers. In general we want to determine whether $S = 2$ or $S = 3$ is better, and the difference between the average costs for the simulations will be made up of the difference between the decisions and the difference between the random numbers used. It seems prudent to use the same random numbers and we will do so. It is a means of getting better estimates of the *difference* between the expected weekly costs arising from each decision, but the reader should be aware of the fact that this is not always the case and each problem has to be judged in its own context as to whether the procedure is valid. In its very simplest term the reason for using common random numbers is as follows for the above example. Suppose that for the 50-week simulation we simulate for decisions S and S', and suppose that the series of demands consists of $\{X_1, X_2, \ldots, X_{50}\} \{X'_1, X'_2, \ldots, X'_{50}\}$ for the two simulations. Let K, K' be the total stockholding plus shortage cost per week for the two simulations. Then it is seen that the cost difference $K - K'$ depends on two aspects of the simulations:

(1) the decisions S and S' are different
(2) the sequences of demands $\{X_1, X_2, \ldots, X_{50}\}$ and $\{X'_1, X'_2, \ldots, X'_{50}\}$ may be different.

Intuitively therefore a better estimate of the difference between the cost effects of S and S' might be expected to occur if we make $X_t = X'_t, t = 1, 2, \ldots, 50$.

This method is used widely in practice, but it must be repeated that it does not work theoretically in all cases. Even in inventory problems there are cases where it does not work theoretically. However the evidence is that in practice it does work.

An alternative justification, which a decision maker may accept, is that it is helpful to see how different decisions work for the same chance circumstances. Again the reader should be aware that such circumstances will be a sample from a population of possible samples, although this sort of reasoning has a plausibility about it.

Let us now carry out the formulation for the case $S = 3$. Again note that we do not include the fixed and order costs since they are independent of S. The results are given in Table 13.5.

Table 13.5

Period	Y	X	Initial inventory	Order quantity	Final inventory	Shortage	Cost
1	74	4	3	3	0	1	$20\frac{5}{8}$
2	92	5	3	4	0	2	$45\frac{1}{2}$
3	20	2	3	5	1	0	10
4	19	2	3	2	1	0	10
5	31	2	3	2	1	0	10
6	33	2	3	2	1	0	10
7	22	2	3	2	1	0	10
8	62	3	3	2	0	0	$7\frac{1}{2}$
9	05	1	3	3	2	0	$12\frac{1}{2}$
10	42	3	3	1	0	0	$7\frac{1}{2}$
11	05	1	3	3	2	0	$12\frac{1}{2}$
12	23	2	3	1	1	0	10
13	87	5	3	2	0	2	$45\frac{1}{2}$
14	04	0	3	5	3	0	15
15	36	3	3	0	0	0	$7\frac{1}{2}$
16	59	3	3	3	0	0	$7\frac{1}{2}$
17	29	2	3	3	1	0	10
18	17	2	3	2	1	0	10

Table 13.5 (continued)

Period	Y	X	Initial inventory	Order quantity	Final inventory	Shortage	Cost
19	95	6	3	2	0	3	$78\frac{3}{4}$
20	23	2	3	6	1	0	10
21	17	2	3	2	1	0	10
22	06	1	3	2	2	0	$12\frac{1}{2}$
23	92	5	3	1	0	2	$45\frac{1}{2}$
24	48	3	3	5	0	0	$7\frac{1}{2}$
25	43	3	3	3	0	0	$7\frac{1}{2}$
26	18	2	3	3	1	0	10
27	37	3	3	2	0	0	$7\frac{1}{2}$
28	65	4	3	3	0	1	$20\frac{5}{8}$
29	06	1	3	4	2	0	$12\frac{1}{2}$
30	86	5	3	1	0	2	$45\frac{1}{2}$
31	45	3	3	5	0	0	$7\frac{1}{2}$
32	35	3	3	3	0	0	$7\frac{1}{2}$
33	02	0	3	3	3	0	15
34	74	4	3	0	0	1	$20\frac{5}{8}$
35	08	1	3	4	2	0	$12\frac{1}{2}$
36	47	3	3	1	0	0	$7\frac{1}{2}$
37	05	1	3	3	2	0	$12\frac{1}{2}$
38	82	4	3	1	0	1	$20\frac{5}{8}$
39	69	4	3	4	0	1	$20\frac{5}{8}$
40	62	3	3	4	0	0	$7\frac{1}{2}$
41	35	3	3	3	0	0	$7\frac{1}{2}$
42	54	3	3	3	0	0	$7\frac{1}{2}$
43	35	3	3	3	0	0	$7\frac{1}{2}$
44	00	0	3	3	3	0	15
45	49	3	3	0	0	0	$7\frac{1}{2}$
46	41	3	3	3	0	0	$7\frac{1}{2}$
47	54	3	3	2	0	0	$7\frac{1}{2}$
48	28	2	3	3	1	0	10
49	75	4	3	2	0	1	$20\frac{5}{8}$
50	76	4	3	4	0	1	$20\frac{5}{8}$

Average cost per week (excluding fixed and order costs)	15.00

The simulation produces an average weekly cost of 15.0, whereas the actual expected weekly cost is 14.5. Again further simulations would be needed to get a better estimate. It is also seen that the actual expected cost (14.5) for $S = 3$ is lower than the actual expected cost (19.1) for $S = 2$, and that the simulation average cost (15.0) for $S = 3$ is lower than the simulation average cost (23.2) for $S = 2$. Thus if we chose $S = 2$ on the basis of the simulation we would take the right decision.

Note, however, that where solutions are fairly close together one must also expect errors unless the simulation run lengths are increased.

Although the simulation may be run to determine estimates of the expected cost per period when the cost factors are explicitly given, in many instances such factors are difficult to pin down. If these costs are not known, simulation can give the average inventory levels, order quantities, and average shortages, and the decision maker may feel able to decide on this basis even without the explicit costs.

Let us now turn to the simulation of queueing problems, as discussed in Chapter 10.

A queueing example

In Chapter 10 the M/M/1 queue is discussed. This queueing problem is a continuous-time one in which arrivals can occur at any point in time. In this case we will not deal with continuous-time processes and will therefore make use of a discrete analogue of the M/M/1 queueing problem, which may be used as an approximation providing the time intervals are small.

Customers will be allowed to arrive at the beginning of each of a sequence of unit time intervals. Either one customer will arrive, with probability $p = 0.4$, or none will arrive, with probability 0.6. If there are any customers in the system immediately after this event one of them is served with probability $q = 0.6$; otherwise none are served, with probability 0.4. Arrivals and departures are independent random events for different periods. We will simulate the queueing system over 50 periods, but in practice a much longer simulation is needed.

We must now determine the random number–random event equivalence for both the arrivals and services. We will use (Y_a, X_a), (Y_s, X_s) respectively for the arrivals and service, where $X_a = 1$ if an arrival takes place, $X_a = 0$ otherwise, $X_s = 1$ if a service takes place, providing the queue is not empty, and $X_s = 0$ otherwise. Table 13.6 gives the results.

Table 13.6

Y_a	X_a	Y_s	X_s
0–39	1	0–59	1
40–99	0	60–99	0

For a specific set of random numbers we may then generate the sequence of arrivals, departures and queue size over the 50 periods as given in Table 13.7. We begin with no customers in the queue.

In the following simulation we will use the following random numbers for the arrivals and services respectively. Note that we will generate all the numbers for

Table 13.7

Period	Initial queue size	Y_s	X_s	Y_a	X_a	Final queue size
1	0			59	0	0
2	0			43	0	0
3	0			50	0	0
4	0			51	0	0
5	0			18	1	1
6	1	44	1	01	1	1
7	1	11	1	10	1	1
8	1	38	1	32	1	1
9	1	08	1	94	0	0
10	0			99	0	0
11	0			83	0	0
12	0			53	0	0
13	0			40	0	0
14	0			05	1	1
15	1	94	0	75	0	1
16	1	93	0	72	0	1
17	1	64	1	74	0	0
18	0			43	0	0
19	0			17	1	1
20	1	82	1	53	0	0
21	0			59	0	0
22	0			35	1	1
23	1	44	0	62	0	1
24	1	41	0	58	0	1
25	1	15	0	08	1	2
26	2	72	0	93	0	2
27	2	23	1	08	1	2
28	2	91	0	23	1	3
29	3	87	0	53	0	3
30	3	69	0	70	0	3
31	3	32	1	76	0	2
32	2	93	0	90	0	2
33	2	55	1	50	0	1
34	1	69	0	78	0	1
35	1	41	1	94	0	0
36	0			24	1	1
37	1	00	1	61	0	0
38	0			05	1	1
39	1	53	1	80	0	0
40	0			25	1	1
41	1	73	0	97	0	0
42	0			18	1	1
43	1	11	1	10	1	1
44	1	82	0	59	0	1
45	1	96	0	12	1	2
46	2	31	1	08	1	2
47	2	04	1	37	1	2
48	2	89	0	03	1	3
49	3	96	0	01	1	4
50	4	86	0	58	0	4
Average	1.02					1.10

service in advance, but, if at any time, the system is empty, no service can take place and hence the corresponding random numbers will be ignored in the simulation.

Inter-arrival random numbers: (taken from the middle top blocks of Table 13.3)

59, 43, 50, 51, 18, 01, 10, 32, 94, 99
83, 53, 40, 05, 75, 72, 74, 43, 17, 53
59, 35, 62, 58, 08, 93, 08, 23, 53, 70
76, 90, 50, 78, 94, 24, -61, 05, 80, 25
97, 18, 10, 59, 12, 08, 37, 03, 01, 58

Service random numbers: (taken from the middle blocks of the second line of Table 13.3)

81, 59, 78, 81, 33, 44, 11, 38, 08, 37
33, 01, 26, 42, 94, 93, 64, 80, 98, 82
08, 56, 44, 41, 15, 72, 23, 91, 87, 69
32, 93, 55, 69, 41, 79, 00, 75, 53, 95
73, 90, 11, 82, 96, 31, 04, 89, 96, 86

Table 13.7 is constructed as follows. We begin with the system empty. The values of Y_s, X_s are discarded since we cannot have a service now in the first period. $Y_a = 59$, corresponding to no arrival in Table 13.6. The final queue size is 0, which is the initial queue size for the next interval. The process is repeated, noting that we assume that any arrivals take place at the end of each period, for our purposes. The average initial and final queue sizes are 1.02 and 1.1 respectively. They differ only because the last final queue size is not included as an initial queue size.

For this problem the proportion of time that the queue is empty, in the long run, is $1 - p/q$, and the expected number in the queue is $p(1 - p)/(q - p)$. The reader may wish to prove this, noting that if there are n in the queue at the beginning of a period, these n remain until the end where transitions take place. If p is small, these reduce to $1 - \rho$, $\rho/(1 - \rho)$ respectively as for the M/M/1 case. For this problem the values are 0.33 and 1.2 respectively. Note that the simulation gives eighteen 0s for the initial queue size, and hence a proportion of time 0.36 is spent with no-one in the system.

If we wish to determine the effect of changing the service parameter from $q = 0.6$ to $q = 0.5$, we re-run the simulation, again using the random numbers used in the first part.

The method used to generate the simulation for the queueing and inventory problems uses a **fixed time advance** procedure, in which the simulation records the position and decisions at each successive time interval. An alternative procedure is to operate the simulation on a **variable time advance** procedure, in which the simulation behaviour is recorded only when events occur. The former is easier to follow, but is inefficient in its operation. The latter is called an **event-scheduling process**. The former comes under the heading of a **process-interaction**

approach. We will now look at the queueing problem again as an event-scheduling process.

An alternative approach to the queueing problem

Let p be the probability of an arrival at the beginning of any specific period, and q be the probability that a customer being served in any period will complete his service in that period. Let X_a be the number of periods between successive arrivals, and X_s be the number of periods taken to serve a customer. Then we have the following probabilities for $l \geqslant 1$, $k \geqslant 1$:

$$P(X_a = l) = (1 - p)^{l-1}p \quad \text{(no arrivals in the first } l-1 \text{ periods and an}$$
$$\text{arrival in the next period)}$$

$$P(X_s = k) = (1 - q)^{k-1}q \quad \text{(no services in the first } k-1 \text{ periods and a}$$
$$\text{service in the } k\text{th period).}$$

For the case $p = 0.4$, $q = 0.6$ we have

$$P(X_a = l) = 0.4 \times 0.6^{l-1}$$
$$P(X_s = k) = 0.6 \times 0.4^{k-1}.$$

The tabulations are given in Table 13.8, where we have rounded off the probabilities. In order to keep matters simple we will assume that the first customer arrives at time 0.

Table 13.8

X_a	Probability	X_s	Probability
1	0.400	1	0.600
2	0.240	2	0.240
3	0.144	3	0.096
4	0.086	4	0.038
5	0.052	5	0.015
6	0.031	6	0.006
7+	0.047	7+	0.005

We have the possibility of indefinitely large values of l, k, and hence we truncate at 7 and assume all numbers greater than 7 are represented by 7. In actual practice we have to justify exactly where we truncate, but we will simply take 7 for illustrative purposes. We will also round off the probabilities as in Table 13.9 and put in the corresponding random number ranges.

Although we will run the simulation for only 50 arrivals it must be stressed that in practice many more will be required in general. Table 13.10 gives the simulation results in which waiting is specifically recorded, since this is of prime consideration in designing queueing systems.

Table 13.9

Y_a	X_a	Probability	Y_a	X_s	Probability
0–399	1	0.400	0–599	1	0.600
400–639	2	0.240	600–839	2	0.240
640–783	3	0.144	840–935	3	0.096
784–869	4	0.086	936–973	4	0.038
870–921	5	0.052	974–988	5	0.015
922–952	6	0.031	989–994	6	0.006
953–999	7+	0.047	995–999	7+	0.005

Table 13.10 is generated as follows. The random numbers $\{Y_a, Y_s\}$ to determine inter-arrival times and service times $\{X_a, X_s\}$ for the first 50 customers are determined (taken from the top and bottom rows of Table 13.3). The time of arrival of each of the instances is determined.

We begin with customer 1. He arrives at $t = 1$, finds the queue empty, and leaves at $t = 6$. Customer 2 arrives at $t = 4$, and hence has to wait 2 units of time before commencing service, and then leaves at $t = 7$. The rest of the table is determined in the same way.

We have chosen only to calculate the average waiting time. This is 2.66. The theoretical value is 3. Had we wished to determine the average number in the queue we would have had to tabulate the number in the queue at each of the epochs at which an arrival or service takes place. Alternatively it can be calculated from the fact that the total waiting time (133) is equal to the total duration (114) × the average queue size, which gives 1.17 for the estimate of the average queue size (true value is 1.2).

Our final example will be taken from the production overage problem of Chapter 12.

A production overage problem

Let us consider the problem given in Section 12.5, and consider the simulation of the policy given in Table 13.11.

For this problem we have to set up random number–random event correspondences for each value q. Let X_q be the number of good vases produced if we put q into production. We then have the following correspondences in Table 13.12, where Pr. is an abbreviation for probability.

It is to be noted that for the particular policy chosen we do not need $\{Y_1, X_1, \text{Pr.}\}$ columns, but put them in for completeness sake.

Let us now begin with $n = N = 4$ and simulate the policy given for 10 set-ups, stopping if the requisite number is produced before the 10th set-up. It is possible for the process to continue for a large number of set-ups, and the length of the simulation may have to be much larger. We also need to run many simulations in order to get a good estimate of the true expected cost.

Table 13.10

Customer	Y_a	X_a	Arrives at time	Y_s	X_s	Waits for service	Leaves at time
1	214	1	1	978	5	0	6
2	775	3	4	398	1	2	7
3	485	2	6	547	1	0	8
4	901	5	11	433	1	0	12
5	837	4	15	055	1	0	16
6	259	1	16	917	3	0	19
7	937	6	22	184	1	0	23
8	624	2	24	547	1	0	25
9	970	7	31	354	1	0	32
10	886	5	36	144	1	0	37
11	952	6	42	220	1	0	43
12	303	1	43	342	1	0	44
13	674	3	46	300	1	0	47
14	482	2	48	089	1	0	49
15	325	1	49	160	1	0	50
16	550	2	51	971	4	0	55
17	431	2	53	922	3	2	58
18	053	1	54	223	1	4	59
19	374	1	55	290	1	4	60
20	350	1	56	637	2	4	62
21	890	5	61	350	1	1	63
22	061	1	62	554	1	1	64
23	183	1	63	548	1	1	65
24	744	3	66	988	5	0	71
25	109	1	67	438	1	4	72
26	622	2	69	163	1	3	73
27	134	1	70	612	2	3	75
28	394	1	71	596	1	4	76
29	661	3	74	688	2	2	78
30	603	2	76	220	1	2	79
31	503	2	78	628	2	1	81
32	240	1	79	717	2	2	83
33	043	1	80	926	3	3	86
34	622	2	82	502	1	4	87
35	350	1	83	823	2	4	89
36	051	1	84	528	1	5	90
37	003	1	85	628	2	5	92
38	221	1	86	491	1	6	93
39	154	1	87	954	4	6	97
40	380	1	88	883	3	9	100
41	834	4	92	814	2	8	102
42	175	1	93	433	1	9	103
43	867	4	97	171	1	6	104
44	495	2	99	905	3	5	107
45	194	1	100	049	1	7	108
46	051	1	101	548	1	7	109
47	758	3	104	067	1	5	110
48	537	2	106	469	1	4	111
49	880	5	111	007	1	0	112
50	590	2	113	567	1	0	114
				Average		2.66	

Table 13.11

n	1	2	3	4
q	2	3	4	4

Table 13.12

Y_1	X_1	Pr.	Y_2	X_2	Pr.	Y_3	X_3	Pr.	Y_4	X_4	Pr.
0–39	0	0.4	0–19	0	0.2	0–9	0	0.1	0–9	0	0.1
40–99	1	0.6	20–59	1	0.4	10–29	1	0.2	10–19	1	0.1
			60–99	2	0.4	30–59	2	0.3	20–39	2	0.2
						60–99	3	0.4	40–69	3	0.3
									70–99	4	0.3

In practice the random numbers will be drawn after each event when we know what the next value of q will be. To simplify matters we will draw the random numbers in advance and use them in sequence as they are required. Table 13.13 gives the set used.

Table 13.13

Y_2	X_2	Y_3	X_3	Y_4	X_4
11	0	26	1	81	4
43	1	12	1	59	3
93	2	62	3	78	4
49	1	01	0	81	4
36	1	87	3	33	2
74	2	93	3	44	3
36	1	88	3	11	1
80	2	04	0	38	2
54	1	31	2	08	0
76	2	26	1	37	2

We will run several simulations using the random numbers in sequence as required, beginning each simulation with the next random number in Table 13.13, which has not been used. Table 13.14 gives the results.

The actual expected cost $v_4 = 141$, and further simulations would be needed to obtain this result. Each policy can be simulated as a basis for final decisions. It is to be noted that the simulations will also give information on the probabilities of various numbers of set-ups, and so on.

Finally let us now look briefly at the random number–random event structure underlying these simulations.

Table 13.14

Simulation number	q	X_q	Cost
1	4	4	78
2	4	3	
	2	0	
	2	1	186
3	4	4	78
4	4	4	78
5	4	2	
	3	1	
	2	2	198
6	4	3	
	2	1	132
7	4	1	
	4	2	
	2	1	210
8	4	0	
	4	2	
	3	1	
	2	2	286
		Average	155.75

13.3   Random number – random event structure

Let us assume that the random event is X, and takes values $X = X_j, j = 1, 2, \ldots$ with probability $P(X = X_j) = p_j, j = 1, 2, \ldots$.

We now need to set up the random number scheme. The random number will be Y, with Y_j being a set of random numbers corresponding to X_j in such a way that $P(X = X_j) = P(Y \text{ is in } Y_j) = p_j$.

The reader should check back with the illustrations given to see how they fit in with the general framework.

The range of Y chosen depends upon the problem and on the precision required. We have chosen ranges from 0–99 or from 0–999, although in the first inventory problem, for example, we could have chosen the range 0–9 equally well. If, in the second approach to the queueing problem, we had not rounded off the probabilities, the range would have been 0–999 999.

The nature of the random variables governing the problem influences the design of the simulation. In our simple inventory and queueing problems the random variables were independently and identically distributed for each occurrence. In practice, the demand in one period may be correlated with the demand in another period, or the inter-arrival time for one arrival may be correlated with the inter-arrival time of another arrival. For the product overage problem the number of defectives depends on previous decisions and on previous numbers of defectives. For such problems the simulation has to be designed to match the circumstances.

Finally, we have restricted ourselves to discrete events, X, in order to keep the text simple. For many problems a continuous random event X may be more appropriate. Consider, for example, the negative exponential queueing problem described in the text. In this case the random variable X is the inter-arrival time T between successive customers and is continuous. The key to handling such cases is the *cumulative probability function*:

$$F(x) = \text{Pr.}\ (X \leqslant x).$$

For the queueing problem, with T, t respectively replacing X, x we have

$$F(t) = 1 - e^{-\lambda t}.$$

The graph of $F(t)$ against t is given in Fig. 13.1.

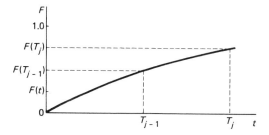

Fig. 13.1

For continuous problems we cannot cater for all possible realisations of X. For the queueing problem we would need to select a subset $\{T_1, T_2, \ldots, T_{j-1}, T_j, \ldots\}$ of the possible values of T. From Fig. 13.1 we see that

$$\text{Pr.}\ (T_{j-1} < T \leqslant T_j) = F(T_j) - F(T_{j-1}).$$

The random numbers $\{Y\}$ are then chosen so that

$$\text{Pr.}\ (Y \text{ is in } Y_j) = F(T_j) - F(T_{j-1}),$$

and whenever Y falls in Y_j some representative T in the interval T_{j-1} to T_j is chosen e.g. $T = T_j$. In practice when the simulation is run on a computer, the computer selects random numbers $Y \in [0, 1]$ and then sets $T = F^{-1}(Y)$, where F^{-1} is the inverse function of F. The numbers to be selected in $[0, 1]$ will be from a predetermined set $\{T_j\}$. It is easily seen that had the only realisations of T been the discrete set $\{T_1, T_2, \ldots, T_j, \ldots\}$, then this would fit in with the simple framework because

$$F(T_j) - F(T_{j-1}) = \text{Pr.}\ (T = T_j) = p_j.$$

This is only a very rudimentary presentation of the simulation of continuous systems, but it should be enough to convey the basic ideas.

13.4　Final comments

As has been indicated, the proper design and control of simulations requires consideration of the lengths and number of repetitions of simulations in order to get good estimates of the parameters which are being sought, such as expected costs per unit time. Each simulation is a realisation of a series of random events and, individually, may give results some way from the true expected values, as shown, for example, by Table 13.4 for the simple inventory problem. Hence a deeper study of simulation requires an appropriate use of statistical analysis which we have not covered.

We have made reference to the generation of a sequence of random numbers. We have used a preset table of random numbers in Table 13.3. However, there are methods of generating such numbers directly. For example *pseudo-random numbers* $\{Y_n\}$ may be generated by applying recurrence relationships of the kind:

$$Y_{n+1} = (aY_n + c) \bmod (m)$$

where a, c are specially chosen constants, $Z \bmod (m)$ = the remainder when Z is divided by m, and Y_0, the initial number, called the *seed*, is specially chosen. Great care has to be given to the choice of the scheme used in order to ensure that the $\{Y_n\}$ do indeed behave like random numbers.

Finally, real-life simulations need the use of a computer. Many languages have been developed to assist efficient simulation. Two languages developed to use the event-scheduling approach mentioned earlier are GASP and SIMSCRIPT. A language developed to use the process interaction approach is GPSS. A more recent language SIMSCRIPT II.5 allows a choice of which of the two approaches to use.

Exercises

1　Carry out the simulation for the inventory control problem of Section 13.2, using the same random numbers, but with the probability distribution (Table 13.15) of demand X, and with $S = 2, 3$.

Table 13.15

X	0	1	2	3	4
P_X	0.20	0.32	0.20	0.20	0.08

Calculate the theoretical costs per week for $S = 2, 3$ and compare with the simulation results.

2　Carry out the simulation for the queueing problem of Section 13.2, where the probability p of an arrival is 0.5 and the probability q of a service, when a customer is being served, is 0.7. Compare the average number in the queue given by the simulation with the theoretical result.

Repeat the simulation using the alternative approach given in the text.

3 Simulate the production overage problem given in Section 13.2 for the following policy given in Table 13.16.

Table 13.16

n	1	2	3	4
q	1	2	3	4

Calculate the theoretical expected cost for $n = N = 4$ and compare with the simulation results.

4 Consider the problem of Section 10.9 where there are two mechanics to look after four machines. When in service, each machine will work for a time given by a negative exponential distribution with mean 120 hours. When one fails, it is repaired by a mechanic if one is free, and the time for the repair is also negative exponential with mean 30 hours. If both mechanics are busy the machine has to wait until one is free before it can be serviced.

(a) Show that if a number X is chosen randomly between 0 and 100, then if

$$T = -\mu \log_e ((100 - X)/100),$$

then it can be considered as a random time from a negative exponential distribution with mean μ.

(b) In order to simulate the break down times for each machine, we could either (i) simulate the breakdown time for each machine or (ii) simulate the breakdown time for the next machine to breakdown. Use (i) to describe how to perform both methods and comment on which you would prefer.

(c) Simulate the queueing system described above for 200 hours, starting when one machine has just broken down and using the random variable Table 13.3.

Describe all the events when they occur and from this calculate the average queue size, the average waiting time, and the average time for which both mechanics are free.

5 Simulate the optimal policy for the production problem in Exercise 12.7 over ten three-year periods. How close is the expected cost of the optimal policy to its average cost in the ten simulations?

14
The Operational Research Process

14.1 Introduction

This text has concentrated on a selection of techniques of operational research. The intention has been to understand their working in the broadest of terms and to illustrate their use by applying them to some very simple examples. In doing so the information required to define the problems required has been given, whereas in practice it must be collected. Moreover, there are other aspects of the operational research process which require consideration before any formal modelling and analysis can be carried out. For example, in the linear programming chapter the objectives to be minimised or maximised are already given, whereas in practice these have to be identified as part of the operational research process.

In this chapter we will briefly discuss several aspects of the operational research process so that the techniques we have discussed may be seen in proper perspective as only one part of a fuller operational research study.

14.2 Problem formulation

Identifying the problem

In real life, it is rarely the case that a decision maker can say, 'I have a problem of mixing products so as to minimise the cost. Can you solve it by linear programming?' Much more likely is that the decision maker feels he has a problem in the production-marketing area but is not quite sure what the problem is. Thus the first process in a study is often to identify the problem, or the facet of the problem, that is causing concern to the decision maker. This involves good communication skills to elucidate what is required, and an ability to distinguish the kernel of the problem from the peripheral considerations. It may be that the problem is not one that is amenable to operational research modelling but is more to do with man management or interpersonal relationships. If it is an operational research problem one needs to know what information is available, and how reliable this information is. Finally one needs to know how important the problem is to the decision maker. Is he prepared to wait some time and spend resources searching for an optimal solution, or is he concerned only with finding an improvement on the present solution provided that it is available next week. These questions lead naturally to the second stage.

Formulation of the problem

The process of formulating the model of the problem can be broken down into several steps, namely:

(a) identification of the decision makers
(b) identification of the possible actions, or options
(c) identification of the constraints on the actions
(d) identification of the objectives to be improved
(e) identification of an overall criterion, or a way of combining the objectives in (d).

Let us briefly comment on each component in turn.

(a) Decision makers
The choice between actions depends crucially on who is doing the choosing. Which decision maker's problem is the model describing? For example in queueing problems, it is very likely that an operational research model describing the situation from the viewpoint of the decision maker who controls the servers will come up with different actions from one viewing the situation from the customers' viewpoint—what's best for the group need not be best for an individual. Similarly a decision on how much a firm should produce or how frequently products should be inspected will be seen differently by the marketing manager and the production manager because they have different objectives. It is necessary to clarify who is the decision maker—the production department, the sales department or the firm as a whole.

(b) The actions
So far in this text, the set of possible actions has been specified at the outset. In reality, part of the operational research process is to find out which actions are possible. Sometimes company policy or procedures mean that activities that at first seem possible cannot be implemented. On other occasions, the problem may be recast in a broader framework, so that there are many more actions possible than appeared on first inspection. Thus in the case of scheduling the overhaul of a piece of machinery (Chapter 11) the problem can be extended to allow replacement of the equipment as well as overhaul; in the sequencing of jobs on machines (Chapter 6) one might also consider increasing the number of machines.

(c) Constraints on the actions
In some operational research problems the possible actions are well specified—whether we should buy machine A or machine B, for example. In other cases, especially in the linear programming problems of Chapter 2, the actions are given implicitly by setting constraints on them. Such constraints tend to be classified as *hard* or *soft* depending on the flexibility one has in dealing with them. A *hard* constraint is one which cannot be violated. Every job must be done and every person must do one job is a hard constraint in an allocation problem for example. On the other hand a constraint which gives a limit on the average amount of

money tied up in stock in an inventory problem is a soft constraint. It reflects the undesirability of having too much stock, which is not making interest, but it prejudges whether this limit is correct and whether the saving in order cost outweighs this holding cost even at this specified level. These are extremes and some constraints seem to lie in between. Thus in a transportation problem, one could lessen the demand at a destination by allowing it to buy in units directly. Similarly, in the production problem with different types of products, are the constraints on raw materials really inviolable? One could always buy in more and the sensitivity analysis approach suggested at the end of the linear programming chapter would help in deciding if this was worthwhile.

(d) The objectives

A very difficult part of the model formulation process is to determine what objectives are to be considered. Often, as in the queueing problems, there are two or more elements to the problem—cost and service in this case. Service may be defined in terms of expected waiting time for a customer and a waiting cost per unit time estimated to make the final criterion purely financial. However, it may be more important for the customers that they do not wait longer than a specified time and the probability of doing this should be the service criterion. Even if one agrees on a financial criterion, what time horizon should be considered and how should inflation and uncertainty about future costs and profits be incorporated?

Often, soft constraints and objectives are interchangeable: e.g. in the nutritional problem, should we try also to maximise level of nutrition? In other cases, some of the objectives such as safety, flexibility, aesthetic value, etc. become very difficult to quantify.

(e) Overall objective

Ideally one should try to identify a single measure of worth combining the various component objectives. As in the queueing problem described earlier, this may be done by measuring each objective on a common scale and then adding the objectives. Thus the service objective was equated with a cost and the overall cost minimised. It is rare to be able to do this well in practice and it may be necessary to derive a super-objective function from the decision maker. This is sometimes taken as a weighted combination of the individual objectives, where the weights are elucidated from the decision maker. Utility theory gives another approach to finding a super-objective.

In some cases it is not possible to combine the objectives and one must then be satisfied with a set of *efficient* actions—efficient here means there is no other action which does as well in all objectives, and strictly better in at least one. Alternatively one could make all the objectives into soft constraints and ask if there is any solution to the problem with these constraints, which is the approach of goal programming.

Finally, although each of the steps (a)–(e) is involved in the operational research process, not only may the process of identifying these be cyclic, but even at the end (or supposed end) of the study, the problem may need to be reformulated.

Thus, as the study proceeds, identified objectives may suggest sets of actions to look at, which may then suggest other objectives. For example, in the queueing problem the objectives of cost and service may suggest increased machine speeds, which may in turn bring into focus the safety factor, and this in turn may suggest alternative machines.

14.3 Techniques and modelling

The various techniques we have covered revolve around the construction of mathematical models of various kinds, including symbolic analytical representations and simulation models.

When confronted with a problem it is important to realise that there is very often a choice of modelling techniques to use, and this choice has to be made on the basis of the cost and difficulties involved in constructing the model, the information required, and sometimes the ease of communication with the decision makers. In inventory control and in queueing, there are occasions where simulation may be the only real choice open to the operational researcher. However, for simple problems it is far less powerful in its analysis than the analytic optimisation methods which can also be applied (see Chapter 12 for an example).

Three main advantages of simulation are that:

(1) it can deal with much more complex models;
(2) the complete probability distribution of the behaviour of the system can be estimated, which is important if the key parameters governing the decision maker's choice are unknown;
(3) simulation is a look-alike (*iconic*) form of modelling which is more readily understood by the decision maker.

Another factor which might affect our choice of technique is our ability to carry out a sensitivity analysis on the parameters of the model. These parameters are often only estimates from underlying data sets and we need to find out how variations in these parameters affect the overall actions chosen. If there is not much change, then we can feel fairly confident about recommending those actions, but if there are large changes, we need to investigate the data more carefully.

In all our models we have made assumptions about the structure, but have not questioned these assumptions, except perhaps constraint levels and coefficients of objective functions in sensitivity analysis. In practice, all assumptions must be validated. Thus, for example, in our queueing problems we have assumed that arrival and service rates are negative exponential in distribution. In practice, this must be validated by the use of statistical tests, a topic with which we have not dealt in this text, but which is indispensable in operational research. In practice, we have only a finite set of data and we have to test this data to determine whether or not, with any specified degree of confidence, it is compatible with the assumptions.

The approach of this text to all of our modelling is one of synthesis, i.e. various characteristics of the problem are put together to produce a synthesised model and the model is analysed to draw various conclusions. In this sense it differs from some sciences in that no experimentation is performed. However, sometimes the data simply does not exist on which to build a synthesised model. For example, if we are concerned with the performance of entirely new systems such as nuclear reactors, data will not exist from which we may deduce reliability behaviour and maintenance cost behaviour. For such situations experimentation (testing) is the only real mechanism for evaluation. If the operational research project does lead to the implementation of a recommended action, we should experiment by checking that the actual results compare with the predicted performance. This is very important because in reality the structure of the problem changes with time, but our models assume no such changes. It is important to monitor the key structural and parametric assumptions so that, when necessary, the problem can be re-solved and a new decision taken. Thus in inventory problems it is certain that the demand rates and cost parameters will change over time.

Finally we come to an essential feature of a successful operational research project—its implementation.

14.4   Implementation

Ackoff said, 'implementation is often the only real test of the validity of research conclusions and as such should be part of the research.' The first point is arguable, but undoubtedly the purpose of undertaking an operational research study is to seek implementation of some action justified on the basis of the study. It is important to recognise this at the outset of the study and to conduct the study in the light of this aim. There are many factors which need to be borne in mind during the study in order to achieve this aim, some of which are as follows.

(1)   Communications between the operational researcher and the various parties affected can play an important role in the successful implementation. This requires direct involvement of the affected parties, clarity of communications and an acceptable understanding of the basis of the study. Final reports should be clear on the assumptions made and their validation, so that further discussion about the validity of the results is facilitated on a rational basis.

(2)   The ability to implement solutions depends upon the existence of resources available to achieve that implementation. Complicated procedures may be counter-productive, and simpler procedures may be more effective, even at the risk of some loss of optimality in terms of the original objectives.

(3)   The cost and time of implementation have to be set against the anticipated gains from the actions to be implemented.

(4) Successful implementation depends on skills developed in the study itself. For example, the collection and processing of the data needed to operate the decision rule needs to be done effectively just as it was done in estimating the parameters in the study itself. There is a lot to be said for having the person who carried out the study actively involved in supervising its implementation.

14.5 Conclusion

In this chapter we have given a rather superficial description of the operation research process, but our aim has been to emphasise that the techniques developed in the earlier chapters are only part of the skills necessary to do operational research.

Further Reading

The following two books give an insight into the military origins of operational research:

Blackett, P. S., *Studies of War*, Oliver and Boyd, 1962.

Waddington, C. H., *O. R. in World War 2, Operational Research against the U-Boat*, Elek Science, 1973.

The following two books give an insight into the nature of the operational research process:

Ackoff, R., *Scientific Method, Optimising Applied Research Decisions*, Wiley, 1962.

White, D. J., *Decision Methodology*, Wiley, 1975.

The following six books cover the general techniques of operational research in ascending order of depth:

Wicks, C. T. and Yewdall, G. A., *Operational Research*, Pan Piper, 1971.

Makower, M. S. and Williamson, E., *Operational Research*, Teach Yourself Books, English Universities Press, 1967.

Duckworth, W. E., Geer, A. E. and Lockett, A. G., *A Guide to Operational Research*, Chapman and Hall, 1977.

Ackoff, R. L. and Sasieni, M. W., *Fundamentals of Operations Research*, Wiley, 1968.

Daellenbach, H. and George, J., *Introduction to Operations Research Techniques*, Allyn and Bacon, 1978.

Wagner, H., *Principles of Operations Research*, Prentice-Hall, 1969.

The reader would also find the *Journal of the Operational Research Society* useful.

Solutions to Exercises

Chapter 2

1 x_1 is amount processed on process I per day.
x_2 is amount processed on process II per day.
Maximise net revenue

$$M = 285(\tfrac{3}{4}x_1 + \tfrac{1}{4}x_2) + 105(\tfrac{1}{4}x_1 + \tfrac{3}{4}x_2) - 60x_1 - 30x_2$$

$$= 180x_1 + 120x_2$$

subject to

$$x_1 \leqslant 1\tfrac{1}{2}$$
$$x_2 \leqslant 3$$
$$x_1 + x_2 \leqslant 4$$
$$20x_1 + 10x_2 \leqslant 10$$
$$x, x_2 \geqslant 0.$$

Solution is $x_1 = 0.5$, $x_2 = 3.0$, $M = 450$.

2 x_1 is number of diesel trains and x_2 is number of electric trains

$$
\begin{array}{lll}
\text{Maximise} & x_1 + x_2 & \\
\text{subject to} & x_1 + x_2 \leqslant 84 & \text{(drivers)} \\
 & x_1 + 2x_2 \leqslant 114 & \text{(guards)} \\
 & 2x_1 + x_2 \leqslant 250 & \text{(cleaners)} \\
 & 4x_1 + 3x_2 \leqslant 309 & \text{(fitters)} \\
 & x_1 \leqslant 60 & \text{(diesel train)} \\
 & x_2 \leqslant 35 & \text{(electric trains)} \\
 & x_1, x_2 \geqslant 0. &
\end{array}
$$

Maximum number of trains is 84 ($x_1 = 54 + x$, $x_2 = 30 - x$, $0 \leqslant x \leqslant 3$). Can sack 0 drivers, 3 guards, 112 cleaners, 3 fitters. If 4 guards and 4 fitters leave, can run 83 trains ($x_1 = 56$, $x_2 = 27$). Cheapest way is 0 trains $x_1 = 0$, $x_2 = 0$.

3 Let f_j, r_j, i_j be the number of airmen flying, resting and instructing in week i, $i = 1$, 2 and 3.

Minimise $200\,(f_1+f_2+f_3)+5(r_1+r_2+r_3)+80(i_1+i_2+i_3)$

$$f_1+r_1+i_1 \leqslant 120$$
$$f_1+f_2+f_3 \geqslant 720$$
$$f_1 \qquad \geqslant 100$$
$$f_2 \qquad \geqslant f_1$$
$$f_3 \qquad \geqslant f_2$$
$$f_2+r_2+i_2 \leqslant 120+20i_1$$
$$f_3+r_3+i_3 \leqslant 120+20i_1+20i_2$$
$$f_2 \qquad \leqslant 120+20i_1-f_1$$
$$f_3 \qquad \leqslant 120+20i_1+20i_2-f_2.$$

4   Maximise M

$$x_1+x_2+s_1 = 4$$
$$x_2+s_2 \quad\;\; = 1\tfrac{1}{2}$$
$$x_2+s_3 \quad\;\; = 3$$
$$20x_1+10x_2+s_4 = 40$$
$$M-180x_1-120x_2 = 0.$$

Initial solution is $x_1 = 0$, $x_2 = 0$, $s_1 = 4$, $s_2 = 1\tfrac{1}{2}$, $s_3 = 3$, $s_4 = 40$.
Make x_1 basic; limit is $x_1 = 1\tfrac{1}{2}\{s_2, x_2\}$ is non-basic.

$$x_1+s_2 \qquad = 1\tfrac{1}{2}$$
$$x_2+s_1-s_2 \quad\;\; = 2\tfrac{1}{2}$$
$$x_2+s_3 \qquad = 3$$
$$10x_2+s_4-20s_2 = 10$$
$$M-120x_2+180s_2 = 270.$$

Make x_2 basic; limit is $x_2 = 1$ $\{s_2, s_4\}$ is non-basic.

$$x_2+\tfrac{1}{10}s_4-2s_2 = 1$$
$$x_1+s_2 \qquad\;\; = 1\tfrac{1}{2}$$
$$s_1-\tfrac{1}{10}s_4 \;+s_2 = 1\tfrac{1}{2}$$
$$s_3-\tfrac{1}{10}s_4+2s_2 = 2$$
$$M+12s_4-60s_2 = 390.$$

Make s_2 basic; limit is $s_2 = 1$, $\{s_3, s_4\}$ is non-basic.

$$\tfrac{1}{2}s_3-\tfrac{1}{20}s_4+s_2 = 1$$
$$x_2+s_3 = 3$$
$$x_1-\tfrac{1}{2}s_3+\tfrac{1}{20}s_4 = \tfrac{1}{2}$$
$$s_1-\tfrac{1}{2}s_3-\tfrac{1}{20}s_4 = \tfrac{1}{2}$$

$M + 30s_3 + 9s_4 = 450$.

Solution is $x_1 = \frac{1}{2}$, $x_3 = 3$, $M = 450$.

5 (a) $M = 3x + 2y = 7.5 - 0.5u - 0.15v$. So solution is optimal as $M + 0.5u + 0.15v = 7.5$ and coefficients are non-negative.

(b) $M = \alpha x + \beta y = \frac{1}{2}\mu + 3\beta + (\frac{1}{2}\alpha - \beta)u - \alpha/20v$. Solution is optimal if $\frac{1}{2}\alpha - \beta \leqslant 0$ and $-\alpha/20 \leqslant 0$, i.e. $0 \leqslant \alpha \leqslant 2\beta$.

6 x_1 is number of Pixie Mixie, x_2 number of Super Mixer, x_3 number of Mixmaster.

$$\text{Maximise } 2x_1 + 3x_2 + 4x_3$$
$$\text{subject to } 10x_1 + 12x_2 + 18x_3 \leqslant 12\,200$$
$$x_1 + 2.5x_2 + 3x_3 \leqslant 2000$$
$$x_1, x_2, x_3 \geqslant 0.$$

Dual is Minimise $12\,200u_1 + 2000u_2$

$$10u_1 + u_2 \leqslant 2$$
$$12u_1 + 2.5u_2 \geqslant 3$$
$$18u_1 + 3u_2 \geqslant 4$$
$$u_1, u_2 \geqslant 0.$$

Solution is $u_1 = \frac{2}{13}$, $u_2 = \frac{6}{13}$ with value £2800. Complementary slackness gives $u_1 = 0$ or $10x_1 + 12x_2 + 18x_3 = 12\,200$; $u_2 = 0$ or $x_1 + 2.5x_2 + 3x_3 = 2000$: $x_1 = 0$ or $10u_1 + u_2 = 2$; $x_2 = 0$ or $12u_1 + 2.5u_2 = 3$; $x_3 = 0$ or $18u_1 + 3u_2 = 4$. Therefore $x_3 = 0$, $x_1 = 500$, $x_2 = 600$. u_2 is shadow value of warehouse space so company would pay £$\frac{6}{13}$ = 46.2p per ft.[3]

7 x_1 is number of colour televisions, x_2 number of black and white televisions, x_3 number of radios, x_4 number of record players and x_5 number of speakers.

$$\text{Maximise } 50x_1 + 40x_2 + 10x_3 + 30x_4 + 8x_5$$
$$\text{subject to } 20x_1 + 10x_2 + 5x_3$$
$$+ 8x_4 + 2x_5 \leqslant 1000$$
$$x_5 + 10 \leqslant x_4 \text{ or } (-x_4 + x_5 \leqslant -10)$$
$$x_1, x_2, x_3, x_4\, x_5 \geqslant 0.$$

Dual is Minimise $1000u_1 - 10u_2$

$$20u_1 \geqslant 50$$
$$10u_1 \geqslant 50$$
$$5u_1 \geqslant 10$$
$$8u_1 - u_2 \geqslant 30$$
$$2u_1 + u_2 \geqslant 8$$
$$u_1, u_2 \leqslant 0.$$

Solution is $u_1 = 4$, $u_2 = 2$, $M = 3980$. Complementary slackness gives $x_1 = 0$, $x_2 = 92$, $x_3 = 0$, $x_4 = 10$, $x_5 = 0$.

8 (a)   Let x be the amount transported from A to C; let y be amount transported from A to D. So $3 - x$ go from B to C, $7 - y$ from B to D, $10 - x - y$ from A to E and $x + y - 4$ from B to E.

$$\text{Maximise } 5x + 4y + 2(10 - x - y) + 4(3 - x) + 6(7 - y) + 3(x + y - 4)$$

$$\text{subject to } 3 - x \geqslant 0$$
$$7 - y \geqslant 0$$
$$10 - x - y \geqslant 0$$
$$x + y - 4 \geqslant 0$$
$$x, y \geqslant 0.$$

Solution $x = 0$, $y = 7$, $M = 55$.

(b)   Let x_{ij} be amount transported from i to j.

$$\text{Maximise } 5x_{AC} + 4x_{AD} + 2x_{AE} + 4x_{BC} + 6x_{BD} + 3x_{BE}$$

$$\begin{aligned}\text{subject to } x_{AC} + x_{AD} + x_{AE} &= 10 \\ x_{BC} + x_{BD} + x_{BE} &= 6 \\ x_{AC} + x_{BC} &= 3 \\ x_{AD} + x_{BD} &= 7 \\ x_{AE} + x_{BE} &= 6 \\ x_{ij} &\geqslant 0\end{aligned}$$

(c)
$$\text{Minimise } 10u_1 + 6u_2 + 3v_1 + 7v_2 + 6v_3$$
$$\text{subject to } u_1 + v_1 \geqslant 5; \; u_1 + v_2 \geqslant 4; \; u_1 + v_3 \geqslant 2$$
$$u_2 + v_1 \geqslant 4; \; u_2 + v_2 \geqslant 6; \; u_2 + v_3 \geqslant 3$$

9
$$\begin{aligned}x_1 + x_2 + s_1 &= a \\ x_1 + s_2 &= b \\ x_2 + s_3 &= c \\ 20x_1 + 10x_2 + s_4 &= d\end{aligned}$$

At $x_1 = \frac{1}{2}$, $x_2 = 3$, non-basic variables are $\{s_3, s_4\}$, so

$$\begin{aligned}x_2 + s_3 &= c \\ x_1 + \tfrac{1}{20}s_4 - \tfrac{1}{2}s_3 &= \tfrac{1}{20}d - \tfrac{1}{2}c \\ s_2 - \tfrac{1}{20}s_4 + \tfrac{1}{2}s_3 &= b - \tfrac{1}{20}d + \tfrac{1}{2}c \\ s_1 - \tfrac{1}{2}s_3 - \tfrac{1}{20}s_4 &= a - \tfrac{1}{2}c - \tfrac{1}{20}d.\end{aligned}$$

So solution remains feasible if $c \geqslant 0$, $\tfrac{1}{20}d - \tfrac{1}{2}c \geqslant 0$

$$b - \tfrac{1}{20}d + \tfrac{1}{2}c \geqslant 0, \; a - \tfrac{1}{2}c - \tfrac{1}{20}d \geqslant 0.$$

(b) $M = 180(\tfrac{1}{20}d - \tfrac{1}{2}c) + 120(c) = 9d + 30c.$

10 x_1 is number of cheap presents; x_2 number of expensive ones.

$$\begin{aligned}
\text{Cost objective function} \quad &\text{Min } 5x_1 + 20x_2 \\
\text{Time objective function} \quad &\text{Min } 2x_1 + x_2 \\
\text{subject to} \quad &x_1 + x_2 \geqslant 12 \\
&x_2 \geqslant 3 \\
&5x_1 + x_2 \geqslant 20.
\end{aligned}$$

  (a)   Cost solution is $x_1 = 9$, $x_2 = 3$, cost 105.
  (b)   Time solution is $x_1 = 2$, $x_2 = 10$, time 14 hours.
  (c)   Efficient points are $x_1 = x$, $x_2 = 12 - x$, $2 \leqslant x \leqslant 9$. With cost/time objective of $(240 - 15x, 12 + x)$.
  (d) $x_1 = x$, $x_2 = 12 - x$ $8 \leqslant x \leqslant 9$.

Chapter 3

1 (a) $x_{11} = 1$, $x_{12} = 6$, $x_{23} = 2$, $x_{24} = 6$, $x_{31} = 4$, $x_{32} = 7$, $x_{ij} = 0$ otherwise; minimal cost $= 31$; solution not unique.

    (b) $x_{11} = 15$, $x_{21} = 1$, $x_{24} = 25$, $x_{32} = 10$, $x_{33} = 30$, $x_{34} = 10$, $x_{ij} = 0$ otherwise; minimal cost $= 538$; solution is unique.

    (c) $x_{11} = 1$, $x_{13} = 5$, $x_{21} = 10$, $x_{31} = 3$, $x_{32} = 12$, $x_{ij} = 0$ otherwise; minimal cost $= 93$; solution is unique.

    (d) $x_{11} = 14$, $x_{12} = 6$, $x_{22} = 10$, $x_{32} = 4$, $x_{33} = 4$, $x_{34} = 27$, $x_{43} = 16$, $x_{ij} = 0$ otherwise; minimal cost $= 211$; solution is not unique.

    (e) This is an unbalanced problem; hence add dummy destination with requirement 1. $x_{13} = 1$, $x_{21} = 1$, $x_{23} = 2$, $x_{31} = 1$, $x_{32} = 1$, $x_{ij} = 0$ otherwise; minimal cost $= 142$; solution is unique.

2 (a) The coefficients $c_{ij} - u_i - v_j$ are zero in the cells $(2, 4)$, $(3, 1)$. Any extra transportation quantities added to these cells, with adjustment of supplies, would be optimal for the new problem. If we increase the supply level 3 by two units, the increase in cost is 0 for the first problem, and this is the required answer. Similarly, for the second problem, we increase supply level 2 by two units.

    (b) To ensure $m + n - 1 = 8$ basic variables, we select two extra cells to make up a transportation solution to the new problem. In addition to the $\{u_i\}$, $\{v_j\}$ solutions to the first problem, we also have (selecting cells $(4,4)$, $(4,5)$) equalities $u_4 + v_5 = c_{45}$, $u_4 = c_{44}$, $v_5 = c_{45} - c_{44}$. Calculating all the values of $c_{ij} - u_i - v_j$, sufficient conditions are the non-negativity of these:

$$c_{15} \geqslant 1 + c_{45} - c_{44}, \quad c_{25} \geqslant c_{45} - c_{44}, \quad c_{35} \geqslant c_{45} - c_{44},$$
$$c_{41} \geqslant c_{44}, \quad c_{42} \geqslant c_{44} + 1, \quad c_{43} \geqslant c_{44} + 2.$$

    (c) The value of $c_{21} - u_2 - v_1$ is zero. If we reduce the requirement of destination 1 to 15, we can simply make $x_{21} = 0$, and this will remain optimal. The solution is unique.

(d) Put in a dummy destination and a dummy supply, with requirement and availability levels M sufficiently large (e.g. $M \geqslant 31$). Extend the solution in Exercise 1(c) by two cells (e.g. $x_{14} = 0$, $x_{44} = 31$) to obtain $m + n - 1 = 7$ basic variables. Then, with $u_1 = 0$ in Exercise 1(c), we obtain $v_4 = p_1, u_4 = -p_1$. Calculating the $c_{ij} - u_i - v_j$ values gives $p_2 \geqslant p_1 - 2$, $p_3 \geqslant p_1 - 5$, $q_1 \geqslant 6 - p_1$, $q_2 \geqslant 7 - p_1$, $q_3 \geqslant 4 - p_1$.

3 (a) The problem is set up as a transportation problem with six supply sources (production in any month either normal time and/or overtime) and four destinations (each of the three months plus a dummy). The unit cost matrix is in Table S3.1. A solution is $x_{11} = 6$, $x_{21} = 1$, $x_{22} = 3$, $x_{32} = 5$, $x_{34} = 1$, $x_{44} = 4$, $x_{53} = 6$, $x_{63} = 4$, $x_{ij} = 0$ otherwise, i.e. produce 6 in month 1 at normal time for use in month 1, produce 4 in month 1 at overtime, using 1 in month 1, and 3 in month 2, and so on. The minimal total cost is 105. The solution is not unique.

Table S3.1

i		j 1	2	3	4	A	
	1	2	3	4	0	6	Source 1 is production
	2	3	4	5	0	4	in month 1 at normal
	3		6	7	0	6	time.
	4		9	10	0	4	Source 2 is production
	5			4	0	6	in month 1 at overtime.
	6			6	0	4	The rest are similar.
R		7	8	10	5		

(b) If the unit stock holding cost is $1 + \varepsilon$, then, in Table S3.1, $x_{12}, x_{13}, x_{22}, x_{23}, x_{33}, x_{43}$ become $3 + \varepsilon$, $4 + 2\varepsilon$, $4 + \varepsilon$, $5 + 2\varepsilon$, $7 + \varepsilon$, $10 + \varepsilon$ respectively. Calculate the row and column shadow costs for the optimal solution of (a), in terms of ε. Then, setting $c_{ij} - u_i - v_j \geqslant 0$ gives $0 \leqslant \varepsilon \leqslant 3$.

4 (a) There are seven initial constraints in the variables $\{x_{ij}\}$, but any one is deducible from the remaining six and may be removed. The problem is a balanced one and constraints are all equalities.

(b) The basic variables are $x_{12}, x_{23}, x_{24}, x_{31}, x_{32}, x_{33}$. Use the equations in (a) to express these in terms of the non-basic variables, and then do the same for the objective function M, to derive

$$M = 102 + x_{11} + x_{13} + 4x_{14} + 4x_{21} + x_{22} + x_{34}$$

with positive coefficients for each non-basic variable, and hence the solution is uniquely optimal.

5 (a) The transportation matrix is as shown in Table S3.2, with a dummy destination since the problem is unbalanced.

Table S3.2

		j					
		1	2	3	4	5	*A*
	1	2	3	4	5	0	20
	2	3	4	5	6	0	20
i	3	4	5	6	7	0	30
	4	5	6	7	8	0	10
R		15	35	15	10	5	

An optimal solution is $x_{11} = 15$, $x_{12} = 5$, $x_{22} = 20$, $x_{32} = 10$, $x_{33} = 15$, $x_{34} = 5$, $x_{44} = 5$, $x_{45} = 5$. The minimal cost is 340. The solution is not unique.

(b) (i) If $\{a_i\}$, $\{b_j\}$ are the loading and unloading unit charges, we see that $c_{ij} = a_i + b_j$. Then, with some manipulation, we have

$$M = 360 - x_{15} - 2x_{25} - 3x_{35} - 4x_{45}.$$

The smallest value of M is taken when $x_{45} = 5$, $x_{i5} = 0$, $i \neq 4$. All solutions giving these values are equally optimal.

(ii) Suppose we select $\{u_i\} = \{a_i\}$, $\{v_j\} = \{b_j\}$, $i = 1, 2, 3, 4$, $j = 1, 2, 3$, 4, $v_5 = a_4$. Then $c_{ij} - u_i - v_j = 0$, $i = 1, 2, 3, 4$, $j = 1, 2, 3, 4$, $c_{i5} - u_i - v_5 = a_4 - a_i > 0$ for $i \neq 4$, $c_{45} - u_4 - v_5 = 0$. Hence, all solutions with $x_{i5} = 0$, $i \neq 4$, are equally optimal, and any solution with $x_{i5} \neq 0$, for some $i \neq 4$, is not optimal.

6 By replacing c_{ij} by $-c_{ij}$, from the linear programming chapter we may replace the maximisation problem by a minimisation problem. Alternatively, since $\{c_{ij} - u_i - v_j\}$ are simply the objective function coefficients in linear programming form, we may look for *positive* $c_{ij} - u_i - v_j$ values when seeking improvements, as distinct from looking for *negative* values.

Chapter 4

1 (a) (1, 5), (2, 3), (3, 4), (4, 1), (5, 2). The maximal value is 36. The solution is not unique.

(b) (1, 2), (2, 1), (3, 3), (4, 4), (5, 5). The minimal value is 154. The solution is not unique.

(c) (1, 2), (2, 4), (3, 1), (4, 5), (5, 3). The minimal value is 31. The solution is not unique.

    (d)   (1, 4), (2, 5), (3, 3), (4, 1), (5, 2). The maximin value is 5. The solution is not unique.

    (e)   (1, 1), (2, 5), (3, 4), (4, 2), (5, 3). The minimal value is 13. The solution is not unique.

2 (a)   After the first minimising pass, we obtain (1, 3), (2, 1), (3, 2), (4, 4) with minimal value 10 and is unique.

    (b)   The second minimising pass then gives (1, 2), (2, 4), (3, 1), (4, 3) with value 11 and is unique. Thus the total value is 21.

    (c)   Yes. The total minimal value cannot be less than 20. For a minimal value of 20, the second pass would need to give a value of 10, but this is not possible since only one assignment has value 10.

    (d)   No. Consider the example shown in Table S4.1.

Table S4.1

		j			
		1	2	3	4
	1	0	100	1	4
i	2	100	0	4	100
	3	100	4	0	1
	4	4	100	100	0

Using the suggested procedure we derive assignments (1, 1), (2, 2), (3, 3), (4, 4), (value 0) and (4, 1), (3, 2), (2, 3), (1, 4) (value 16) with a total value of 16. The following two assignments give a total value of 14: (1, 1), (2, 3), (3, 2), (4, 4) and (1, 3), (2, 2), (3, 4), (4, 1).

3 The assignments are as shown in Table S4.2, considering firm 1 as three firms, firm 2 as two firms, and firm 3 as one firm.

Table S4.2

		Jobs			Dummies		
		1	2	3	4	5	6
Firm 1	1	20	35	8	0	0	0
	2	20	35	8	0	0	0
	3	20	35	8	0	0	0
Firm 2	4	15	40	K	0	0	0
	5	15	40	K	0	0	0
Firm 3	6	12	33	6	0	0	0

The solution is $(1, 2), (2, 3), (3, 4), (4, 5), (5, 6), (6, 1)$ with a minimal value of 55 (firm 1 gets jobs 2 and 3, and firm 3 gets job 1). The solution is unique.

4 Define an assignment table by $c_{ij} = 1$ if the cell (i, j) is a zero, and otherwise set $c_{ij} = 0$. Then the problem of finding the maximal number of independent zero cells is equivalent to the linear program:

$$\text{maximise } \sum_i \sum_j c_{ij} x_{ij}$$

$$\text{subject to } \sum_j x_{ij} = 1, \text{ for all } i$$

$$\sum_i x_{ij} = 1, \text{ for all } j.$$

The dual problem is

$$\text{minimise } \sum_i u_i + \sum_j v_j$$

$$\text{subject to } u_i + v_j \geqslant c_{ij} \text{ for all } i, j.$$

The complementary slackness conditions give $u_i + v_j = c_{ij} = 1$ or 0, when $x_{ij} = 1$. We see that the u_i and v_j may be taken to be 0 or 1 without loss. Then the condition $u_i + u_j \geqslant c_{ij}$ is precisely the condition that the cell (i, j) is covered by either a row line and/or a column line, and $\Sigma_i u_i + \Sigma_j v_j$ is the total number of lines used.

5 Let x_{ij} be a starting solution for the transportation problem and $t = \max_{(i,j):x_{ij} > 0} [t_{ij}]$. Construct a new transportation problem with

$$c_{ij} = 1 \text{ if } t_{ij} = t$$

$$= 0 \text{ if } t_{ij} < t$$

$$= K \text{ (large) if } t_{ij} > t$$

and find the minimal total cost for this transportation problem. A better value than t will exist only if the minimal value of this transportation problem is zero. The procedure is repeated until an optimal solution is found.

6 Put 1 when all $c_{ij} = c_{ij}$ value for circled solution in column j (Table S4.3).

Table S4.3

		Job				
		j				
		1	2	3	4	5
	1	①✓	K	0	K	K
	2	K	K	1✓	K	①
Person *i*	3	K	①	0	0	1✓
	4	K	0	①	0✓	1
	5	K	0✓	K	①	K

Put 0 for values less than the c_{ij} value of the circled solution in column j. Put K (≥ 5) in the other cells. Then the solution in the circled position is dominated if and only if a solution to the new problem exists which contains no K and at least one 0, i.e. a solution with value < 5. This may be tackled as a new assignment problem. By inspection the circled solution is dominated by the ticked solution.

Chapter 5

1 Apply Lawler's algorithm.
Optimal sequence is $(J_6, J_1, J_2, J_8, J_5, J_4, J_3, J_7)$ with max $\{\alpha_i T_i\} = 18$. If objective changed, then optimal sequence is $(J_8, J_6, J_1, J_2, J_5, J_3, J_4, J_7)$ with max $\{\alpha_i T_i^2\} = 162$.

2
$$\overline{W} = \frac{1}{n} \sum_{l=1}^{n} W_i = \frac{1}{n} \sum_{l=1}^{n} (C_i - p_i) = \overline{C} - \frac{1}{n} \sum_{l=1}^{n} p_i = \overline{C} - \text{constant}.$$

So minimising $\overline{W}$ is equivalent to minimising $\overline{C}$. Apply Smith's algorithm to problem. Optimal sequence is either $(J_3, J_6, J_2, J_7, J_4, J_5, J_1)$ or $(J_6, J_3, J_2, J_7, J_4, J_5, J_1)$, both with $\overline{C} = 94$ and $\overline{W} = 64$.

3 Using Lawler's algorithm to minimise either $T_{\max}$ or $L_{\max}$ in a problem without precedence constraints, we see immediately that the last position in the processing sequence will be given to a job with the latest possible due date, the penultimate position to a job with the second latest due date, etc. An EDD sequence is therefore constructed.

4 See Figs. S5.1 and S5.2.

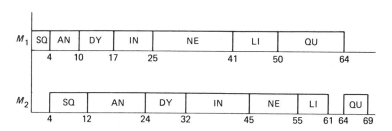

Fig. S5.1 Gantt diagram for part (a)

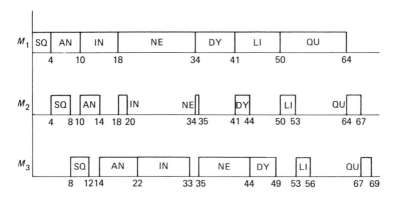

Fig. S5.2 Gantt diagram for part (b)

5 Johnson's algorithm gives the sequence (J_1, J_2, J_4, J_3) which has $C_{max} = 23$. Interchanging the first two jobs reduces idle time on the second machine, giving $C_{max} = 22$ for the sequence (J_2, J_1, J_4, J_3).

6
$$T_{max} = \max_{i=1}^{n} \{\max\{L_i, 0\}\}$$

$$= \max\{L_1, L_2, L_3, \ldots, 0\}$$

$$= \max\{L_{max}, 0\}.$$

So minimising L_{max} minimises T_{max}.

Chapter 6

1 The critical activities are A, D, F, H and the length of the critical path is 12. The network is shown in Fig. S6.1

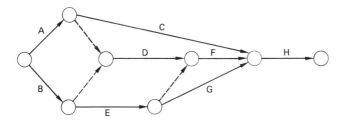

Fig. S6.1 Network for Exercise 6.1

If only 1 man is available, then he clearly must take 25 days (= sum of activity durations) to complete the project.

If two men are available, then they must take at least 25/2 days. In fact, since activities take whole numbers of days, they must take at least 13 days. It is possible to complete the project with 2 men in 13 days, as the Gantt diagram in Fig. S6.2 shows. Hence the quickest it can be done with 2 men is 13 days.

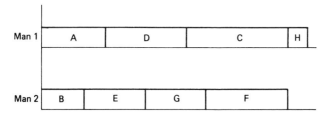

Fig. S6.2   Gantt diagram for Exercise 6.1

2   The critical activities are D, E, F, G, H, I, K, N, and the earliest possible opening date (i.e. earliest that it is possible to start activity 0) is 38 weeks. It is possible to complete the project with 7 men as Fig. S6.3 shows. Note that *at least* 7 men are required because A must overlap F for at least one day. So 7 is the minimum number.

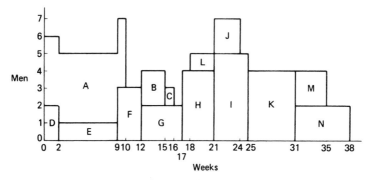

Fig. S6.3   Allocation of men to activities for Exercise 6.2

3   The critical path is A, C, E, H and its length is 20 weeks. Table S6.1 gives the cost of crashing each activity by 1 week and Fig. S6.4 shows the project network.

On A–C–E–H, C is cheapest, so crash C by 1. B and D now become critical. Cheapest to crash C and B together by 1. F and G now critical also. Cheapest to crash C, D, F by 1. C is now fully crashed. Only possible combinations for crashing are A and F; A and G; H. All cost more than £600. So algorithm terminates. Final cost of project is

$$£800 + 500 + 1100 + 700 + 1000 + 900 + 400 + 1000 + 17 \times 500$$
$$\text{A}\quad\text{B}\quad\text{C}\quad\text{D}\quad\text{E}\quad\text{F}\quad\text{G}\quad\text{H}$$

$$= £14\,900.$$

Table S6.1 Cost of crashing each activity in Exercise 6.3

	Cost/week's crashing (£)	No. of weeks that may be crashed
A	500	2
B	100	1
C	100	3
D	200	1
E	0	0
F	100	2
G	200	4
H	600	1

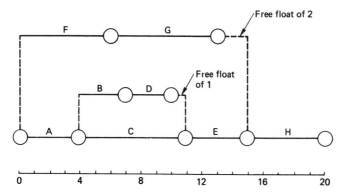

Fig. S6.4 Project network for Exercise 6.3

4 The critical path is A, C, F, G and its length is 19 weeks. Table S6.2 gives the cost of crashing each activity by 1 week and Fig. S6.5 shows the project network.

Table S6.2 Cost of crashing each activity in Exercise 6.4

	Cost/week's crashing (£)	No. of weeks that may be crashed
A	—	—
B	150	2
C	300	3
D	100	1
E	—	—
F	200	1
G	250	1

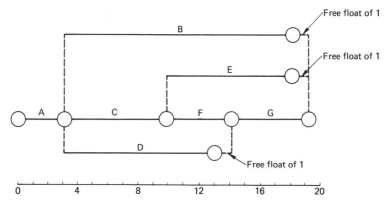

Fig. S6.5 Project network for Exercise 6.4

Cheapest to crash F on critical path. So crash F by 1 week. B, D and E now critical. Can only reduce critical path by crashing B, C and D simultaneously. Cost of crashing is £550 < £600 so crash by 1 week. Algorithm now stops. But if B, C and G are all crashed by 1 further week and F uncrashed by 1 week (i.e. returned to its normal time), the critical path length reduces by 1 week at a direct cost of £$(150 + 300 + 250) - 200 = 500 < 600$. So a further saving can be achieved.

5   Using *Johnson's algorithm* for the two-machine flow shop, an optimal schedule for producing the cogs is 3, 7, 2, 5, 4, 1, 6.

The minimum total processing time is given by the Gantt diagram in Fig. S6.6.

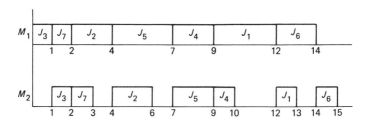

Fig. S6.6 Gantt diagram for producing cogs

Note the maximum processing time on $M_4 = 2 <$ minimum processing time on $M_3 = 3$.

Johnson's algorithm may be used to schedule production of the spindles:

Spindle	1	2	3	4	5
$M_3 + M_4$ times	5	4	5	6	4
$M_4 + M_5$ times	6	5	8	5	5

so optimal schedule is 2, 5, 1, 3, 4. The Gantt diagram is given in Fig. S6.7.

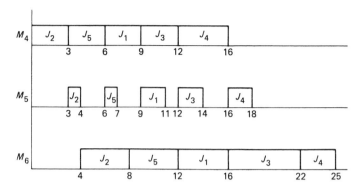

Fig. S6.7 Gantt diagram for producing spindles

Inserting these times into the project network shown in Fig. S6.8 gives the critical path B, D, F, H, J.

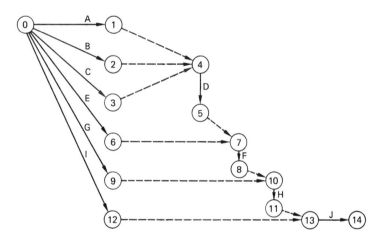

Fig. S6.8 Project network for Exercise 6.5

A naive application of the resource levelling procedure given in Section 6.5 suggests that at least 5 men are needed. *But* a little cunning shows it can be done with 4 men. Note that M_2 jobs can be delayed, and therefore one man can do the M_3 jobs and then do the M_2 jobs. See Gantt diagram in Fig. S6.9.

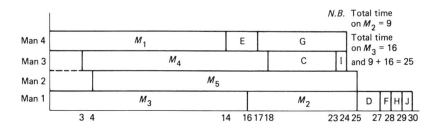

N.B. Total time
on M_2 = 9
Total time
on M_3 = 16
and 9 + 16 = 25

Fig. S6.9   Gantt diagram for Exercise 6.5

Chapter 7

1 (a)

	2	3	4	5	6	7
d	5	8	3	6	12	15
π	4	5	1	4	3	6

The shortest-path tree is shown in Fig. S7.1.

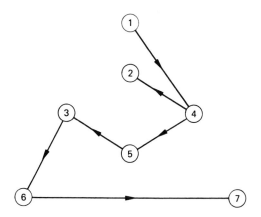

Fig. S7.1

(b)

	2	3	4	5	6	7
d	5	8	3	6	11	8
π	4	5	1	4	7	4

1 to x via 3: $10\frac{1}{2}$ miles, 1 to x via 6: $12\frac{1}{2}$ miles. So $1 \to 4 \to 5 \to 3 \to x$ is shortest.
When x is $3\frac{1}{2}$ miles from 3, routes via 3 and 6 are equidistant.

(c)

	2	3	4	5	6	7
d	3	3	3	3	4	4
π	4	5	1	4	3	6

(d) The optimal solution and $k(i, j)$ are given in Tables S7.1, S7.2.

$6 \to 3 \to 2$ is shortest from 6 to 2

$6 \to 7 \to 4 \to 1$ is shortest from 6 to 1.

Table S7.1

—	5	8	3	6	11	8
	—	4	2	2	8	7
		—	5	2	4	7
			—	3	8	5
				—	6	8
					—	3
						—

$k = 7$

Table S7.2

—	4	5	0	4	7	4
	—	0	0	0	3	4
		—	5	0	0	6
			—	0	7	0
				—	3	4
					—	0
						—

$k(i, j)$

In (e) and (f) let $d(i, j)$ be the length of a shortest path from i to j. Let $\pi(j)$ be the population of j.

(e)

i	1	2	3	4	5	6	7
$\sum_j d(i,j)\pi(j)$	1364	1017	1050	920	984	1279	1200

Build the hospital in town 4.

(f)

i	1	1	1	1	3	3	3	4	4	6
j	3	4	6	7	4	6	7	6	7	7
$\max_k \{\min \{d(k,i), d(k,j)\}\}$	7	8	6	7	5	8	8	4	5	8

Build the schools at 4 and 6.

(g) Use the algorithm of Section 7.4 with

$$\phi_{ij}(t) = 1.3t + l(i, j).$$

	2	3	4	5	6	7
d	5.9	10.97	3	6.9	14	18
π	4	5	1	4	1	1

2 $K(i, j)$ at iteration m is the second vertex on a shortest path from i to j with intermediate vertices restricted to $1, 2, \ldots, m$.

If $d(i, j)$ changes at this iteration, the new shortest path is $i \to \cdots \to m \to \cdots \to j$, so $K(i, j)$ changes to $K(i, m)$. $K(i, j)$ for Exercise 1(d) appear in Table S7.3.

Table S7.3

—	4	4	4	4	4	4
4	—	3	4	5	3	4
5	2	—	5	5	6	5
1	2	5	—	5	7	7
4	2	3	4	—	3	4
7	3	3	7	3	—	7
4	4	4	4	4	6	—

$K(i, j)$

3 Apply Floyd's algorithm to Table 3.44 to get Tables S7.4 and S7.5
    Solve the transportation problem in Table S7.6 to get Table S7.7 (not unique, cost = 194).

Table S7.4

	1	2	2	1′	2′	3′	4′
1	0	6	5	13	11	13	17
2	5	0	4	16	14	12	13
3	4	4	0	17	15	15	12
1′	14	17	18	0	5	4	5
2′	10	12	15	5	0	2	8
3′	12	13	14	4	2	0	8
4′	17	12	14	5	8	9	0

Table S7.5

	1	2	3	1′	2′	3′	4′
1	—	0	0	0	0	5	3
2	0	—	0	6	0	0	0
3	0	0	—	1	1	0	0
1′	0	5	6	—	0	0	0
2′	0	0	1	0	—	0	0
3′	5	0	0	0	0	—	0
4′	2	0	0	0	0	0	—

$k(i, j)$

Table S7.6

	1′	2′	3′	4′	
1	13	11	13	17	2
2	16	14	12	13	6
3	17	15	15	12	7
	3	3	4	5	

Table S7.7

1	1		
	2	4	
2			5

The shortest path from 3 to 1′ is $3 \to 1 \to 1′$. So transport $1 + 2 = 3$ from 1 to 1′ and tranship 2 units from 3 to 1. No other shortest path has intermediate vertices.

Chapter 8

1   (a) $q^* = 200$
   (b) (i) 100   (ii) 200
   These maximise $40\,000\,q^{-1} + q$ subject to $\leqslant 100$ (300).
   (c)   (i) The additional storage cost per cycle is

$$\begin{cases} \tfrac{1}{2}(q - 100)\,(q - 100)/d = \tfrac{1}{2}(q - 100)^2/d & \text{if } q \geqslant 100 \\ 0 & \text{otherwise.} \end{cases}$$

Thus, the total cost per unit time is

$$cd + \frac{dA}{q} + \tfrac{1}{2}hq + \tfrac{1}{2}(q - 100)^2/q = 19\,900 + \frac{45\,000}{q} + \tfrac{3}{2}q$$

$$\text{for } q > 100 \qquad\qquad \text{(A)}$$

$$20\,000 + \frac{40\,000}{q} + q \qquad \text{for } q \leqslant 100 \qquad\qquad \text{(B)}$$

(A) is minimised at $q = 100\sqrt{3}$ and, as we have seen, (B) at $q = 100$. Since (A) also applies for $q = 100$ (why?), the overall minimum is at $q = £173$.
   (ii) The additional storage cost per unit time is $q - 100$, so (A) is modified to

$$19\,900 + \frac{40\,000}{q} + 2q.$$

The minimum is at $q = 100\sqrt{2} = £141$.

2   Let q be the order quantity and n/d be the cycle length. (It must be a multiple of $1/d$. Why?) From Section 8.1, the ordering plus shortage costs per cycle are

$$A + cq + \tfrac{1}{2}hq(q - 1)/d.$$

The revenue per cycle is kq, so the profit per unit time is

$$[dkq - dA - dcq - \tfrac{1}{2}hq(q-1)]/n$$

to be maximised subject to $n \geqslant q$.

The argument of Section 8.2 can be carried through to conclude that the maximum over n, for given q, is

$$\max \{(k-c)d - \frac{dA}{q} - \tfrac{1}{2}h(q-1), \, 0\}$$

and this must be maximised over integer q.

As before, we can conclude that lost sales are not worthwhile.

By Section 8.1, the maximum of

$$19(k-8) - \frac{437}{q} - 16(q-1)$$

over integer q is at

$$\left\lceil \sqrt{\frac{437}{16} + \frac{1}{4}} \, \right\rceil - \tfrac{1}{2} = 5\tfrac{1}{4} = 6.$$

Thus, operate with $q^* = 6$ if

$$19(k-8) - \frac{437}{6} - 16 \times 5 \geqslant 0,$$

i.e. $k \geqslant 16.04$. Otherwise, don't operate.

3 (a) Order 6 items, timed to arrive $1\tfrac{1}{2}$ weeks after inventory drops to 0.

   (b) Add ks to the cost per cycle, to give total cost per week

$$\frac{27}{q} + 3q + [4s^2 - 6qs + 3ks]/q + \text{constant}.$$

This is minimised over s at

$$s^* = (6q - 3k)/8$$

provided $s^* \geqslant 0$, i.e. $q \geqslant \tfrac{1}{2}k$. Otherwise the minimum is at $s = 0$, for $q < \tfrac{1}{2}k$.

Dropping the 'constant' terms, the minimal cost is then

$$\frac{27}{q} + 3q \qquad\qquad\qquad \text{if } q < \tfrac{1}{2}k$$

$$\left(27 - \frac{9k^2}{16}\right) \Big/ q + \tfrac{3}{4}q + \tfrac{9}{4}k \qquad \text{if } q \geqslant \tfrac{1}{2}k$$

The first expression is minimised at $q = 3$ and this is $< \tfrac{1}{2}k$ if $k > 6$. The second is minimised at

$$q = \left(36 - \frac{3k^2}{4}\right)^{1/2}$$

and this is $\geqslant \frac{1}{2}k$ if

$$36 - \frac{3k^2}{4} \geqslant \frac{1}{4}k^2 \text{ i.e. } k \leqslant 6.$$

So order $(36 - 3k^2/4)^{1/2}$ items timed to arrive $(\sqrt{(144 - 3k^2)} - k)/8$ weeks after the inventory drops to 0, if $k \leqslant 6$. Otherwise, order 3 items without backlogging.

4 (a) $q = 10$ is optimal.

(b) The cost of q items is

$$3.2 + 24.3q \qquad \text{for } 0 \leqslant q < 5$$
$$3.2 + 24.3 \times 5 + 20.1(q - 5) = 24.2 + 20.1q \qquad \text{for } 5 \leqslant q \leqslant 10.$$
$$3.2 + 24.3 \times 5 + 20.1(q - 5) = 51.2 + 17.4q \qquad \text{for } q \geqslant 10.$$

This gives a total cost per week of

$$\frac{9.6}{q} + 0.6q + 72.9 \qquad \text{for } 0 \leqslant q \leqslant 5$$

$$\frac{72.6}{q} + 0.6q + 60.3 \qquad \text{for } 5 \leqslant q \leqslant 10$$

$$\frac{153.6}{q} + 0.6q + 52.2 \qquad \text{for } q \geqslant 10.$$

The three expressions are minimised at $q_1^* = 4$, $q_2^* = 11$ and $q_3^* = 16$ respectively. Since $q_1^* \leqslant 5$, $q_3^* \geqslant 10$, but $q_2^* > 10$, the minimum is at q_1^* (cost 77.7) or q_3^* (cost 71.4) (Why?). Thus $q_3^* = 16$ is optimal.

5 Cost per day, as in Section 8.5, is

$$\frac{d'A}{q'} + cd + \frac{1}{2}hq'$$

where $d' = 40(r - 40)/r$ and $q' = d'q/40$.

When $r = 400$, $d' = 36$, so optimal $q' = 360$. Hence $q^* = 400$ and minimal cost is

$$cd + \sqrt{2d'Ah} = 560.$$

For general r, the minimal cost is

$$20 + 120\sqrt{10 - \frac{400}{r}}$$

and, of course, $r \geqslant 40$. This is minimised at $r = 40$.

S is given as Table S9.1. We see that $S^* = 3$.

$\circ$	1	2	3	4	5
13.4	9.875	8.15	7.825	8.5	9.7

2 Take $A = 40$, $h = 6$, $k = 100$, giving $(k - \tfrac{1}{2}h)/(k + \tfrac{1}{2}h) = 97/103$ and thus $S^* = 3$. The approximate cost per month is $1.75c + 46.75$.

For bi-monthly deliveries, we must change h to 12 (storage cost per item, per two months), and p_x, the probability of X being demanded in two months, is given in Table S9.2.

Table S9.2

X	0	1	2	3	4	5	6
P_x	0.0225	0.075	0.1525	0.24	0.24	0.18	0.09

Hence, we now have $S^* = 5$ and the approximate cost *per two months* is $3.5c + 87.65$. Since this is smaller than $2(1.75c + 46.75)$, bi-monthly deliveries with $S^* = 5$ are preferable.

3 Using the procedure of Section 9.3 we find $r_1 = 0$ and $\beta(0) = 57$, giving $q_1 = 9.06 = 10$. Thus, $r_2 = 2$ and $\beta(2) = 38$, giving $q_2 = 7.3 = 8$. Then $r_3 = 3$ and $\beta(3) = 31$ giving $q_3 = 6.6 = 7$. Hence $r_4 = 3$, so that $r^* = 3$, $q^* = 7$.

Chapter 10

1 Cafeteria queue is M/M/1, $\lambda = 25$ per hour, $\mu = 30$ per hour. $\mathrm{Exp}\{W\} = 1/(30 - 25) = 12$ min. Total time is $12 + 10 = 22$ min, which is quicker than restaurant.

2 Queue is M/M/c with waiting room limited to c. $\lambda = 60$ per hour, $\mu = 10$ per hour. $p_1 = 6p_0$, $p_2 = 18\,p_0$, $p_3 = 36p_0$, $p_4 = 54p_0$.

With c researchers profit per hour is $\pounds(60(1 - p_c) - 7.5c)$.

$c = 2 \quad p_0 = \tfrac{1}{25}, p_1 = \tfrac{6}{25}, p_2 = \tfrac{18}{25}$, so profit is $\pounds 1.80$

$c = 3 \quad p_0 = \tfrac{1}{61}, p_1 = \tfrac{6}{61}, p_2 = \tfrac{18}{61}, p_3 = \tfrac{36}{61}$, so profit is $\pounds 2.09$

$c = 4 \quad p_0 = \tfrac{1}{115}, p_1 = \tfrac{6}{115}, p_2 = \tfrac{18}{115}, p_3 = \tfrac{36}{115}, p_4 = \tfrac{54}{115}$, so profit is $\pounds 1.29$.

3 M/M/1 with $\lambda = 20$ per week $\mu = \mu$ per week. $\bar{W} = (\mu - 20)^{-1}$ so cost per week is $1000(\mu + 4(\mu - 20)^{-1})$ Differentiating w.r.t. μ and setting equal to 0 gives minimum at $\mu = 22$ with cost 24 000. With new machine tool cost per

week is $14\,000 + 1000(\mu + 4(\mu - 5)^{-1})$ which is minimum at $\mu = 7$ with cost $23\,000$. So it is better.

4   $M/M/c$ with waiting room of $3c$. $\lambda = \mu = 2$ per minute. So for $c = 1$, $p_1 = p_2 = p_3 = p_0$ and $p_i = \frac{1}{4}$, $i = 0, 1, 2, 3$. For $c = 2$, $p_1 = p_0$, $p_2 = \frac{1}{2}p_0$, $p_3 = p_0/4$, $p_4 = p_0/8$, $p_5 = p_0/16$, $p_6 = p_0/32$. Therefore $p_0 = \frac{32}{95}$ and $p_6 = \frac{1}{95}$.

$$\text{Exp \{number of servers\}} = 0 \times \tfrac{1}{4} + 1 \times \tfrac{3}{4} = \tfrac{3}{4}(c = 1);$$

$$0 \times \tfrac{32}{95} + 1 \times \tfrac{32}{95} + 2 \times \tfrac{31}{95} = \tfrac{94}{95}(c = 2)$$

(a)   For $c = 1$, average profit on goods per week

$$= \pounds\tfrac{3}{4} \times 0.20 \times 60 \times 38 = 342, \text{ so (a) is } \pounds302.$$

For $c = 2$, average profit on goods per week

$$= \pounds\tfrac{94}{95} \times 60 \times 38$$

$$= \pounds451.2, \text{ so (a) is } \pounds371.2.$$

(b) $c = 1$ is $\pounds(\tfrac{1}{4} \times 0.2 \times 60 \times 38) + 4 = \pounds154.$

$c = 2$ is $\pounds(\tfrac{1}{95} \times 0.2 \times 60 \times 38) + 80 = \pounds84.8.$

(a) + (b) is total possible weekly profit.

5   $M/M/1$ with two types of customers—outgoing calls and incoming calls

$$\lambda_0 = 16, \ \lambda_i = 20, \ \lambda = 36, \ \mu = 60, \ \rho = 0.6.$$

Exp {number in the queue} $= \rho(1 - \rho)^{-1} = 1.5.$

Exp {waiting time for queues} $= (60 - 36)^{-1} \text{ hr} = \tfrac{1}{24} \text{ hr} = 2\tfrac{1}{2} \text{ min.}$

Exp {total waiting times of outgoing calls} $= 16 \times 2\tfrac{1}{2} \text{ min} = 40 \text{ min.}$
Cost per hour $= \pounds9.00 \times \tfrac{2}{3} = \pounds6.00.$

New equipment $\lambda_0 = 8$, $\lambda_i = 20$, $\lambda = 28$, $\mu = 60$.
Exp {waiting time in the queue} $= (60 - 28)^{-1} = \tfrac{1}{32} \text{ hr} = \tfrac{15}{8} \text{ min.}$
Exp {total waiting times of outgoing calls} $= 8 \times \tfrac{15}{8} = 15 \text{ min.}$
Cost per hour $= \$9.00 \times \tfrac{1}{4} + \$1.20 = \$3.45.$

6   For expert $\lambda_0 = \tfrac{1}{30}$, $\lambda_1 = \tfrac{1}{40}$, $\lambda_2 = \tfrac{1}{60}$, $\lambda_3 = \tfrac{1}{120}$. $\mu_i = \tfrac{1}{20}$.
Gives $p_0 = \tfrac{54}{115}$, $p_1 = \tfrac{36}{115}$, $p_2 = \tfrac{18}{115}$, $p_3 = \tfrac{6}{115}$, $p_4 = \tfrac{1}{115}$.
Cost is $\pounds(4 + 4(\tfrac{36}{115}) + 8(\tfrac{18}{115}) + 12(\tfrac{6}{115}) + 100(\tfrac{1}{115})) = \pounds8.00.$

For two apprentices $\lambda_0 = \tfrac{1}{30}$, $\lambda_1 = \tfrac{1}{40}$, $\lambda_2 = \tfrac{1}{60}$, $\lambda_3 = \tfrac{1}{120}$, $\mu_1 = \tfrac{1}{30}$, $\mu_2 = \tfrac{1}{15}$, $i \geqslant 2$. So $p_0 = \tfrac{256}{635}$, $p_1 = \tfrac{256}{635}$, $p_2 = \tfrac{96}{635}$, $p_3 = \tfrac{24}{635}$, $p_4 = \tfrac{3}{635}$.
Cost is $\pounds(5 + 4(\tfrac{256}{635}) + 8(\tfrac{96}{635}) + 12(\tfrac{24}{635}) + 100(\tfrac{3}{635})) = \pounds8.75.$
So get expert.

7   M/M/1 with limited waiting of 4. $\lambda = 24$ per hour, $\mu = 20$ per hour.
   (a) $p_1 = 6p_0/5$, $p_2 = 36p_0/25$, $p_3 = 216p_0/125$, $p_4 = 1296p_0/625$.
         So $p_0 = 0.1344$, $p_1 = 0.1613$, $p_2 = 0.1935$, $p_3 = 0.2322$, $p_4 = 0.2786$.
   (b)   13.44 %
   (c)   0.2786, profit loss is £6.69.
         Waiting time is 3 min

$$\times \left(\frac{1 \times 0.1344 + 2 \times 0.1613 + 3 \times 0.1935 + 4 \times 0.2322}{1 - 0.2786} \right)$$

$$= 8.177 \text{ min.}$$

   (d)   M/M/2 with limited waiting of 4. $\lambda = 24$ per hour, $\mu = 20$ per hour,
         $p_1 = 6p_0/5$, $p_2 = 18p_0/25$, $p_3 = 54p_0/125$, $p_4 = 162p_0/625$, $p_0 = 0.2769$,
         $p_1 = 0.3323$, $p_2 = 0.1994$, $p_3 = 0.1196$, $p_4 = 0.0718$
   (e)   27.69 %, 33.23 %, 39.08 %.
   (f)   0.0718
   (g)   Cost with two attendants and profit loss = £6.25 + £24 × 0.0718
         = £7.973. So one is better.

Chapter 11

1   Call each 5000 miles a period. So preventive replacement $R_p = 10$, and failure
     replacement $R_f = 35$. $\bar{P}_0 = 1.0$, $\bar{P}_1 = 0.9$, $\bar{P}_2 = 0.8$, $\bar{P}_3 = 0.6$, $\bar{P}_4 = 0.4$,
     $\bar{P}_5 = 0.1$, $\bar{P}_6 = 0$. $C(n) = (10\bar{P}_n + 35P_n)/(\bar{P}_0 + \bar{P}_1 + \ldots + \bar{P}_{n-1})$. $C(1) = 12.5$,
     $C(2) = 7.89$, $C(3) = 7.40$, $C(4) = 7.57$, and $C(5) = 8.78$.

2    $C(n)$ is the cost per period if we replace after n periods (i.e. start preparation at
     $n - 2$ periods) unless there is an earlier failure.

$$C(n) = (4000 + 20\,000P_{n-2} + 10\,000p_{n-1})/(3p_1 + 4p_2 + \cdots$$
$$+ n(1 - p_{n-3}))$$
$$C(2) = 2250, \ C(3) = 1833, \ C(4) = 1772, \ C(5) = 2061, \ C(n) > 2000$$
$$n \geqslant 5.$$

So $n = 3$ is optimal.

3    $$\int_0^T tf(t)\,dt + TF(T) = [-t\bar{F}(t)]_0^T + \int_0^T \bar{F}(t)\,dt + T\bar{F}(T) = \int_0^T \bar{F}(t)\,dt.$$

$$C(T) = \frac{(20T + 10(100 - T))}{\displaystyle\int_0^T (100 - t)\,dt} = \frac{(1000 + 10T)}{(100T - \tfrac{1}{2}T^2)}.$$

Maximised at $T = 131.7$, so in range $0 \leqslant T \leqslant$ optimum is $T = 100$ i.e. never
replace.

4 $C(n)$ is cost at time replacement every n periods.

$$C(n) = (0.3 + 1.25(f_1 + \cdots + f_n))/n.$$
$$f_1 = 0.1, f_2 = 0.11, f_3 = 0.131, f_4 = 0.3331, f_5 = 0.486.$$
$$C(1) = 0.425, C(2) = 0.281, C(3) = 0.242, C(4) = 0.286, C(\infty) = 0.350.$$

So take $n = 3$ as replacement period.

5 $r(t) = f(t)/\bar{F}(t) = \alpha$. Integrating both sides gives

$$\log(\bar{F}(t)) = k - \alpha t.$$

Therefore $\bar{F}(t) = Ce^{-\alpha t}$, $F(t) = 1 - Ce^{-\alpha t}$. $F(0) = 0 = C = 1$. $f(t) = F'(t) = \alpha e^{-\alpha t}$; therefore

$$\text{Exp }\{\text{lifetime}\} = \int_0^\infty t\alpha e^{-\alpha t}\, dt = \frac{1}{\alpha}.$$

$$C(t) \text{ cost per unit time} = \frac{c_1 + c_2 \text{ Exp }\{N(t)\}}{t}.$$

$\text{Exp }\{N(t)\} = \alpha t$, so $C(t) = (c_1/t) + c_2\alpha$, which is minimised at $t = \infty$, i.e. never preventively replace. New equipment has same failure rate as used.

6 $C(n) = (I + Dn + (R - D(1-p)^{-1})(1-p^n))/n$. $I = 10$, $D = 30$, $R = 1000$, $p = \frac{5}{6}$, so

$$C(n) = 30 + (10 - 80(1 - (\tfrac{5}{6})^n))/n$$

$C(1) = 26.67$, $C(2) = 22.77$, $C(3) = 22.09$, $C(4) = 22.14$, $C(5) = 22.43$. So $n = 3$ is optimal.

Chapter 12

1 Let $v_n(i)$ be the cost of the optimal policy over a period of n years if it is i years since the machine's last overhaul.

Define $v_0(i) = 0$ for all i.

Then for $n \geqslant 1$:

$$v_n(i) = \min\{c_i + v_{n-1}(i+1), £1200 + c_0 + v_{n-1}(1)\} \quad (\text{S12.1})$$

where c_i is the cost of operating a machine for 1 year when its last overhaul was i years ago. Define

$$d_n(i) = \begin{cases} K & \text{if the minimum in (S12.1) occurs on the first term;} \\ & \text{i.e. if the machine is used without overhaul.} \\ O & \text{if the minimum in (S12.1) occurs on the second term; i.e. if the machine is overhauled immediately.} \end{cases}$$

Then it is straightforward to construct Table S12.1.

Table S12.1

$(v_n(i), d_n(i))$	n				
	1	2	3	4	5
1	$(1500, K)$	$(3500, K)$	$(5200, K)$	$(7200, K)$	$(8900, K)$
2	$(2000, K)$	$(3700, O)$	$(5700, K)$	$(7400, O)$	$(9400, K)$
3	$(2200, O)$	$(3700, O)$	$(5700, O)$	$(7400, O)$	$(9400, O)$
i 4	$(2200, O)$	$(3700, O)$	$(5700, O)$	$(7400, O)$	$(9400, O)$
5	$(2200, O)$	$(3700, O)$	$(5700, O)$	$(7400, O)$	$(9400, O)$
6	$(2200, O)$	$(3700, O)$	$(5700, O)$	$(7400, O)$	$(9400, O)$

The machine begins 2 years from previous overhaul.

$d_5(2) = K =$ do not overhaul at beginning of first year.

$d_4(3) = O =$ overhaul at beginning of second year.

$d_3(1) = K =$ do not overhaul at beginning of third year.

$d_2(2) = O =$ overhaul at beginning of fourth year.

$d_1(1) = K =$ do not overhaul at beginning of last year.

2   Let $v_n(a) =$ total revenue brought in by investing £a optimally in activities $1, 2, \ldots, n$. Using the methods of Section 12.4 it is straightforward to produce Table S12.2 (all sums in units of £1000).

Table S12.2

a	0	25	50	75	100	125	150	175	200
$v_1(a)$	0	10	20	30	40	55	65	75	80
$v_2(a)$	0	15	25	35	60	70	80	90	100
$v_3(a)$	0	15	25	35	60	70	80	90	100

Optimal allocation $v_3(200) = 100$ is given by allocating 100 to each of activities 1 and 2 and nothing to activity 3.

To formulate as a linear program, let

x_1 be amount allocated to activity 1,

x_2 be amount allocated to activity 2,

x_3 be amount allocated to activity 3.

Then the problem becomes

$$\text{Maximise } (0.5x_1 - 20\,000) + (0.6x_2 - 30\,000) + (0.7x_3 - 25\,000).$$

$$\text{Subject to } x_1 + x_2 + x_3 = 200\,000 \qquad x_1 \geqslant 0,\ x_2 \geqslant 0,\ x_3 \geqslant 0.$$

3 Using the notation and method of Section 12.5, you should calculate:

$$v_1 = 106.25, \quad q_1 = 2$$
$$v_2 = 159.375, \ q_2 = 3$$
$$v_3 = 178.1, \quad q_3 = 4$$
$$v_4 = 225.3, \quad q_4 = 4.$$

Thus the optimal policy is:

Put 4 into production until at least 2 perfect made.
If 2 remain to be made, put 3 into production.
If 1 remains to be made, put 2 into production.

The method can be modified in a straightforward way to deal with the scrap value of excess vases. Consider the development leading to expression (12.16) for v_{n+1}. Assume for generality that the scrap value of a vase is s.

$$v_{n+1}(q) = a + cq + p_q(0)v_{n+1}(q) + p_q(2)v_{n-1}$$
$$+ \cdots + p_q(n)v_n + p_q(n+1) \times 0$$
$$+ p_q(n+2)s + p_q(n+3)2s + \cdots + p_q(q)(q-n-1)s.$$

Hence

$$v_{n+1} = \min_{q=1}^{\infty} \frac{\left\{ \left(a + cq + \sum_{r=1}^{n} p_q(r)v_{n+1-r} + \sum_{r=n+2}^{q} p_q(r)(r-n-1)s \right) \right\}}{1 - p_q(0)}.$$

Note. In the above we have implicitly assumed that $q \geqslant n+2$. However, the expression is valid in general if we adopt the convention that a summation is 0 if the upper summation limit is less than the lower. This expression leads to the following values.

$$v_1 = 101.25, \ q_1 = 2$$
$$v_2 = 134.72, \ q_2 = 3$$
$$v_3 = 173.02, \ q_3 = 4$$
$$v_4 = 221.80, \ q_4 = 4.$$

So introducing a scrap value of £10 does not change the policy, but it does, of course, reduce the expected cost of the optimal policy.

4 Let $v_n(q) = $ cost of optimal policy for meeting requirements in the remaining n months if at the beginning of month $(3 - n + 1)$ there are q items in stock and *we ignore costs already incurred.*

We require to calculate $v_3(0)$ since initially there are no items in stock.

First, we calculate $v_1(q)$. Now note two things:

(i) q may feasibly be 0, 1, 2, 3, 4 or 5;

(ii) the demand must be exactly satisfied in month 3 with no items left in stock.

Thus $(10 - q)$ must be manufactured in the last month, and clearly as much as possible will be made in normal time. Therefore,

$$v_1(q) = \min\{10 - q, 6\} \times 4 + \max\{10 - q - 6, 0\} \times 6.$$

The first term gives the normal time production costs; the second term gives the overtime production costs. Hence we construct the values in Table S12.3.

Table S12.3

q	0	1	2	3	4	5
$v_1(q)$	48	42	36	30	24	20

Next consider $v_2(q)$. Suppose x items *in total* are produced in the second month. Feasibility demands that $8 - q \leqslant x \leqslant 10$, since the demand in the second month must be met. If there are q items in stock at the beginning of the month and x items are produced, the following costs will be incurred.

Normal time production costs $= \min\{x, 6\} \times 6$

Overtime production costs $= \max\{x - 6, 0\} \times 9$

Storage costs of excess items $= (x + q - 8) \times 1$

Costs incurred in later months $= v_1(x + q - 8)$

Hence we see that

$$v_2(q) = \min_{x = 8 - q}^{10} \{\min\{x, 6\} \times 6 + \max\{x - 6, 0\} \times 9 + \{x + q - 8\} \times 1$$

$$+ v_1(x + q - 8)\} \tag{S12.2}$$

Evaluating this over the possible values of q, we get the results shown in Table S12.4.

Table S12.4

q	0	1	2	3
$v_2(q)$	102	93	84	78
minimising x in (S12.2)	8	7	6	5

Finally we need to calculate $v_3(0)$. Suppose that x items are produced in the initial month. Then the cost will be, by an argument similar to that which led to (S12.2),

$$\min\{x, 6\} \times 2 + \max\{x - 6, 0\} \times 3 + (x - 7) \times 1 + v_2(x - 7).$$

Clearly for feasibility $7 \leqslant x \leqslant 10$. So

$$v_3(0) = \min_{x=7}^{10}\{12 + (x - 6) \times 3 + (x - 7) \times 1 + v_2(x - 7)\}$$

$$= 105, \text{ with the minimising value of } x \text{ being } 10.$$

As before we have found the optimal cost is 105 and the optimal production policy produces 10 in the initial month, 5 in the second month, and 10 in the last month.

5 Using formulation (12.17), we get Table S12.5.

Table S12.5

$v_n(j)$		n				
	1	2	3	4	5	6
2	6	5	5	5	5	5
3	11	10	8	8	8	8
4	3	3	3	3	3	3
j 5	∞	6	6	6	6	6
6	14	14	14	12	12	12
7	18	17	16	16	15	15

At each iteration of Dijkstra's algorithm the minimisation operations each involve two quantities only. Moreover, the number of minimisations is N for the first iteration, $(N - 1)$ for the second, $(N - 2)$ for the third, etc. In the DP formulation the number of quantities in each minimisation is the number of vertices from which there are arcs to the vertex concerned. Moreover, there are $(N - 1)$ minimisations per iteration. Clearly for all but the sparsest networks, Dijkstra's algorithm will be much more efficient. However, there are advantages to the DP formulation. For instance, it can allow for negative length arcs. (Negative 'length' arcs occur, might occur, when the 'lengths' are costs and some arcs allow a profit.)

6 A little thought shows that extra capacity need only be installed when demand and capacity are equal. Let us suppose that demand and capacity are equal at the end of some period n. Then the minimal discounted cost, *discounted to the end of period n*, from the optimal policy operating from the end of period n to the end of period N depends only on n. Let this minimal discounted cost be v_n.

Suppose that the decision is taken to put in enough capacity to be installed is $D_r - D_n$ at a cost $(1 + D_r - D_n)$. From year r to year N the discounted cost *discounted to the end of year r* of the optimal policy is v_r. Thus discounting v_r to the end of year n

$$v_n = 1 + D_r - D_n + \alpha^{r-n} v_r.$$

Since we are free to choose r optimally,

$$v_n = \min_{n < r \leqslant N} \{1 + D_r - D_n + \alpha^{r-n} v_r\}.$$

Clearly $v_N = 0$. We may now solve the problem starting with v_N, calculating v_{N-1}, and so on until v_0 is calculated. The optimal policy may now be determined in the usual way.

7   Let $v_n(q)$ be the expected cost of the optimal policy running over the final n years when the number of satellites in stock at the beginning of the n-year period is q. Thus we require $v_3(1)$ and the production policy that achieves it.

We shall allow $q = -1$ as a convention to indicate that there is an unfulfilled order from the previous year. In each year the company can manufacture 0, 1 or 2 satellites. However, since it knows that the demand will be 1 or 2, we can be sure it will manufacture

2	if $q = -1$
1 or 2	if $q = 0$
0, 1 or 2	if $q = 1$

Let $d_n(q)$ be optimal number of satellites to manufacture in first of the n years. Whence, adding production costs to expected penalty costs:

$$v_1(-1) = 18 + 0.7 \times 0 + 0.3 \times (3 + 10)$$
$$= 21.9$$
$$v_1(0) \quad = \min \{10 + 0.7 \times 0 + 0.3 \times (3 + 10), \ 18 + 0.7 \times 0 + 0.3 \times 0\}$$
$$= 13.9$$
$$v_1(1) \quad = \min \{0 + 0.7 \times 0 + 0.3 \times (3 + 10), \ 10 + 0.7 \times 0 + 0.3 \times 0,$$
$$18 + 0.7 \times 0 + 0.3 \times 0\}$$
$$= 3.9.$$

From the minimising terms it is seen that

$$d_1(-1) = 2$$
$$d_1(0) = 1$$
$$d_1(1) = 0.$$

Next calculate $v_2(q)$ and remember that for $n \geqslant 0$ there are production costs, penalty costs, storage costs and the costs of production in future periods.

$$v_2(-1) = 18 + 0.7 \times (0 + v_1(0)) + 0.3 \times (3 + v_1(-1))$$
$$= 35.2$$

$$v_2(0) = \min\{10 + 0.7 \times (0 + v_1(0)) + 0.3 \times (3 + v_1(-1)),$$
$$18 + 0.7 \times (0 + 2.5 + v_1(1)) + 0.3 \times (0 + v_1(0))\}$$
$$= 26.65$$

$$v_2(1) = \min\{0 + 0.7 \times (0 + v_1(0)) + 0.3 \times (3 + v_1(-1)),$$
$$10 + 0.7 \times (0 + 2.5 + v_1(1)) + 0.3 \times (0 + v_1(0)),$$
$$18 + 0.7 \times (0 + 2.5 + v_1(1)) + 0.3 \times (0 + 2.5 + v_1(1))\}$$
$$= \min\{17.2, 18.65, 24.4\}$$
$$= 17.2.$$

From the minimising terms

$$d_2(-1) = 2$$
$$d_2(0) = 2$$
$$d_2(1) = 0.$$

Finally

$$v_3(1) = \min\{0 + 0.7 \times (0 + v_2(0)) + 0.3 \times (3 + v_2(-1)),$$
$$10 + 0.7 \times (0 + 2.5 + v_2(1)) + 0.3 \times (0 + v_2(0)),$$
$$18 + 0.7 \times (0 + 2.5 + v_2(1)) + 0.3 \times (0 + 2.5 + v_2(1))\}$$
$$= \min\{29.215, 31.785, 37.3\}$$
$$= 29.215.$$

Thus $d_3(1) = 0$.

The optimal policy is thus given by Table S12.6 (compare Table 12.6).

Table S12.6

			n	
	$d_n(q)$	3	2	1
	-1		2	2
q	0		2	1
	1	0	0	0

Chapter 13

1 The theoretical weekly costs for $S = 2, 3$ respectively are, excluding fixed and order costs, 10.61, 11.85.

2 The theoretical expected queue size is 1.25.

3 The theoretical expected cost for $N = 4$ is 146.

4 The theoretical expectations are, 838, 33.41 hours and 40.31% of the time respectively.

Index